The 33rd

Editor-In-Chief	Scott Stein
Senior Editors	Albert DiBartolomeo
	Kathleen Volk Miller
Layout Editor	William Rees
Graphic Design	Hannah Dillon
	Lauren Frain
Editorial Co-ops	Maia C. Livengood
	Julia Perch
Student Interns	Olivia DiPasquale
	Michael A. Filippone
	Katrina D. Gaudier
	Giby V. George
	Emily G. Homrok
	Kurt R. McCrohan
	Nicolle Morales Kern
	Laura Knoll
	Carolynn McCormack
	Amanda Panicali
	Sonal Patel
	Daniel Savage
	Jordan Schilling
	Heather M. Schwartz
	Matthew Strickland

Sponsors

Drexel University
The College of Arts and Sciences at Drexel University
The Department of English and Philosophy at Drexel University

Dr. Donna M. Murasko, Dean, College of Arts and Sciences,
Drexel University
Dr. Abioseh Michael Porter, Department Head, English and Philosophy,
Drexel University

The 33rd Volume 3
Drexel University
Department of English and Philosophy
3141 Chestnut Street
Philadelphia, PA 19104
www.drexelpublishing.org

Cover photo by Lauren Frain

Copies of this volume are available for $10 by writing to the above address.

ISBN 978-0-9820717-2-4

Thank you, thank you, thank you and thank you to: Dr. Donna M. Murasko; Dr. Abioseh Michael Porter; all the judges from the Drexel Publishing Group Essay Contest, the Week of Writing Contest, and the Freshman Writing Contest (Harriet Millan, Lynn Levin, Valerie Fox, Dan Driscoll, Cassandra Hirsch, Robert Finegan, Elizabeth Thorpe, Susan Spaid, Ingrid G. Daemmrich, Kathy McNamee, Emilie Passow, Rebecca Ingalls, Gail Rosen, Stacey Ake, Don Riggs, Scott Warnock, Ken Bingham, F. Elaine DeLancey, Karen Nulton, Jonathan Seitz, Nianli Sang, Kathryn Steen, Al Stegemen, Anne-Marie Obajtek-Kirkwood, Alexander Friedlander, Genevieve Betts, Rebecca Hoffman and Ron Bishop); Department of English and Philosophy, especially Mary Beth Beyer, Eileen Brennen and Nicole Kline; contest participants; Drexel Publishing Group staff.

Printed by T-Shore, Dexter, MI
Distributed by the Drexel Publishing Group
The fonts used within this publication are Archer and Avenir

Credits:

Betts, Genevieve. "Nepantla." *red.* 2 (2007): 138-140. Print.

Cohen, Paula Marantz. "Shylock, My Students, and Me." *The American Scholar.* (2010). Web.

DiBartolomeo, Albert. "Double Life." *Philadelphia Inquirer.* July 12, 2007.

Fox, Valerie. "Manifesto." *Sentence* 8. 2010.

Fox, Valerie. "We Wrote…" *Quarrtsiluni.* 2009.

Hnaraki, Maria. "We Speak What We Eat." *The Smart Set.* 2010.

Knowles, Scott Gabriel. "Building Under Peril." *Next American City Magazine.* 2008.

Kotzin, Miriam N. "Hag." *Just Desserts.* Star Cloud Press, 2010.

Kotzin, Miriam N. "Should, Shouldn't." *Just Desserts.* Star Cloud Press, 2010.

Levin, Lynn. "The Fox and the Neighbors." *Fair Creatures of an Hour.* Loonfeather Press, 2009.

Levin, Lynn. "Thistledown." *Fair Creatures of an Hour.* Loonfeather Press, 2009.

Millan, Harriet. "Girl in Cap and Gown." *Girl in Cap and Gown.* Mammoth Books, 2010.

Millan, Harriet. "In the Community Garden." *Girl in Cap and Gown.* Mammoth Books, 2010.

Obajtek-Kirwood, Anne-Marie. "*Le Monde* on a 'Likely' Iraq War." *Leading to the 2003 Iraq War The Global Media Debate.* New York: Palgrave Macmillan, January 2006. 129-147.

Stein, Scott. "Big Switch." *National Review.* April 20, 2009.

Thorpe, Elizabeth. "Punctuation." *Per Contra.* 2010.

Warnock, Scott. "School Budgets? We Vote Every Day with Our Wallets." *Burlington County Times.* April 25, 2010.

Wilson, Jason. "A Game Journey." *The Smart Set.* November 20, 2007.

Welcome

The 33rd continues to be a visible expression of the College of Arts and Sciences' commitment to writing excellence. Within its pages you will find an eclectic mix of faculty and student writing, from thoughtful essays to entertaining short stories, from moving poetry to scholarly articles on scientific topics. This volume is a reminder that good writing is vital to the success of students and professionals in *all* fields, not only in the humanities, but also in the social and natural sciences.

The 33rd illustrates our aptitude for observation and analysis, and our willingness to look both inward and outward, as we continually evaluate this world and our place within it, coming back always to share our diverse perspectives with our fellow students, colleagues and friends. Please enjoy this anthology, enjoy it for both entertainment and academic study, but most importantly, recognize that what is bound within these covers is an example of the many accomplishments you, as a Drexel student, are capable of achieving. Let these pages motivate you to do more than you ever imagined.

Donna M. Murasko, Ph.D
Dean
College of Arts and Sciences

Preface

As is often noted, the Department of English and Philosophy has established a well-deserved reputation not only as a place where instructors of all ranks are passionate about teaching and learning—derived from classroom and other such experiences—but also as the one locale at Drexel where excellent writing is seen as a daily, achievable goal. Because our ultimate objective is to make excellent writing a defining characteristic of a Drexel education, we will continue to help our students understand that a fine blend of traditional literary skills and modern thought and practice will help to make them excellent, even outstanding, writers.

We are thus pleased to present the third volume of this yearly anthology. In *The 33rd* 2010, we have as a primary aim the encouragement of our students to fuse insights derived from their varied experiences and the knowledge to create a document that truly should impress readers because of the complex web of writing the authors present, even with an occasional undergraduate self-consciousness.

Using varying approaches that, even in these early stages, reveal the complexity, density of texture and meaning, and the richness of vision and artistry that often characterize good quality writing, the students—guided by their very able instructors—have carefully demonstrated in print some famous words of wisdom by Diane Stanley, author and illustrator: "Good writing is clear thinking." What I now hope the students, again with guidance from all of us, will continue to do from this point on is to apply the other half of Ms. Stanley's statement: "Reading is how you learn what good writing sounds like."

My personal congratulations—as well as those of the whole department—go to all who participated in this laudable and practically useful project. To those whose selections were published, I would like to conclude by offering some more words by the British writer, Thomas Carlyle: "In every phenomenon the beginning remains always the most notable moment." Bravo!

Abioseh Michael Porter, Ph.D
Department Head
Department of English and Philosophy

Table of Contents

Week of Writing
Introduction

Poetry

Fiction

Faculty Writing
Introduction

Freshman
Writing

Introduction

Each year, Drexel freshmen write thousands of projects and papers. Many of these are excellent, yet they are often only read by the students' instructors and classmates. The goal of the Freshman Writing Award is both to recognize student excellence and to provide students with an opportunity to communicate to a broader audience. This contest is a highlight of the Freshman Writing Program (FWP). The awards for this contest are given at the English Awards Ceremony in the spring term, and for years this contest has been generously supported by Ingrid Daemmrich, one of our faculty members.

The contest process is rigorous. In the fall, faculty members from the 140 freshman writing courses nominate the best examples of student writing. These papers and projects are distributed to a panel of faculty judges. This year these judges narrowed down 70 initial entries to a finalist list of 19. A smaller panel of faculty judges then re-read the final 19 and ranked them to make the final determination of the top three prize winners and seven honorable mentions.

The winning writers gain an audience beyond their own classrooms. This anthology, now in its third year, allows them to reach many readers. I continue to be amazed each year at the array of academic disciplines represented by the winning entries. To me, this emphasizes the importance of writing in the careers and lives of all of our students. In addition, this contest, with its winners from across Drexel's curriculum, helps us recognize our students as *writers*; that is fitting, because I think that is exactly what they are.

Scott Warnock, Ph.D
Director
Freshman Writing Program

Kellie Chiu

Is the Western Way the Only Way?

I loved visiting my third great uncle because he had huge tanks of colorful fish, a cute little Shih Tzu, and always something delicious to eat. I remember wandering around his house when I was about six or seven years old and stumbling upon my third great uncle treating my grandfather, laying on his stomach with his shirt off, with acupuncture. I had no idea why there were needles all over his body, and I was slightly scared. My mom explained to me simply that the needles would make my grandfather, who was suffering from dizziness while undergoing treatment for bladder cancer, feel better.

Despite being exposed to Chinese medical practices, my family predominantly believes that the Western, conventional remedy is usually the best option. After all, my oldest sister earns money as a pharmacist based on the belief that prescriptions and over-the-counter medicines will alleviate health problems. When I got sick for the first time in college, my mother kept calling me to make sure that I was taking medicine like Advil to help deal with the symptoms. It was not until my roommate revealed to me that she had never heard of Advil and had taken mostly Chinese herbal medicine all of her life that I began to question the mentality I had towards Western medicines. I had always discounted Chinese herbal medicine and acupuncture as options that only worked because people believed that they did. How could acupuncture or Chinese herbal medicine save a person dying of cancer? Why would any cancer patient want to be treated by Chinese physicians that base their judgments on those made by people that lived thousands of years ago when Western physicians base their judgments on clinical trials and clear, up-to-date scientific data?

In order to evaluate Western Medicine (WM) and Traditional Chinese Medicine (TCM) in regards to cancer treatment, a better understanding of the difference in ideologies is important. Using the concepts of yin and yang, TCM emphasizes the maintenance of balance between the human body and its environment as well as internal balance between the organs of the body. Yin and yang correspond with aspects that are opposite to each other yet cannot exist without each other. J. Tsuei remarks in her article, "Eastern and Western Approaches to Medicine," that "everything in life can be classified according to its yin and yang components" (554). In this way, TCM follows a holistic approach, looking at the whole body in terms of emotional and physical balance. Eastern medical students must learn about not only how the human body works but also how the world works. In order to gain a sense of balance between humans and their environment, Eastern medical students study astrology and geology as a supplement to their knowledge of human physiology (552). In contrast to those who practice TCM, physicians trained in Western, conventional medicine, focus on localizing the disease and treating the patient by addressing only specific targets in the body. After being treated by Western doctors, "The majority of people may be free from serious disease but not from discomfort, either physical or mental" (Tsuei 552).

This statement seems at first to be counterintuitive. If a person is free from disease, why would they still have discomfort? Someone who receives antibiotics to treat an infection and is subsequently cured of the infection should be healthy again. However, if this same person continues to be plagued by infections and needs different antibiotics to treat them, then this could be a sign of a systematic problem which could be better evaluated and recognized by a TCM doctor. Unlike WM, which would have in the previous example continued to categorize the illness as a bacterial infection or to explain the processes on the cellular level, TCM takes into account a patient's emotions and environment when determining the cause of the disease. The cause of disease is attributed to six physical factors as well as seven emotional factors, which include anger, joy, worry, grief, anxiety, fear, and fright (Hsiao 85). This idea of emotions affecting overall health has been a longstanding principle of TCM. J. Tsuei quotes from the ancient Chinese text, *Yellow Emperor's Canon of Medicine*, which states that "a skilled physician will go one step further [rather than examining only physical appearance] and examine the emotions of his patient as well" (556).

Because TCM and WM hold different philosophies, their respective approaches to cancer lead to different treatments. S.M. Sagar and R.K. Wong describe Western cancer therapies that kill cancer cells as "aggressive and destructive" while TCM methods like acupuncture aim to balance the whole "body-mind network" (Sagar 43). This concept of the body-mind network comes back to the principle of yin and yang. Instead of treating each system as a separate process in the body, TCM categorizes organs in terms of how they balance each other psychologically and physiologically. There are yin organs, known as the five zang, which "store fundamental substances" like blood and chi (energy), as well as yang organs, known as the six fu, which transport these important substances (Hsiao 84). Each yin organ can be paired with a yang organ based on similar psychological function. For example, both the liver, which is one of the five zang, and the gall bladder, which is one of the six fu, are associated with the psychological characteristic of equilibrium and tranquility (Tsuei 555). To make further connections between the mind and the body, TCM associates cancer with "'liver fire'(representing anger), and [there is] recent scientific evidence that repressed anger both suppresses the immune system and may increase the risk of breast cancer in the so-called Type C personality" (Sagar 44). Because the liver represents feelings of equilibrium and tranquility, it makes logical sense that "liver fire" would correspond with cancer, which causes a large imbalance in the body. Whether repressed anger itself can cause cancer is debatable, but emotional distress should not be completely ignored by physicians.

Since WM is based on data collected from clinical trials and minute observation of cells, most conventional doctors view cancer as simply the result of mutations in DNA that cause cells to divide at an uncontrolled pace rather than incorporating psychosomatic explanations as well. Western medicine makes conclusions based on observations of the body itself, which is illustrated in many museums and exhibits in the United States. For example, I visited the Mütter Museum, located in Philadelphia, Pennsylvania, in October 2009, which contains many real and wax body parts that demonstrate specific afflictions. The museum itself is split into body systems, from the integumentary system to the skeletal system. Preserved in special fluids, body parts ranging from cancerous livers to gangrenous hands demonstrate the Western mentality of studying the disease in terms of the location of the disease and its symptoms. At a certain time, medical students were allowed to borrow these body parts like books in a library, demonstrating the general acceptance of this view of human health.

In keeping with this Western mentality, Western cancer treatments aim to kill or remove specific cells from the body through chemotherapy, radiation, or surgery in the hopes that removal of the cancer cells will cure the patient of sickness. Chemotherapy attempts to kill all cells that are dividing in the body by circulating certain drugs in the bloodstream, which can cause many painful side effects in a cancer patient because many healthy cells in the digestive lining and hair follicles are killed by chemotherapy along with the cancer cells ("Chemotherapy and You"). Radiation therapy and surgery are more localized treatments that attempt to remove cancer cells in specific parts of the body. Radiation therapy can shrink or destroy tumors in the area treated, but like chemotherapy, it can affect healthy cells as well, causing side effects like fatigue and skin changes during treatment ("Radiation Therapy and You"). Surgery, the most straightforward treatment of cancer, can effectively remove tumors that have not spread to other parts of the body as well as the lymph nodes that surround the tumor ("Surgery to Treat Cancer"). While Western doctors believe that ridding the body of cancer cells with these treatments will leave the cancer patient happy and healthy, treatments can cause such great levels of pain that the patient may still be alive at the price of an altered state of mind.

My aunt had breast cancer and became a different person after undergoing surgery and chemotherapy. I had always thought of her as a strong woman who could take any joke and deal with any conflict thrown at her, but the pain of chemotherapy proved to be overwhelming. She stopped attempting to live a normal life, falling into a deep depression and reverting to childlike behavior. She refused to go anywhere, even the bathroom, without her husband accompanying her, and she frequently threatened to kill herself. The Western, conventional cancer treatment, while eliminating the breast cancer, produced a different kind of imbalance in her body. Although she eventually began seeing a psychiatrist, psychological treatment was not deemed necessary at first because her body was cured of cancer. It took many years before my aunt started to interact normally with others, slowly but not fully coming back to us as though she was living as a ghost of herself.

While my aunt's doctors had prescribed her pain medication, my aunt refused to take them. For those patients who are afraid of becoming addicted to medication or who prefer not to allow excessive synthetic compounds in their body, acupuncture is a viable option. My third great uncle, an acupuncturist, helped my aunt deal with her pain by giving her periodic acupuncture treatments. Acupuncture uses needles to stimulate certain nerves in the body.

This ancient technique has been proven in modern clinical trials to significantly alleviate pain and acute vomiting in cancer patients (Konkimalla 208). As a result of these treatments, my aunt believed that it gave her better balance and strength, complaining less about her pain although she still had difficulty accepting her physical appearance after losing her hair and her breast. While acupuncture can help to alleviate pain, it can also help with other side effects of western cancer treatment like hot flashes caused by the chemotherapy drug Tamoxifen, which is given to many women who have had surgery for breast cancer. Jill Hervek and Odd Mjaland's study, "Acupuncture for the treatment of hot flashes in breast cancer patients, a randomized, controlled trial," found that breast cancer patients treated with traditional acupuncture showed a significant decrease in mean hot flashes both night and day for the duration of the study, which spanned from four weeks before treatment (surgery and chemotherapy) to twelve weeks after treatment, while the group of patients treated with sham acupuncture showed little change in the mean number of hot flashes (Hervik 314). This study used the same acupuncture points for each person in the study, but customizing the points for each patient would most likely make the acupuncture treatment even more effective. Another side effect from treatment that acupuncture has been proven to effectively treat is Xerostomia, which is dry mouth induced by radiation therapy (Lu 639). Because acupuncture can have multiple positive effects on the body, it fits within the TCM model of targeting many parts of the body in order to create balance as opposed to treating only one part of the body. It may not be a panacea, but with scientific proof to support its validity, acupuncture seems to be more than just ancient Chinese quackery.

While acupuncture can help treat the side effects of Western cancer treatment, Chinese herbal medicine can enhance Western treatments as well as fight cancer on its own. In 26 clinical trials that tested the effects of Chinese herbal medicine in conjunction with chemotherapy, a significant increase in tumor response and patient survival was observed as opposed to just chemotherapy alone (Konkimalla 208). If Chinese herbal medicine can increase the survival rate, then Western doctors should be more willing to recommend it to their patients. Some Chinese herbs have even proven to be effective against tumors on their own. For example, a study found that the Chinese herb liqi significantly reduced the size of tumors in mice (Deng-Bo et al). However, it seems that in order to completely remove a tumor, conventional surgery must be done.

Many Western professionals discount the effectiveness of Chinese herbal medicine because "quality control and safety issues are of major importance" (Konkimolla 209). Proper regulation of Chinese herbal medicine is a serious issue because herbal stores are not like regular pharmacies. There is no guarantee that the herbs that people buy contain exactly what the sellers tell them they contain. Despite the risk, people have been using Chinese herbal medicine for thousands of years and continue to do so today. While walking through any Chinatown in an American city, you will easily see at least two or three markets selling Chinese herbs, illustrating the prevalence of TCM in today's world. My own roommate swears by her Chinese herbal medicine for upset stomach, and my great-grandmother lived to be 93 supposedly by taking a few spoonfuls of a special family recipe of ginseng, a mix of other Chinese herbs, berries, and rice wine each day.

Despite the fact that there have been many studies supporting both acupuncture and Chinese herbal medicine, further research must be carried out in order for these practices to become more widespread in the Western world. There needs to be a higher level of certainty in regards to the effects of TCM treatments on cancer patients. My father, who was diagnosed with chronic lymphocytic leukemia a couple of years ago, has mainly relied on conventional blood analysis as his treatment, seeing a hematologist every month. My mother also had a benign tumor surgically removed from her breast recently. These kinds of treatments are what help me keep my faith in WM, despite some of its failings in regards to treating overall health, because its practices have helped the people I care about stay healthy. Since I will most likely enter a medical school that teaches WM, I will be learning how to treat the patient by treating the disease rather than the TCM method of holistic analysis. However, I should not limit my view of medicine by only considering

Western, conventional treatments. In conjunction with WM, TCM could greatly improve the quality of life of cancer patients, alleviating side effects of WM treatment and emphasizing a balanced, healthy life in the future.

Works Cited

"Chemotherapy and You: Support for People with Cancer." National Cancer Institute. 29 June 2007. Web. 10 Nov. 2009. <http://www.cancer.gov/cancertopics/chemotherapy-and-you>.

Ji, Deng-Bo, et al. "Anti-Tumor Effect of Liqi, a Traditional Chinese Medicine Prescription, in Tumor Bearing Mice." *BMC Complementary and Alternative Medicine* 9.1 (2009): 20. *Pubmed*. Web. 11 November 2009.

Hervik, J., and O. Mjåland. "Acupuncture for the treatment of hot flashes in breast cancer patients, a randomized, controlled trial." *Breast Cancer Research and Treatment* 116.2 (2009): 311-316. Health Module, *ProQuest*. Web. 27 Oct. 2009.

Hsiao, C., H. Tsou, A. Pong, J. Liu, C. Lin, Y. Chang, and S. Chow. "Statistical Validation of Traditional Chinese Diagnostic Procedures." *Drug Information Journal* 43.1 (2009): 83-95. Health Module, *ProQuest*. Web. 26 Oct. 2009.

Konkimalla, V. Badireenath, and Thomas Efferth. "Evidence-based Chinese medicine for cancer therapy." *Journal of Ethnopharmacology*. 116 (2008): 207–210. *Pubmed*. Web. 3 Nov. 2009.

Lu, Weidong, et al. "The Value of Acupuncture in Cancer Care." *Hematology/oncology clinics of North America* 22.4 (2008): 631-48. Pubmed. Web. 11 November 2009.

"Radiation Therapy and You: Support for People with Cancer." National Cancer Institute. 20 April 2007. Web. 10 Nov. 2009. <http://www.cancer.gov/cancertopics/radiation-therapy-and-you>.

Sagar, S.M., and R.K. Wong. "Chinese medicine and biomodulation in cancer patients—Part one." *Current Oncology*. 15(2008): 42-48. Pubmed. Web. 30 Oct. 2009.

"Surgery to Treat Cancer." Cancer Research UK. Web. 10 November 2009. <http://www.cancerhelp.org.uk/about-cancer/treatment/surgery/surgery-to-treat-cancer>.

Tsuei, MD, Julia J. "Eastern and Western Approaches to Medicine." *Western Journal of Medicine* 128 (1978): 551-57. *Pubmed*. Web. 22 Oct. 2009.

"What is Cancer?" National Cancer Institute. 11 May 2009. Web. 7 November 2009. <http://www.cancer.gov/cancertopics/what-is-cancer>.

Amanda Decker

Walk a Mile in Her Shoes

Her name was simple and ordinary. She should have had a simple and ordinary life. Mary. She heard her name every day during her prayers, "Hail Mary, full of grace-." In the 1930s, countless Marys wandered through the South Street markets, shopping for their families. Mary O'Donnells and Mary Bishops were common, with their fiery red hair and pale, freckled skin. But Mary Buemi? Her name conjured visions of a young woman in blue, cradling a child. But was this who she really was? She was Italian, with an Anglicized name. No one is quite sure if she was born Mary or if immigration officials took the liberty to grant her a more befitting American name. She was a Mary, not a Marie or Maria, and she was an outcast in her own society. Her name made her an outcast. Her culture made her an outcast. Her disability made her an outcast. Not quite ignored and not quite shunned, but she was an oddity nonetheless. Where most people want to make themselves unique, Mary wanted to have a normal life, and she was determined to make that ordinary life possible.

In 1916, my grandmother's childhood and future were put in jeopardy when she suddenly stopped moving. At nine months old, after she had just learned how to crawl, *Poliomyelitis* fevered her brow and froze her little muscles. America's first major outbreak of polio occurred in New York the same year that it attacked Mary (Gould xi). As unfortunate as this diagnosis was, Mary was extremely lucky to contract the virus in the United States, instead of in her native Italy. Although the outbreak was sudden and devastating, American hospitals, especially those in major cities like Philadelphia, tended to have a larger assortment of working instruments than smaller treatment facilities like those in the Buemis' native Sicily. The primary treatment for polio required an "iron lung," a device that lowered the air pressure around a victim's body so that respiration would be easier, even in the patient's weakened state (Gould xiv). One example of this inequality in treatment was that in a small clinic based in a rural Spanish church, much like the aging Catholic Church in Sicily, iron lungs were constructed out of old, previously used coffins (Gould 288). American hospitals also offered experimental treatments. The Buemis usually took their ailing daughter to the hospital as soon as they heard about the risky surgeries. Doctors promised that stretching the muscles surgically, transplanting muscle, and grafting bone would help restore Mary's mobility, if only for a short time.

The multitude of risky, expensive surgeries that my grandmother endured may have pained her physically, but emotionally, they were the best things for her. Many polio victims do not want their physical deformities to define who they are as individuals. They want their achievements to be recognized before the wheelchairs and braces. "By labeling themselves as 'overachievers,' instead of high achievers, they may at the same time conclude that, along with much of society-at-large, they did not expect themselves to achieve much at all" (Gould 222). Mary and her parents refused to subject Mary to society's disrespect and scorn because of a tiny, incurable virus. Despite the fact that she never learned to walk before contracting polio, her parents would not accept that their daughter would be wheelchair bound, and Mary would not accept that she would be a cripple. With her strong will and determination to be a regular child, Mary did learn to walk, without the aid of a walker or braces. She was almost a normal Italian girl.

My grandmother's determination to overcome the odds stemmed from her desire to be the exception to society's view on people with disabilities. The American cinema of the mid-1900s exemplified how society felt about people like Mary: "Whether represented as menacing or pathetic, physically handicapped people were thereby defined as unfit for normal social roles" (Longmore 14). Many disabled children were barred from attending public school, as doctors deemed hospitals and institutions more appropriate for their physical needs (Longmore 11). Perhaps the specialized hospitals could assist as the physically disabled learned to speak with their hands, or read with their fingers, or walk again, or breathe on their own, but those institutions could never help mental and emotional healing. Even those who were not so disabled to have to be in a hospital were not welcomed in everyday life. A Chicago law in the 1930s stated, "No person who is diseased, maimed, mutilated, or in any way deformed so as to be an unsightly or disgusting object or improper person to be allowed in or on the public ways or other public places in this city, shall therein or thereon expose himself to public view" (Longmore 11). My grandmother could have succumbed to society's expectations and lived a life with leg braces or in a wheelchair, hiding from the world. Yet, she was determined to live as normal a life as possible. A life where she walked with her head held high, surrounded by a husband and children.

Her friends at school looked at her with pity. A girl with special needs did not deserve the love of another. But Mary disagreed. She wanted the love her parents had, and she was determined to stop a man in his tracks like any normal girl. Like any normal girl, she did eventually fall in love. She picked the wrong time and place to fall in love, but she did. In 1940, Mary still needed help for everyday tasks, her family lost their business thanks to the Great Depression, and World War II was growing worse by the day. Nevertheless, when her Fleicher Trade School friends introduced her to Edward Decker, she fell in love with a blonde-haired, blue-eyed German. To say that there was tension in the family is an understatement. "No *figlia* of mine is marrying a *Nazista!*" Despite the objections there was hidden blessing in the marriage, however unconventional. With aging parents, Mary's future was uncertain. Even a mobile, respiratory polio victim requires help to put on shoes, boil water for supper, wash the dishes, dust the mantle, do the laundry, and care for the children. Up until then, Mary always had her parents to rely on. A polio victim's greatest fear is not the paralysis or the unknown, but facing "the death of their parents who now care for them. They will be faced with the soul-killing prospect of vegetating in county homes with the senile" (Gould 198). Her marriage to Edward became her escape from that life and her ticket to a new adventure, a family of her own and the new difficulties that came along with it.

However, despite the sudden hardships and eccentricities of the new family, the unlikely marriage of Edward and Mary ushered in a new lifestyle for Mary. Even with her weak legs and weakening arms, she could now be the head of her household. The only problem was that there was no house for her to head. In the 1940s, the Italian area of Philadelphia was still recovering from the economic crisis commonly known as the Great Depression. As of 1936, 40 percent of the Italian-American population in Philadelphia was on federal relief (Luconi 61). In March of 1937, the family's hardware enterprise closed its doors for good, and the Buemi family was left to try to put their lives back together with the unsold screws, nuts, and bolts. Even as immigrants, "Italian families remained in rented housing only long enough to accumulate sufficient money to purchase their own homes" but, the newlyweds were not as fortunate (Juliani 203). Edward had a huge heart, but small savings. Mary had seamstress and beading work only just before a neighbor walked down the aisle. They could not, and would never be able to, afford their own home. More than anything, this is what Mary wanted. Owning her own family home was the only obstacle she had never overcome in her life. Instead, she grew up, studied, married, raised her children, and passed away in the same house.

Similar to her childhood, her adult life and family almost fifteen years later were unusual. The conventional 1950s mornings of rushing off to office jobs, egg and bacon breakfasts, and calls of "Did you wash behind your ears?" were not to be found in the Decker house. Instead of a sterile, bleach scent, the stale aroma of Mary's long snuffed out, calming cigarettes and smoldering wood carried in after Edward's firefighter shifts mingled in the house. Usually, my grandmother woke to the midday sunlight streaming through the slated blinds, casting oblong shadows across the bed and door. She always heard her mother, Mama Rosieboom, puttering around the house, getting ready to make lunch for Judy and Joey. With a cane and unsteady legs, dressing herself was a challenge, but soon, her homemade cotton dress would swish around her legs. The hemline was just long enough to hide the scars behind her knees, her evidence of failed polio operations. At noon my father and aunt would take a break from school and come home for lunch to chat with their mother and grandmother. Their uniforms were stiff with starch, and little Joey often pulled at his collar. "*Giuseppe*, the nuns will yell if you muss yourself, *fermata che*." All too soon, the children would return to school and leave the adults alone again. Edward would stir from the bedroom, trying to rub out the soot and ash from his last shift as Mary would settle down to her beading and Mama Rosieboom would wait at the makeshift desk for the optimistic gamblers.

In a society that values men over women, it is easy for a girl to lose herself in the complicated workings of everyday necessities, especially when that young girl is stricken with polio. The neighbors wondered what was she to do as a woman besides cook, clean, and keep the house? Yes, she was beautiful, smart, and like all Sicilians, driven, but the legs that did not want to support her body also gave way under the load of her society's expectations. In the neighbor's eyes, Mary could do no more than sit at home. Society deemed her worthless and severely underestimated her potential.

Much like the daughter in Chimamanda Adichie's story, "Cell One," Mary was expected to be a certain way because of a society ignorant of her inner strength. Mary's role in life was to take care of her parents as much as possible and be happy with only that opportunity. The daughter in "Cell One" was expected to support her brother and family, no matter what her opinions were. Both young women faced constricting expectations from society and family, but had the courage to make their individuality be seen. Mary was defined by her disability, while the unnamed sister was defined by her familial relationships, not their own potential. In "Cell One," brother Nnamabia looked flawless on the outside, but his immorality created a hideous monster under the beautiful façade. After years of his breaking rules with no retribution, Nnamabia's sister is resentful and disgusted with her kin. In keeping with society's vision of a proper daughter, she calmly voiced her opinion, that it hurt the family, emotionally and financially, to continue to visit Nnamabia in jail. However, she forgot her place as a caring, supportive sister, saying that "it would not hurt for Nnamabia to fend for himself for a day" (Adichie 14). This blatant disrespect of society's norms and expectations threatened to tear the family apart, yet her point was made and no one visited the family's caged prince that day. It was a small victory, but for a young woman in a family and society where men are favored and women seen as useful as the household appliances, it was enough.

Like the daughter in "Cell One," my grandmother refused to accept her life as it was. God did not intend for Mary Buemi's life to be simple. An immigrant crippled with polio was not destined to do great, or even mediocre, things. Society assumed that someone in her condition would accept their physical shortcomings and live a minimalistic life, possibly in an institution. She should never have considered an education, let alone a career, and a marriage, let alone children. However, the tough Sicilian demeanor of her homeland dominated her life. Mary accomplished everything society told her to give up.

The phrase, "Don't judge someone until you've walked a mile in their shoes," holds special meaning to my family. My grandmother led an extraordinary life. She was destined to be paralyzed and essentially useless as a woman, yet with hard work through daily struggles, she exceeded the expectations of doctors who claimed she would never walk again and the neighborhood *paesani* who pitied her shuffling gait. Despite everything she endured, my grandmother taught all of those around her that she could overcome obstacles and change her world. Mary's overwhelming drive to make her world a better place led her to help anyone in need. She exercised with the other neighborhood polio victims, ignoring the generation gap, and gave them a glimpse into their own future, a future where they could walk, attend school, and have a family. She granted freedom to new immigrants in the community by creating a link from Italian to English. Even as she grew older and her legs finally gave up, bills were paid, houses were repaired, and children went to school with Mary's help. Who would have ever thought that she would have been such an important part of so many people's lives? Her life may have been unconventional and at times scandalous, but very few people would have the strength to walk a mile in her shoes.

I regret not remembering much of my grandmother. I vaguely recall spending a day in the house at the corner of 11th and Durfor. My three-year-old brain thought it strange that there was a ramp leading up to a bedroom, that the house was so unbearably hot, and that this snowy-haired woman in a wheelchair was holding me. I remember attending a funeral but I never realized whom we were mourning for. Years later, I had a chance to really "meet" my grandmother for the first time, and she taught me more about overcoming adversity and being a strong woman than any classic literary heroine.

Works Cited

Adichie, Chimamanda Ngozi. "Cell One." *The Thing Around Your Neck*. New York: Knopf, 2009. 3-21. Print.

Briggs, John W. *An Italian Passage: Immigrants to Three American Cities,* 1890-1930. London: Yale UP, 1978. Print.

Decker, Joe, Sr., Judy Nardella, and Rosetta Abbruzzee. Telephone interview. 7 November 2009.

Eileen R Chasens, & Mary G Umlauf. (2000). "Post-polio syndrome." *The American Journal of Nursing*, 100(12), 60-67. Research Library Core 30 October 2009.

Gould, Tony. *A Summer Plague: Polio and Its Survivors*. Google Books. Google, 1997. Web. 10 Nov. 2009.

Juliani, Richard. *The Social Organization of Immigration:The Italians in Philadelphia*. Ed Steve Bedney: Arno, 1971. Print.

Luconi, Stafano. *From Paesani to White Ethnics: The Italian Experience in Philadelphia*. Albany: State U of New York P, 2001. Print.

Mallory, Staphen L. *"The Italian-American Mafia." Understanding Organized Crime*. Jones and Barlett, 2007. 90-113. Print.

Paul K Longmore, and David Goldberger. "The League of the Physically Handicapped and the Great Depression: A case study in the new disability history." *Journal of American History* 87.3 (2000): 888-922. ProQuest. Web. 24 Nov. 2009 Rothman, Edwin.

"The Gang Problem in Philadelphia: Proposals for Improving the Programs of Gang-Control Agencies." Philadelphia: Bureau of Municipal Research, 1974. Print.

Saladino, Maria, et al. "Testimonies." *Mafia and Outlaw Stories from Italian Life and Literature*. Trans. Robin Pickering-Iazzi. Toronto: U of Toronto P,2007. 138-166. Print.

Marquerita Algorri

Cannibalism

In her book, *A Natural History of the Senses,* Diane Ackerman ponders the relationships linking taste, food, and human socialization. She discusses how Western society established food taboos to differentiate acceptable consumables from inedible substances. Protein sources such as pigs, chickens, and cows are considered suitable for consumption, while human flesh is forbidden. However, Ackerman questions the logic behind the taboo and presents a paradoxical statement: In a society which eagerly sacrifices numerous human beings during warfare, cannibalism is morally wrong, not because human lives are valued, but because of a societal taboo (Ackerman 137-138). In this essay, I explore Ackerman's paradox.

Cannibalism, formally known as anthropophagy, is the age-old practice of man eating man. Though the act is presently regarded as taboo in Western society, its practice dates back to the origin of human development. It can be argued that cannibalism is a part of human instinctual behavior, comparable to sexuality, forbidden only by the modern formation of social constraints. Human consumption, if advocated, could be the solution to several of the world's most problematic issues, such as hunger, overpopulation, crime, and excess waste. It is ironic that the violence of war is tolerated and encouraged, while the practicality of cannibalism is deemed repulsive and inhumane. With the Earth's resources steadily diminishing, human flesh could serve as an apt and easily obtainable replacement for many of our daily needs as the thriving society of the man-eating ancient Aztecs of Mesoamerica proved.

The exact origins of this practice are unclear. Archeologists have found limited evidence in the form of distinctive cutting marks on human bones similar to those found on animal bones. This evidence suggests that the regular consumption of human flesh for nutritional purposes was common among prehistoric humans (Collinson 192). Most notably, the Aztecs of Mesoamerica were, as documented by Spanish explorers such as Cortés, advocates of human sacrifice and consumption for religious and political purposes. Aztec gods were believed to require human hearts and blood for sustenance. The Aztecs recognized the needs of their gods by sacrificing male prisoners of war and slaves during a sacred ceremony. After the ceremony, the Aztecs cooked and devoured the bodies of their victims, including their organs and blood (Harris 102). The Spanish, and many other European cultures with blossoming agricultural systems, perceived such behavior as barbaric. Even cultures that had previously advocated the practice of cannibalism, such as the Greeks and Romans, had come to reject it after the establishment of government-ruled societies (Harris 114).

More recent instances of cannibalism have been documented in Western society after the social criminalization of the practice, such as the cases of Jeffrey Dahmer, a serial murderer and sex offender who often consumed the bodies of his victims, and Armin Meiwes, a German man who, via the Internet, found volunteers to murder and consume. In addition, cases of human consumption for survival were found among a group of players from a Uruguayan rugby team, stranded in the Andes after a plane crash (Collinson 191-192).

Cannibalism is not simple: there are a series of subtypes that define who is eaten and the purposes behind their consumption. There are two categories for who is eaten, exocannibalism and endocannibalism. Exocannibalism is the consumption of individuals outside of one's respective social group, while endocannibalism refers to the eating of those within one's own group. The Aztecs, for example, practiced exocannibalism by consuming their prisoners of war, invaders from outside of their culture. However, they also practiced endocannibalism by eating their slaves, who were, despite their low status, considered to be a part of Aztec society. The purposes of human consumption can be defined as nutritional, ritual, demographic, competitive, and dysfunctional (Collinson 190). Practiced both by prehistoric humans and by the Uruguayan rugby team, nutritional cannibalism uses humans as a primary protein source on a regular dietary basis and in survival situations. Ritual cannibalism, practiced by the tribes of New Guinea, can be performed for significant religious and celebratory events, and to compensate for disasters, plagues, and the like. Endocannibalism and exocannibalism are found most commonly within cannibalistic rituals. Demographic cannibalism can be used for population control and where resources are limited. Competitive cannibalism occurs when the powerful consume the weak, often within the same social group, such as when adults consume the young, or a powerful nation consumes its enemies. Dysfunctional cannibalism is explained by a psychological disturbance or mental disorder, such as in the case of Jeffery Dahmer.

The Aztecs, in particular, justified their methods of cannibalism through their religion. However, it is likely that the practice was also necessary for their survival, as the land of Mesoamerica had few animal protein resources. The animal protein sources that were available, such as dogs, turkeys, deer, and fish, were consumed by the higher class individuals, leaving the lower class individuals with only corn, beans, and algae, which are not significant sources of protein. Marvin Harris states, "While corn and beans in sufficient quantity could provide all of the essential amino acids, recurrent production crises throughout the fifteenth century meant that protein levels were frequently depressed to levels which would have biologically justified a strong craving for meat" (Harris 110). Therefore, Aztec society used the only abundant protein resource available: humans. Their ritual cannibalism was, in essence, nutritional cannibalism. The biological urge for meat and protein is comparable to the human sexual libido, a natural, instinctual craving.

Human sexuality and cannibalistic urges are closely related as natural instinctual processes. Often sexual activity is combined with concepts that suggest consumption, such as kissing and oral sex. The human mouth's functionality relies upon both hunger and passion, and serves as a primary source of physical pleasure, comparable to the genitals. Food, flesh, and sex essentially always correlate in the human mind, as an infant's first source of food traditionally originates from the breast, a dominant symbol of sexuality in society. In fact, several cannibal tribes report their taste preference of the penis, breasts, and vulva (Crumpacker 209-210).

However, the relationship between cannibalism, sex, and food is presented most vividly in literature and linguistics. For example, Bram Stoker, author of the classic horror story of *Dracula* in 1897, "capitalized on the always ready connection between food and sex, between love and the love bite, in his story of the bloodsucking vampire who found his way to the staid, repressed side of a pale English lady" (Crumpacker 212).The tale of the vampire is a compellingly erotic mixture of sexual activity, as the attractive Dracula first seduced his victims, and consumption, as he then proceeded to drain them of blood. In linguistics, it is evident that several phrases, such as "I could eat you up, "metaphorically insinuate both sex and consumption. The phrase "is said by Claude Levi Strauss to exist in the erotic vocabulary of most cultures and to embody an 'analogie très profonde'" or a profound analogy (Rawson 82). In the French language, the verb "*consommer* can refer equally to sexual and gastronomic transactions" (Rawson 82), which highlights the close relationship of the two acts by merging them into a single word, depending only upon context to distinguish intended meaning. Similarly, in the English language, Rawson also states that the word "consume" is contained within the word "consummate" which describes the initial occurrence of sexual intercourse of a married couple (Rawson 82). Rawson's linguistic examination proposes that much of human sexual activity is based upon consumption, which suggests that by engaging in sexual activity, we are in a way consuming one another.

Humanity's long history with cannibalistic urges suggests that such behavior is ingrained in the most basic aspects of our psyches. Human instincts are survival methods, which urge us to consume, procreate, and prolong our overall lifespans. Since it is a basic instinct, we need to examine the history of its prohibition. The practice became taboo in Europe after the establishment of cohesive, functional societies with agricultural systems and domesticated animal resources for protein. This taboo disregards our most primal urges. Marvin Harris, author of "Cannibals and Kings," quotes Eli Sagan, who finds that cannibalism is "'the most fundamental form of human aggression'" (Harris 103). Harris also notes the "elaborate theories offered in the Freudian tradition which claim that torture, sacrifice, and cannibalism are intelligible as expressions of instincts for love and for aggression" (Harris 103). Additionally, Bunny Crumpacker also reminds us that "babies have to learn that teeth are for chewing and not for biting. Most of us forget that the mouth itself is a weapon, the first weapon, the most primitive one" (Crumpacker 200). Though we are now repulsed and disgusted by the prospect of eating the flesh of another, it is a part of our development, much like sexuality, which is also hidden and condemned in Western society. Some would argue that our suppression of urges creates a world plagued with overpopulation, excessive waste, and unresolved conflicts and the benefits of cannibalism far outweigh its potential disadvantages, since the practice can be used to solve numerous devastating world issues and not simply for superfluous barbarism. We'll explore the uses of cannibalism in the next section.

There are practical uses for cannibalism. Cannibalism can be used as a method of social control, as demonstrated in primitive societies. Endocannibalism used as punishment for criminals can be an effective crime deterrent. Possible deviants within a society will be less likely to commit crimes if the consequence of such behavior is to be consumed by those of their own social groups. In modern American society, twenty percent of Americans are currently incarcerated. Prisons require physical space to house the prisoners, resources such as food, water, and clothing, to meet the prisoners' basic needs, and manpower to control the prisoners. Therefore, much of our time, energy, and resources are awarded to those who have committed crimes against our societal rules. Instead of wasting such valuables on deviants who chose to violate and disregard the American legal system, such deviants could be used as a source of protein. Manufacturing animals, such as cows, pigs, and chickens, as a protein source depletes the Earth of fossil fuels and requires a vast amount of energy. If Americans instead slaughtered and ate prisoners, society would blossom with more land, less crime, and a more environmentally sustainable source of protein. As our resources inevitably become scarce in the future from overuse and exploitation, this human protein could be used as a reward, as in Aztec society where, "the cost/benefits of political control underwent a favorable shift as a result of using human flesh to reward selected groups at crucial periods" (Harris 110). Individuals will be more motivated to obey societal rules if they are aware that they will receive rewards, particularly rewards that are scarce. Additionally, exocannibalism could deter foreigners from committing crimes against other societies, which could potentially reduce looming threats of international wars and terrorism.

In addition to establishing a more effective means of social control, cannibalism can also solve the issue of overpopulation. Overpopulation is a problem that effects the Earth as a whole, as it depletes resources and causes issues such as hunger, housing shortages, excessive waste, increased carbon dioxide production, and steadily destroys the Earth's natural resources. Instead of continuing to consume the irreplaceable natural resources of our environment, societies should use resources that are overproduced and readily available, such as human beings. Using fellow humans as a primary protein source will lead to the eventual decrease in population size, as Aztec society has proven.

> Aztec war and sacrifice were part of a system for
> regulating population growth. [Cooke] calculated that the
> combined effect of combat deaths and sacrifices produced
> an annual elevation of 25 percent in the death rate. Since
> 'the population was reaching a maximum consistent
> with the means of subsistence...the effect of warfare and
> sacrifice would have been very effective in checking an
> undue increase in numbers (Harris 107).

Instead of mindlessly enforcing infanticide or placing boundaries upon childbirth, we could instead eat humans deemed as unneeded or menaces to society, such as criminals and the homeless. Those who do not wish to benefit society's advancement and instead inhibit its improvement should be used as food sources.

If cannibalism can reduce overall world population size, resources can then be preserved and the production of waste can be minimized. Modern society exploits natural resources by using food, clean drinking water, and oil, in excess, which thus instills in individuals the concept that our resources are expendable, leading to the creation of more waste. Therefore, cannibalism is an environmentally sustainable option to combating problems such as pollution and global warming. Using humans as a protein resource would also have a monumental impact upon modern industrialized food companies that rely upon the slaughter and manufacture of animals. Mass-produced animal protein, which creates a large amount of waste and drains the Earth of vital energy, could be relied upon less often. To use human protein most effectively, with the least amount of waste, the bodies of the dead could be consumed instead of burned or left to rot in the Earth. Though diseased flesh would be discarded and regarded as unfit for consumption, healthy deceased humans, such as war casualties, could be salvaged for food.

However, cannibalism does not exist without risks and possible disadvantages. Kuru, a prion disease related to Creutzfeldt-Jakob disease, also known as Mad Cow disease, is a health concern in cannibalistic societies. It was first displayed in 1950 amongst the cannibalistic tribes of New Guinea. Kuru, a word that means "shaking," has a long incubation period and causes neurological degeneration, bodily trembling, and ultimately death. An American neurologist, Daniel Gajdusek had originally hypothosized that a "slow virus" was the cause of the condition, but later learned, when the tribe ceased practicing rituals that involved consuming undercooked human brain tissue, that the disease was caused by prions in the human brain tissue (Collinson 197). This condition, however, could likely be avoided in a futuristic cannibalistic society by cooking human flesh thoroughly and heating it to a temperature that would destroy all existing prions, as we do now with pork and certain other problematic proteins.

Cannibalism, the primitive concept of man eating man, can be used to solve numerous contemporary issues in society today, as exemplified in the society of the ancient Aztecs of Mesoamerica. Although the Aztecs existed in the 15th century, they faced many of the same problems we, as members of modern society, are currently experiencing. The Aztecs used cannibalism as a method of social control, population control, and as a source of protein in a land of scarce resources. Today, our world suffers from overpopulation, diminishing resources, and increasing crime rates. While cannibalism seems like an effective solution, its practice is forbidden and regarded with disgust because of societal taboos. However, cannibalism is a natural part of our development, not a mindless display of barbarism, as it has existed since the origins of humanity, much like sexuality. Cannibalistic and sexual urges are related as natural human instincts, as most clearly demonstrated in literature and linguistics. Instincts exist to prolong our survival and assist our senses; therefore by ignoring them, we are ultimately reducing our productivity and quality of life as human beings.

Works Cited

Ackerman, Diane. "Taste." *A Natural History of the Senses. Vintage*, 1991. 127-172. Print.

Crumpacker, Bunny. T*he Sex Life of Food: When Body and Soul Meet to Eat*. New York: Thomas Dunne Books, 2006. Print.

Harris, Marvin. *Cannibals and Kings: Origins of Culture*. New York: Random House, 1977. Print.

Henry, Jaya, et al. "Consuming the Inedible: Neglected Dimensions of Food Choice." New York: Berghahn Books, 2007. Web.

Rawson, Claude. "I Could Eat You Up: The Life and Adventures of a Metaphor." *The Yale Review* 97.1 (2009): 82. Humanities Module, *ProQuest*. Web. 5 Nov. 2009.

Adam Barnett

Discourse Communities

Classmates, family members, and friends assume that I remain a part of a variety of discourse communities that define my course in life based on acquired mannerisms and lifestyles. However, none of these exchanges that take place between fellow manatee enthusiasts or accordion players appear quite as interesting as that of, say, an actual manatee, a dinosaur, or a Vietnam War veteran. Presently, the majority of my generation flocks to one gigantic general system of education and community. Although the details of the educational system and the communities may differ, in that one may focus on science and another on minimalist art, and customs may vary greatly between religions and heritage, these seemingly intricate communities represent the same, general relationships most humans maintain; that is mainly, family, friends, school, and work. However, because of the trite differences between specific interest groups, members of such exclusive communities refuse to journey outside of their monotonous comfort zone that they seem to share with the majority of the population. Let me explain this concept through poetry:

Patrick pokes a pretty hole through his perfect plaster wall of his perfectly pretty dormitory room.

He exclaims to himself, "Oh boy! A whole new world for me to explore!"

However, he realizes that the hole in the wall leads to his neighbor, Patricia, who is mirroring his every move, thinking the exact same thoughts.

They both ponder the coincidence, and know exactly what the other is thinking:

"I expected as much. Might as well go get some tape and then study for my English test."

They both tape the wall from either side, reinforcing the wall, the barrier.

They both go to English. They both fail the test.

One cries, the other leaves to smoke a cigarette.

Sadly, the friends of a typical man, Joe, who listen to the same music and babble about the same topics daily, his neighbors who dwell in the same location as him, and his coworkers who experience the same basic daily lives as Joe, render him unable to explore and associate with other discourse communities because of a lack of exposure to a varied way of life and far more interesting people, enforcing the divisions of these monochromatic discourse communities. Thus, instead of doggy paddling between a series of disconnected rivers of communities like Joe, I prefer to scuba dive into the ocean where the rivers meet to connect with individuals and groups from all across one gigantic communal spectrum. However, this method may not appeal to other closed-minded fellows less accepting of change and obscurity than myself because they might despise, hate, absolutely detest, and wholly scorn change or something a bit different from their everyday routine, and therefore might not follow suit in my willingness to cross boundaries most men and women my age never imagine crossing.

For instance, I quite enjoy Pokémon, Ultimate Frisbee, Obscure Orchestral Indie Music, X-Men and the color purple (not to be confused with the feature film). Yet, because of intolerance of certain communities towards certain hobbies, interests, and practices, these varied interests jeopardize my participation in various other communities:

Setting: Purple Anonymous
Date/Time: 3/25/2008—9:34 AM
Me: "Hello. My name is Adam, and I love the color purple."

Everyone in Purple Anonymous: "Hi Adam."

Me: "I love purple to the point that I wear it every day. I even wear purple flip flops in the shower. The only time I haven't worn purple was for comic-con last year because I was dressed as Professor Xavier, and—

Leader of Purple Anonymous: "Excuse me, but members of Purple Anonymous require you to commit to wearing purple during all hours of the day. Because of your silly interest in comic books, you have broken our only rule, and thus you are banned from Purple Anonymous and from wearing the color purple ever again because you are a disgrace."

Exclusive Discourse communities require certain sacrifices, usually involving the dissociation of oneself from another group of people. This ultimately leads to segregation amongst high school lunch tables, as depicted in the film *Mean Girls* or any actual high school cafeteria. These sacrifices, possibly involving time, resources, and the notorious "others," also create a specialization of labor, much like that of a factory in the macrocosm of the labor force and higher education system. While one student spends four years earning his bachelor's degree in music, he misses out on his opportunity to gain the same knowledge of biology or field that might prove useful in the event that the student fails in any occupation involving music. To avoid the trap of the typical microcosmic conveyor belt, I journey into other discourse communities to steal bits and pieces of information to construct my own knowledge bank with the intent of combining these discourses into one practical use.

Time to imagine:

Comic Books + Music +Film + Purple + Pineapple +Transcendentalism + Socks = A movie-musical version of Spiderman entitled Spiderman: A Life in the Woods; *it is a film that involves Spiderman's urge to "know [pineapple]," while he wears a pair of nice, purple, wool socks.*

Imagination becomes reality:

January 31, 2024

Dear Mom,

Last night was the premier of Spiderman: A Life in the Woods. The premiere sold out, and the movie is selling out in every other theater in the continental US, as well as France. I'm sorry if you and Dad aren't the biggest fans of Spiderman, pineapple, or Walden. *However, you should consider journeying outside of your comfort zones to witness other concepts, ideas, and cultures that you may not take into consideration individually. They may combine to possibly form something beautiful beyond your wildest dreams. Oh, and can you send me up some socks? Mine were all used up by the time we finished shooting the 4th scene.*

Thanks,

Adam

Acceptance of Reality

February 2, 2024

Dear Adam-kins,

I just saw your movie with your father and have to admit that it's possibly one of the greatest films ever produced since Casablanca. *Since my trip to the theater, we've picked up the first ten issues of* Spiderman, *Henry David Thoreau's* Walden: Life in the Woods, *purple socks, a pineapple upside-down cake, and of course, the soundtrack to your wonderful, wonderful musical. As you can see, you've had quite an influence on your father and me. We're so very proud of you and look forward to the sequel.*

Love,

Mom

P.S: Your socks should reach you within the next few days.

Clearly, an open mind can result in the acquisition of new and exciting interests and lifestyles that one pig-headed man, sadly, might never experience. My mother in the future represents a global example of the how branching out into the vast forest of discourse communities will affect the world.

Because of a collective failure to recognize examples like my mother's, this generation of young adults lacks the open-mindedness necessary to develop new forms of technology and entertainment. Lately, engineers develop instead of invent. Musicians recreate songs instead of write and compose original works of art. Screenplay writers recreate story lines or borrow plots from other movies instead of creating original films. Essentially, this results from the adamancies of these "innovators" to branch out to other industries, trades, practices, and even foreign countries involved in the same field, thus preventing them from creating new and original ideas deriving from combined inspirations from varied sources.

Thus, here is the next assignment for the rest of the world, and I don't care if you think you've started on it already:

Find someone (or something) interested in something completely different from yourself, whether it be a clown, a dinosaur, or a manatee. Ask about his main functions within the world. Become his friend, and learn how to be a manatee, or a clown, because it might prove useful to you in the long run. You might suddenly acquire an interest in riding a unicycle, roaring, or swimming, and thus incorporate it into a movie-musical, a novel, or just share said interest with your friends. Then write a paper on your experiences so that you won't forget about the epiphany you reach after the interaction if you happen to blend, once again, into the same patterns of music, conversation, and life itself.

Ready? Go.

Ryan Debski

The Afghanistan Question

Throughout my life, I have always been one to educate myself on current events of the day, especially when it comes to matters of government and politics. I began watching the evening world news intently when I was in the latter half of my elementary school years. I found that I needed a source to feed my ever growing curiosity about the world and the daily news provided me with a quick overview of current events. At first, headlines such as "Five Bosnian Croats Sentenced Up to Twenty-five Years in Prison for the Killing of Over One-hundred Bosnian Muslims" or "Iraq Rejects Latest UN Security Council Weapons Inspections" meant nothing to me, because I did not have a context for which the events were occurring and I did not understand many of the terms that were being used. I asked myself questions like: What is a Bosnian Croat and why would they murder other Bosnians? Where is Iraq and why would they reject a weapons inspection proposal? As I grew older, I progressively developed the context that I had been missing in years previous, and the headlines on the evening news began to make sense.

Soon enough, my emergent curiosity about the world became a passion for acquiring knowledge. I wanted to learn why certain societies did not get along with other societies and how different governments manipulate each other in order to advance their causes. In short, I wanted to learn how the world worked. However, I soon realized that sometimes knowledge only leads to more confusion.

I find war, in particular, to be confusing. I can understand everything there is to know about a specific war, and yet still not understand why it is being fought. To elaborate, it is possible for me to comprehend why the war is occurring and for what reasons; however, I am unable to fathom the most basic element of war: killing another human being. I am unable to conceive how one society can make the decision to go to war with another knowing that their countrymen will invariably die in the ensuing conflict. War fascinates me for this very reason. How can something that seeks to reach a definite solution to a matter that could not be decided peacefully result in so many questions?

When I turned on the TV the other day I saw President Obama walking side-by-side with a man dressed in his full military officer's uniform on the White House lawn. The caption underneath read, "What Will Obama Do about

Afghanistan?" This alluded to events that took place a few months prior: General Stanley McChrystal, the new American and NATO Commander in Afghanistan, had made an official request to President Obama for a 30,000 to 40,000 troop increase in Afghanistan. The request has sparked a debate about not only whether or not to surge troop levels in Afghanistan, but also over the United States' military and political strategy with the Afghani government. The debate has largely expanded because General McChrystal's request comes at a time when the United States' control over previously captured parts of the country are in jeopardy, the Taliban continues to gain power, and the death toll of American soldiers rises at an increasing rate. I, like many others, including geopolitical experts and military strategists, have asked myself the question, "So what should President Obama and the United States military do about Afghanistan?" Although the question seems simple, it is in fact extremely complex, problematic, and significant. It is all of those things because upon posing the question, it is immediately followed by a flurry of opinions that all have their supporters and critics. The question is also significant in that depending on what course President Obama decides to take, the lives of those 30,000 to 40,000 soldiers are possibly at stake as well as the long-term future of the Afghani people.

When I initially began to research the question, I decided that I would only research possible strategies that were not obscure or that were supported by a large number of people because President Obama would not choose a course that is too politically risky or unpopular with the American public. I also decided that I would research opinions that were derived from both liberal and conservative ways of thinking. From the outset, I wanted to explore a wide array of ideas that would occasionally be in conflict with each other and did not all come from the same perspective so that I could develop my opinion thoughtfully and without bias. If I had only become familiar with ideas from one political ideology or ideas that originated in only one geopolitical region, it would be impossible for me to gain an insight into the proverbial "other side of the story," and I would risk not being able to fully investigate the situation. And as a citizen who participates in the electoral process, I believe that not researching a question of this magnitude thoroughly is not only unethical, but is also irresponsible.

I opened my research with an article written by a writer for *Newsweek* and recognized expert on foreign relations, Fareed Zakaria. I decided to begin with this article because I had become familiar with Zakaria's moderate and seemingly honest opinions on news networks such as CNN. Zakaria believes that at the heart of General McChrystal's request for a major troop surge is the commander's assumption that we are failing in Afghanistan; however, Zakaria argues otherwise. He cites the United States' one central objective to fighting the war in Afghanistan, to deny al Qaeda the ability to plan and carry out major terror attacks, as being reason enough not to surge. For the past eight years, this mission has been largely successful, as al Qaeda is on the run and unable to organize attacks as it had done routinely in the 1990s.

He also cites several reasons the United States' course in Afghanistan should not be changed dramatically. The first reason is that al Qaeda's leadership has already been dismantled through the use of predator drones. In fact, fourteen of the twenty top al Qaeda officials have been killed by air strikes (Zakaria). Additionally, al Qaeda's political appeal in the Islamic world is at an all-time low. Before the war in Afghanistan in 2001, al Qaeda had received covert support and funding from many Islamic political elites, but now because al Qaeda is on the run and because of the United States' ability to track funds, al Qaeda's international support infrastructure is drying up (Zakaria). Furthermore, Zakaria believes that a troop surge could provoke a nationalistic backlash from the Afghani people. There is, of course, plenty of evidence in Afghanistan's history that supports this claim, the most recent evidence being the Soviet Union's failed 1979 invasion. There is also much evidence that suggests that al Qaeda has fled to Pakistan, and despite the Taliban's many pockets of turf control, al Qaeda has not shifted back to Afghanistan.

Zakaria also cites the surge in Iraq as a surprising reason not to surge in Afghanistan. He states, the "lasting element of the surge in Iraq was not the influx of troops, but getting Sunni tribes to switch sides by offering them security, money, and a place at the table" (Zakaria). This argument in particular stood out to me. My previous impression of the surge in Iraq was that troop levels alone helped to stabilize the country. However, as a result of this specific insight, I began to doubt my own support for a troop surge because it undermined what I thought to be a successful strategy that could be easily translated to the context of Afghanistan.

The next article that I read was written by Olivia Hampton of the British daily newspaper, *The Guardian*. Hampton does not explicitly lend her support to any specific strategy; however, she does provide one with a good understanding of the current situation in Afghanistan. Hampton begins by stating that Obama's team of military planners outlined and presented the President with four options, all of which reconciled General Stanley McChrystal's request for 30,000 to 40,000 more troops with Congressional Democrats' ambitions for drawing the war to a close. The first option, the "Gates Option," so-called because it is supported by Defense Secretary Robert Gates, would add 30,000 or more American soldiers to the already serving 68,000, and would require that NATO bridge the gap by adding around 10,000 of its own troops to meet General McChrystal's request. The second option demands that 20,000 American troops be added to defend twelve major Afghani population centers, while a counterterrorism strategy would be implicated in the more rural countryside with Special Operations providing intelligence for unmanned drone attacks. The third strategy involves no troop surge whatsoever, but the sole use of unmanned drones, which would in turn, rely on Special Operations. And finally, the fourth option would only deploy 10,000 to 15,000 additional troops.

Hampton also makes clear that all of these scenarios are further complicated by war weariness in all of the NATO member states as well as a growing belief in Europe and even Afghanistan itself that Hamid Karzai's government is corrupt. She also states that Ambassador Karl Eikenberry, a retired three-star general who served in Afghanistan, was also worried about the Kabul government's legitimacy. Hampton affirms that Eikenberry has "expressed serious misgivings about the plans" because additional US forces would only further the Afghan government's reliance on Washington's support and not challenge it to become increasingly responsible for its own people's security (Hampton).

Perhaps the most poignant and significant part of her piece is her closing statement in which she summarily expresses her opinion on the matter. Hampton believes that "fighters cannot be removed with force alone" (Hampton). This suggests to me that the Afghanistan question cannot be solved through the use of the military alone, but also through a variety of other means. Prior to encountering Hampton's article in *The Guardian*, I had not considered that the issue may be more than one-dimensional, meaning that military force was not the only factor in play. The major media outlets made so much to-do about our military strategy in Afghanistan that the other important factors that also affect the country's stability such as its government and economy were virtually ignored. Olivia Hampton opened my eyes to the fact that bringing stability to Afghanistan would take more than bullets and bombs.

I continued my research with an article written by Boris Johnson for *The Daily Telegraph*, another British daily newspaper. Johnson's article expresses his belief that the fight against the Taliban should not be abandoned by the British government. Johnson asserts that Britain should not pull out of Afghanistan until the United States pulls out because America is Britain's closest ally and the United States, he believes, has a right to be fighting the war. He also considers the United States and Britain to have a moral duty to improve the standard of living of the Afghani people in addition to teaching them the value of democracy and educating women. However, he argues that the most important reason Britain must remain in Afghanistan fighting is that to leave now would be a dishonor to those who have sacrificed their lives to the above causes. This, Johnson states, would be the "biggest betrayal" of all.

Upon reading Johnson's opinion I was struck by how different his ideas about the world were from the ideas in the other articles that I had read, most of which dealt with factual information that supported some sort of a thesis. However, in stark contrast, Johnson's piece used factual information to bolster his opinion as to why the coalition is morally bound to see Afghanistan through to stability. Although I was not interested in using something so based in ideology, as Johnson's ideas are, to aid my own examination of the situation, Johnson did raise important questions about what place morals have on the battlefield, or in a scenario like Afghanistan, and while I continued my exploration, I found that Johnson's article in particular intrigued and troubled me at the same time.

Although I had been committed throughout my inquiry to developing my opinion without preconceptions, I was inclined to favor General McChrystal's request for a troop increase for two reasons. The first was his belief that the war "will likely result in failure" if the quota is not met, and the second was that I did not think that any of my research would sway my opinion. What I found out was that I was wrong. My research allowed me to realize that the question cannot be answered with a simple yes or no, and that such a question requires a true exploration of all of the issues involved and their possible solutions.

Initially, I found merit in the "hybrid" option where American and NATO troops would pull out of the rural Afghanistan countryside and move to major population centers, and Special Operations forces would work in tandem with Air Force unmanned drone attacks. However, while I was conducting my research, I became aware of General McChrystal's emphatic opinion that the strategy would not work. I believe that whatever strategy is chosen by President Obama must also be supported by the military commanders who are carrying out the President's decisions. General McChrystal himself is a Special Forces veteran, and would obviously be well-acquainted with the abilities of that particular option. Additionally, the fact that most civilian deaths are caused by air strikes, a vital aspect of the counter-terrorism strategies, ended any credibility that I had found in that particular strategy.

The other most scaled-back option is not a viable solution in my opinion, because as Richard Cohen puts it in a *Washington Post* article, "Leave Afghanistan to the Drones," "it is designed to do nothing much but look like a strategy designed to do a great deal" (Cohen). It is neither "here nor there" because it does not give General McChrystal the logistics to accomplish his agenda in Afghanistan and it also "provokes the ire of the locals" who are unhappy with the presence of foreign troops in their country in the first place (Cohen).

So that leaves only one option on the table and that is the 30,000 to 40,000 troop deployment that was originally requested by General McChrystal. However, I do not believe that the troop surge alone will solve Afghanistan's many problems. Yes, the troops will certainly aid in the fight against the Taliban, especially in the rural parts of the country. And yes, the troops can provide added security in the country's population centers, but they cannot reform Afghanistan's government or provide the country with a stable economic infrastructure, both of which are desperately needed.

A surge will give the military an increased capacity to end the power struggle with the Taliban for control of Afghanistan's most rural and sparsely populated regions. I believe that fighting the Taliban is still relevant because without their complete elimination, al Qaeda would always have the ability to return to Afghanistan. Furthermore, I contend that an end to the Taliban's rule in Afghanistan can be achieved through a combination of both military force and diplomacy. Despite the risk of higher casualty losses, the United States and NATO could push the Taliban back to the Pakistani border by engaging them, potentially backing both the Taliban and what is left of al Qaeda into a corner with the newly recommitted Pakistani army on one side and the allied nations on the other. Additionally, I believe that by engaging Afghanistan's Pashtun population in a similar manner in which the Sunni tribes of Iraq were, the United States could bring an important local ally in the fight against the Taliban into the fold.

Part of the reason Pashtuns feel disenfranchised is that the current Kabul government has alienated them, thus forcing Pashtuns to migrate toward the Taliban. In general, Hamid Karzai sits at the head of an Afghani government that is largely incompetent and corrupt. Karzai recently won an election in which there have been hundreds of complaints about voter fraud. If that were not enough, his brother has been connected to Afghanistan's illicit drug trade ("Leaders: Obama's War"; "The War in Afghanistan"). In order to create a stable democracy in a fledgling country, the government of the democracy must play by the rules to establish its own right to govern. This is why I strongly believe that the current Kabul government and even its regime should be scrapped to make way for a new democratic system. The current system centralizes the political power with the federal government and not with regional provincial governments, but in a geographically and ethnically diverse country such as Afghanistan, people tend to look to the local governments as the closer source of authority. Therefore, I advocate that Afghanistan's current constitution should be replaced with a new decentralizing constitution that grants more power to the provincial governments than it does a federal government, which to many Afghanis might as well be a world away.

Furthermore, the United States should begin to invest heavily not only in Afghanistan's military, but also in its infrastructure and economy. Helping Afghanistan develop a viable economy would wean the country off of its opium trafficking, and provide a better life for Afghanistan's people, who would no longer see the Taliban as an option to turn to for stability. The answer for Afghanistan's economy could come in the form of the recently proposed Tapi natural gas pipeline that would begin in Turkmenistan and run through Afghanistan, ending in India. The project would bring critically needed jobs to the country in addition to "providing steady transit revenues for a long time" (Sobhani). A trans-Afghani pipeline linking the energy deficient countries of southern Asia with central Asia would also enhance Afghanistan's financial stability by creating long-term stakeholders who would increase foreign investment. By providing the necessary military protection, the financing to fund the project, and the diplomatic wherewithal to invite investors to the table, the United States could potentially be able to secure the ground roots for the country's future economic stability.

Finally, whatever strategy chosen by President Obama must include a detailed exit strategy that includes benchmarks and tentatively scheduled dates to put pressure on the Afghanistan government and the Afghani Security Forces as well as make it clear to the rest of the world that the United States has no intention of staying in Afghanistan longer than it needs to.

Afterword

A few days following the completion of "The Afghanistan Question," President Obama, in an address at the United States Military Academy, outlined his plan to return stability to Afghanistan. After a "thorough review" of all of the possible strategies, the President stated with conviction that it is a "vital national interest to send an additional 30,000 U.S. troops to Afghanistan." I agree with the President's decision to surge as well as his overall strategy in dealing with Afghanistan. However, one thing that I did not understand about the President's address was when he commented on the re-election of Afghani President Hamid Karzai. President Obama acknowledged that the election was "marred with fraud," but because the "election produced a government that is consistent with Afghanistan's laws and Constitution," Hamid Karzai is still the legitimate leader of the country. I understand that President Obama does not want to potentially undermine any progress that has been made in establishing a democratic government in Afghanistan by declaring Karzai illegitimate, but I also believe that President Obama is making a mistake if he does not demand that another election take place. In a democratic system of government, it is imperative that the citizens of a country believe that they have the ability to choose the people that govern them. This is especially true in fledgling democracies where the citizens do not traditionally have any experience with a non-authoritarian form of government. By not challenging the election, President Obama is inadvertently sending a message to the Afghani people that they still do not have the power to influence their government.

The debate over whether or not Karzai's government is indeed legitimate is, like most of the issues addressed in "The Afghanistan Question," a question of morality. I initially began to think about what role morality should play in President Obama's decision after reading Boris Johnson's "To Abandon Afghanistan Now Would Be a Betrayal of the Fallen." His argument for staying in Afghanistan was almost entirely based on morals, which immediately made me skeptical because I have learned that morals are not always rooted in reason. I especially question things whenever morality is brought up in the context of war. Wars are not moral. There is no way to justify the killing of a person that one has never met before and has never done anything wrong besides being the "enemy." I am also skeptical of his argument, especially in this situation, because it was al Qaeda's morals, their belief that the attacks that they carried out on September 11th, 2001 were righteous and justified by their religion, that prompted the war in the first place.

In their most basic components, wars are essentially a struggle between two states that are fighting for different morals. However, the more that I thought about morals within the larger context of war, the more I realized that morals are unavoidable in war for one simple reason: it is impossible for people to kill others that have done them no harm without the belief that they are doing something that is right. And in this paradoxical relationship morality is an inseparable truth of war. What I will truly take away from my research and this assignment is not my opinion or suggestion on how the war in Afghanistan should be handled by our country's leaders, but rather, whatever they decide to do, they will never be able to find a morally correct solution because in war, what is right is wrong, and what is wrong is right.

Works Cited

Cohen, Richard. "Leave Afghanistan to the Drones." *The Washington Post*. Washington Post Company, 10 Nov. 2009. Web. 10 Nov. 2009.

Hampton, Olivia. "Obama's Afghanistan Options." *The Guardian*. Guardian Media Group, 12 Nov. 2009. Web. 12 Nov. 2009.

Johnson, Boris. "To Abandon Afghanistan Now Would Be a Betrayal of the Fallen." *The Daily Telegraph*. Telegraph Media Group, 9 Nov. 2009. Web. 9 Nov. 2009.

"Leaders: Obama's war; The war in Afghanistan." *The Economist* 17 Oct. 2009: ABI/INFORM Global, *ProQuest*. Web. 18 Nov. 2009.

Obama, Barack. "West Point Address." United States Military Academy, West Point. 24 Nov. 2009.

Sobhani, Rob. "A Pipeline to Prosperity in Afghanistan." *Financial Times*. 9 Jan. 2010. Web. 9 Jan. 2010.

Zakaria, Fareed. "The Case Against a Surge: More Troops Won't Solve Afghanistan." *Newsweek*. 19 Oct. 2009: ABI/INFORM Global, *ProQuest*. Web. 30 Oct. 2009.

Manali J. Desai

Sex Trafficking: An Economic View on Slavery Today

In the 2008 hit suspense film *Taken*, a father is in despair when his 17-year-old daughter is kidnapped while on vacation in Paris. Making conversation with a man she randomly meets at the airport, she agrees to share a cab with him. Not knowing at the time that he would be her kidnapper, the naïve high school girl leads the cab to her house, allowing the stranger to have access to her address. The young girl quickly gets thrown into a prostitution ring along with her close friend and together they are humiliated and bid on by many different men. It isn't till her father tracks her down that she escapes this nightmare, unlike her friend who ends up raped and dead. Although this is just a fictional movie, for many women around the world this is their reality. Sex trafficking has grown to become a notorious industry which annually rakes in billions of dollars, unfortunately from the exploitation of innocent women.

Human trafficking has become an extremely lucrative business in which exploiters from around the world actively transport innocent women to and from countries. Trafficked women and children are not terribly hard to spot, as we see prostitutes of all ages pacing the city streets late at night. While not all women who give up their bodies to complete strangers can be classified as illegal aliens, a vast majority of them, more likely than not, are pimped against their own will. Women are hardly being treated as independent individuals, but rather as property, sold to gain a profit. Because of the underground nature of this criminal activity, governments are inadequately handling the situation, leading to more exploitation and inevitably perpetuating the cycle. By understanding the quick thinking and manipulative mindset of the pimps, and exposing their surprising strength in numbers, it can be said that the underlying motive of exploiters around the globe is solely economic.

The media depicts pimps as men who live glamorous lives, with more than one beautiful, busty woman hanging off their shoulders. Even though they are dressed in fancy clothes and expensive jewelry, we see these men as uneducated, usually speaking broken English or using slang terms. What is ironic about this depiction is that being a pimp, or exploiter, requires more brains than many seem to believe. Since trafficking is like a business, the exploiters must be able to play the game well or face termination of their jobs and/or companies. You aren't going to get hired, promoted, or make any money if you have no idea how the game works and what loopholes to go through when obstacles arise. The better an exploiter can operate, the more money he will make in the sex trafficking industry.

Exploiters are constantly trafficking young women and children because when it comes to who they recruit, the process is almost effortless. They have an extremely manipulative force that makes girls either fall in love or believe their best interest is staying with them (Hughes). How does this train of thought contribute to the economic motive that was previously proposed? As Hughes explains, sex trafficking has been thriving due to the ability of men to con girls into believing a better life is awaiting them, with endless money, luscious gifts, and a love so true nothing could tear them apart. Many women are lured into the business because they often come from broken homes with little to no money, and they have no job or education. The future is bleak, and there is no other way out (Hughes). If a man came up to you in this situation and told you he could change all of that, in an instant, what are the odds that you would say no? The luxuries and stability that can be provided by the pimps far outweigh the lifestyles these women are currently living. The recruitment of these vulnerable girls feeds the money pot because the cost to capture is zero and selling the women off makes a hefty profit. The money they save can be thrown into other illegal activities that most exploiters are involved in, including "trafficking arms and drugs" (Pyshchulina).

Conning young women and forcing them to be sex slaves is not the only way exploiters gain access to women. Although this is the more appealing route, another more expensive way is to buy young children off of their parents (Foo). Even this doesn't come at a high cost because poverty-stricken homes are so desperate for money they often sell their offspring for next to nothing (Foo). The image of pre-pubescent children being sold by their own flesh and blood is tragic because adults are supposed to protect their babies. Instead they are selling them out of desperation for only a couple of hundred dollars (Foo). Parents aren't only disposing of their children for money but also, paralleling the manipulation method, they see a better future and more prosperity for their children in more wealthy nations.

Surprisingly, trafficking could not exist without the intricate web that hundreds upon hundreds of individuals are tangled within. Since the business of sexual slavery is a covert operation, it must be closely monitored so the chance of getting caught is slim to none (Foo). To make this possible, there are, according to Woolf, a division of roles including investors, recruiters, transporters, corrupt public officials, and so on. Each sector has a different contribution so that illegally trafficked women may reach their destination countries (Hughes). Along with traffickers, "brothels, corrupt officials, hotels, and taxi drivers" all make a profit off of women because they house the "sex acts, provide rooms, transportation" and anything else necessary to keep the trafficking alive (Hughes). With so many sectors of people to cover up the dirty trail, it is easy to see why so much money keeps flowing into the business of sexual slavery without any questioning. Although only "4.2% of the world's slaves are trafficked sex slaves, they generate 39.1% of slaveholder's profits" (Foo). This is billions of dollars a year just being tossed around with no tabs and no restrictions. The traffickers have inside sources that guide them through the loopholes of the game which is why trafficking continues to expand not only in a sexual sense but a drug and weapons sense as well.

Since there are designated individuals hired to cover up the paper trail, and powerful individuals who indirectly or directly feed trafficking, pimps and exploiters know that their criminal activity is off the radar, which they fully use to their advantage. Corrupt officials such as police officers, politicians, and others who hold powerful positions, pay good money to prostitutes or escort systems for various sex acts (Hughes). If corrupt officials involve themselves in these acts and condone this behavior, then how can they protect the victims and lock up the perpetrators? They cannot, and this is how traffickers are allowed to get away with so much. Sadly, the "penalties for keeping slaves [...] have remained disproportionately low," which says to the criminals that even if you do get caught, it will just be a slap on the wrist (Foo). To make it worse, the receiving countries tolerate prostitution because it draws tourists and boosts their revenue (Hughes). They benefit from this heinous activity, thus not caring about what happens to the people supplying the victims to their country. The inadequate attention that governments give to this ever-growing problem gives traffickers the confidence to continue their illicit activities.

Economics play a crucial role in the success of not only sex trafficking but drug and arms trafficking as well. We see that women in most cases are taken from their homes and their families, not because they are kidnapped but because the men they put their trust in are full of deceit and trickery. If governments had stricter regulations and thoroughly enforced them, we might see the amount of innocent women and children trafficked decrease. Yet if we stand by and do nothing, allowing this brutal crime to go on, who will protect us when we need them the most?

Works Cited

Foo, Janis. "Sex Trafficking: Inside the Business of Modern Slavery." *Far Eastern Economic Review* (2009): 74-76. Web. 6 Nov 2009.

Hughes, Donna. "Sex Trafficking: Supply and Demand." (2006). Web. 6 Nov 2009. Pyshchulina, Olga. "Association Humanitarian Initiative." *Human Trafficking in Ukraine and Perspective of its Prevention*. Web. 6 Nov 2009.

Woolf, Aaron Gwin. "Dying to Leave: Business of Human Trafficking: Business Structures." (2000). Web. 21 Nov 2009.

Grace Leonard

The Breathing Canvas

The brush hits the canvas with a dull thud, like a muted drum. Paint flows as my brush dances across the white expanse of the canvas. Slowly, shapes begin to form, to make sense. A picture is forming. Music thumps in my ears and I fall into a rhythm. Load, paint, clean. Load, paint, clean. A quick check from my teacher, and then I move into color. And this is the true test of my abilities: will I be able to see the colors?—the beautiful reds and yellows and greens that warm the lit side of the object; the full purples and blues that make the shadows sing. I have begun the color study, and I have to paint light into the picture. I am trying to show the effect the light has on the object by using warm colors—the colors of fire—on the lit side of the object. The cool colors—the colors of water—are used on the shadows. The first time this was taught to me, I began to see colors everywhere. My blue shirt went slightly green where the light hit it, and a deep cobalt blue in the shadows. Rebecca returns as I place the final touches of the color study. She squints, making the shadows clearer to see for herself. I wait for her to make a comment or give a piece of advice. "All round objects have round edges" and "Light-dark, warm-cool, both matter" are her two favorite sayings, and those lines run through my mind as I paint, creating a sweet melody with the songs that play on my iPod. To my surprise, Rebecca tells me to proceed to the localizing stage. This is the first time this has happened since I began painting with her, so I don't begin to tune down the garishness of the color study for a few seconds. Happy energy begins to run through my veins, and I start on the background, making the pink and purple background on my canvas look like the magenta sheet in the still life.

I turn from my painting so that I can clear my head of my painting and accurately check my work. As I move away from the easel, I see Rebecca pick up a paint brush and demo a section for a student. When she finishes, she wipes the work she did and explains to the student why she did certain things. After this, she begins telling a story about her time studying under Nelson Shanks, the first great colorist, in order to emphasize her point. The story shows how much she knows about the medium of oil and the technique required to use it successfully. I turn back to my still life and compare my painting to the real thing. I silently reflect on how much Rebecca has taught me in the year and a half that I have been with her. She has passed on her considerable knowledge of colorism, as well as given me a much easier version of Nelson Shank's teaching. She has taught me how to handle five different mediums and the subtle differences between the applications of colorism to each medium.

I step back from my painting so that I can see the mistakes in the painting more easily, taking care to step around the electric heater. Stepping back gives me a better perspective on the still-life and the painting at the same time. I continue to paint, and then Rebecca is back for another check. She looks and squints, and a faint smile appears on her face. It looks good! She turns to me and commends me on working from macro to micro. She points out a few areas that need improvement, and I fix the problems with the energy that comes from having done something well the first time. Quite unexpectedly, the power in the studio goes out. Rebecca had forgotten that the electric heater was still on, and the power has blown out. Now, the only light comes from the sun as it is setting through the trees. Despite this, my painting seems to have a light shining on it. I smile because I know that I was successful in making my painting "breathe." I made it come to life by painting in the effect of light. It's not the first time that I have been able to do this, but this is the most successful instance by far, and as soon as the lights come back on, I return to my painting, wanting to keep painting light into the canvas.

Too soon, clean-up time comes, and Rebecca calls each of us over so that she can collect the oil paints on our palate that we didn't use. I reflect upon my painting while I wipe down my palate, and feel a glow of pride. It is by far my best yet. I walk out to my mom's car and secure my painting carefully in the back seat. When I get into the passenger seat, I remember, for the first time that day, the mound of homework that is waiting for me when I get home. I had realized before how calm painting makes me, but now I realize that it has become a vital part of my life. Without it, I would have no real way to relax and rid myself of the buildup of stress in my life. I wouldn't be able to become truly independent, even if it is only for twelve hours every month.

Michael Meyers

Bilingual Thinking

[handwritten annotations: Logic & structure → presents a self-realization → explores an issue → self-research → sources → conclusions]

Years ago when I was in kindergarten, my teachers introduced me to the Spanish language. I was absolutely baffled by the idea that other people talked this funny way and actually understood each other. The concept of learning a second language fascinated me, until I finally decided to learn one in eighth grade, when I started taking German. This experience invited me to explore the ways a second language can change the way one thinks, and now I want to understand more completely how the acquisition of a second language can influence the mechanism of thought.

I had my own ideas about how a second language can affect one's thought, which were based on my own experiences as I learned to speak German. Throughout my years of learning, I saw that how I thought was actually able to change. Initially, I seemed to keep a key in my mind, and as I heard each word, I looked up what that word meant, then combined my translated words to try to extract meaning from the sentence I had just read. To speak I was able to quickly rearrange sentences to match the German grammar in my head, and then look up the translations in my mental dictionary. Eventually, I realized that this was far too inefficient, because I wanted to be able to speak German the way I could speak English, that is, without thinking about it. Instead of learning translations for words, I tried to simply learn words that I'd never seen before. Each time I learned a new word, I just treated it like another English word for something, rather than a different language. Once I started learning this way, I quickly realized that as my German vocabulary grew, the voice in my head was using fewer and fewer English words, and I needed English less. Grammar automatically switched around when I used these new words. My German teacher always said "Deutsch ist logisch," meaning "German is logical," and now that I could think in German, I understood what she meant. I could understand how grammar worked; I could see subjects performing actions on direct objects, as if language were suddenly the most perfect and obvious way to describe anything. To me, an interaction between two objects became a verb, a relationship became a preposition, and everything matched up. German had revolutionized the way I saw the world. This was just my little theory, though, and before I started claiming it as truth, I needed to find out what more qualified researchers had to say on the subject.

[handwritten annotation: Learning a second language changed the way he thinks]

Originally, I thought that there could not really be much concrete information on how bilingualism affects thought, since thought itself seems to be such an ill-defined process. "How can there be actual science about an idea that abstract?" I asked myself. A skeptical search of Drexel's library's database, however, revealed that there was plenty of information on the subject.

One of the most interesting ideas to me at the start was how a second language could reach backwards and influence a bilingual's native language. I found an article published in *Psychological Science* by a group of researchers about how bilinguals treat cognates, words with similar sounds, as they read. The article, written by Eva van Assche and a team of researchers from Ghent University, describes how researchers tested bilinguals by tracking their eye movement as they read over sentences containing a cognate, and found that cognates took, on average, less time to read than other words.

The conclusion that this article leads to makes plenty of sense. Becoming more familiar with a certain word should make it easier to identify, just like any other learning experience, but the idea that a second language can influence the way one reads in his or her native language is exciting. This idea involves a change in the way a person uses his or her native language, one of the first things that person ever learned.

Although it is significant, I thought that becoming familiar with cognates seemed too obvious of a subject for all of the results that came up when I searched the databases, so I went back to explore other ways that bilingualism can affect a person's thinking. I managed to find an article that seemed to have more of a physical, scientific basis, called "Neural Aspects of Second Language Representation and Language Control," written by a researcher named Jubin Abutalebi at Vita-Salute San Raffaele University in Italy. Abutalebi describes how he wanted to research the neural differences between a person's first and second languages. He discusses conclusions researchers have come to using functional magnetic resonance imaging (fMRI), a way of imaging neural activity, to examine differences in languages, and comes to his own conclusion that, at least on the neural level, differences only exist between languages when one is much more comfortable with one language than with the other. According to his research, the differences in how the brain treats languages disappear if the speaker is able to speak his or her second language as easily as a native could speak that language. For example, imagine a person is asked to speak in his or her first language and an fMRI image is taken of his or her brain. Then the same person is asked to speak his or her second language, and another fMRI image is taken. If the person is equally proficient in the two languages, then the same regions of the brain will light up in the image. But, if the person is stronger in one language than in the other, then different parts

Build off each other (research)

of the brain will light up, indicating that the languages are being processed differently.

Abutalebi's research, in a way, confirms what I originally thought about learning a new language. Language does have ways of influencing one's thought, but eventually, differences between two languages diminish and thoughts are the same whether they are in one language or the other. This explains why it was possible for me to switch my thinking into German; I simply switched which parts of my brain I was using to process the language. It does not, however, account for the way German helped me suddenly understand grammar. *CAN'T THINK IN BOTH LANGUAGES AT THE SAME TIME*

Although it is what I expected, Abutalebi's article was somewhat disappointing, as I hoped to find something really profound that learning a second language would do to one's thinking process. So this time, when I looked again for articles, I searched for something that was as significant as Abutalebi's, but that described a bigger change in the way a person thinks because of being bilingual. I managed to find an article that investigated the links between bilingualism and executive function, which is how a person controls his or her cognitive functions. In this new article, Stephanie Carlson and Andrew Meltzoff, both professors at the University of Washington, reasoned that since bilinguals have to actively inhibit one of their languages from being used, they should have better control over their own cognitive abilities. This study compared test results from native bilingual, monolingual, and second-language immersion kindergarten students, and found that the native bilinguals had higher scores for their executive functioning than the monolinguals did.

This article is more of an exciting one, since it has concrete evidence that knowing a second language actually influences thought unrelated to language. The mechanism for this change is simple: learning to suppress a language would give one practice controlling one's thoughts, and it supports the idea that learning a language changes the way a person thinks, even in ways unrelated to words and language.

After reading this article, I understood something about my own experiences that always seemed a mystery to me. I have always had a short attention span, which for a very long time caused me to do poorly in school. My average in elementary and middle school was a C, but towards the end of my freshman year and beginning of my sophomore year in high school, when I started to try thinking in German, I began to get better grades. In retrospect, I have realized that when I was finally able to think in German, my grades peaked and I was earning straight As.

Carlson's article and my recent realization had me excited to find out more, and I came across an article that delved into something that was very interesting to me: how does the language being used affect the concepts being discussed? I found an article that examined the effect of grammatical gender, which is an arbitrary assignment in most languages other than English, on actual concepts. The article, by Benedetta Bassetti, was published in the *International Journal of Bilingualism*, which contains research on different questions arising from bilingualism. Bassetti's article investigates how children's concept of an object's gender is affected by the object's grammatical gender. The children were asked to assign a male or female voice to a noun with which they were presented. Bassetti provides credibility for this study by comparing the results from children who speak both Italian and German, and children who speak only Italian. She explains that she used objects whose grammatical gender is opposite in German and Italian, to see if the monolinguals, who only have the Italian concept of the object, have a differing concept from the bilinguals, who have both the German and Italian concepts of the object. Her conclusions were that the bilinguals showed less of a preference for assigning an object either gender than Italian monolinguals did.

Bassetti's article fascinated me, because it really provided evidence that differences between languages can and do affect a person's concept of objects. Changing how one defines an object is a profound change to result from learning a new language, and is one of the things I was really hoping to find, although at first it seemed unbelievable.

The research I did gave weight to the idea that learning a language can change the way one thinks, whether neurally, conceptually, or cognitively. Although some of it swayed me to think that two languages are not different in the brain, most of it lent credibility to the idea that different languages do cause differences in how one thinks.

Works Cited

Abutalebi, Jubin. "Neural aspects of second language representation and language control. (Report)." *Acta Psychologica.* 128.3 (July 2008): 466(13). Academic OneFile. 26 Oct. 2009

Bassetti, Benedetta. "Bilingualism and thought: grammatical gender and concepts of objects in Italian-German bilingual children." *International Journal of Bilingualism* 11.3 (2007): 251+. *Academic OneFile.* Web. 16 Nov. 2009.

Carlson, Stephanie M., and Andrew N. Meltzoff. "Bilingual experience and executive functioning in young children.(Report)." *Developmental Science.* 11.2 (March 2008): 282(17). *Academic OneFile.* 26 Oct. 2009

Van Assche, Eva, Wouter Duyck, Robert J. Hartsuiker, and Kevin Diependaele. "Does Bilingualism Change Native-Language Reading? Cognate Effects in a Sentence Context. (Report)." *Psychological Science.* 20.8 (August 2009): 923(5). Academic *OneFile.* 20 Oct. 2009

Rhetoric & Response
Language literacy
Some German

LANGUAGE SHAPES THE WAY IN WHICH WE SEE THE WORLD
EXPLORES THE IDEA

- REFLECT
- TELL STORY
- PROFILE

EXAM/RESEARCH IDEA
WHERE YOU ARE NOW
AND THEN FUTURE

Nirali Patel

Cultural Restrictions on Education

Education is important for furthering a nation's growth. Many cultures have placed restrictions on the education provided to its people. The restrictions are mainly placed upon the women, with many adverse effects, including, at times, the deprivation of education for men as well. Despite the many negative effects of cultural restrictions on education, they continue to exist throughout societies.

There are many restrictions that are placed upon people of certain cultures. One example is the fact that many women receive only minimal education in certain areas. For instance, arranged marriages are very common in Orthodox Jewish religious societies (Antwerp Jewry) and being educated does not look good on women's "marriage applications." When a young person comes of age, they set up what is in a sense a resume that incorporates the life history of the individual, allowing others to see if they can be a possible match. Many times, it is not a suitable trait for women who want to get married to be more educated than their possible suitors. Jewish girls are encouraged to get basic education, but it is not wise to attend universities for further education outside the protected boundaries (Longman 7). These protected boundaries are generally outside of the community and there are no secondary education settings available within the confines of the community. This is then considered problematic because the parents of the young women are not comfortable allowing them to go out of the community. The lack of encouragement due to marriage added to the parents' concerns relating to the women travelling outside of the community boundaries cause many women to receive minimal education.

In many nations, women are taught the household chores above everything else. Being educated is not an important aspect of their lives. This causes women, such as those from Yemen, to believe that the only way they can contribute to the society is by bearing many children, working in the fields, and taking care of their parents. They learn these household chores during their childhood, and generally are married off by the age of 15 or 16 (Metres 9). My great-grandmother herself was not educated in a school system. During that time period in India, especially in rural villages, many women were married off between the ages of 12 and 15. She learned the household chores during her early years of life and by age 13 was married to my great-grandfather. She then went on to have ten children. Her job was to take care of the children and maintain the household, while at times assisting my great-grandfather in the field.

The goal for women in many societies like in Yemen is to have a successful marriage that bears many children (Metres 8). The system that they have leads them to believe that they have nothing more to fight for and thus do not believe in educating themselves. Instead, they work to learn the household chores and do not ask to be educated. Even if they disagree, girls are not allowed to protest because they are bound by the law which states that their fathers are allowed to marry them off to whomever they please (Metres 13). My great-grandmother was the perfect example of this, as she did bear ten children and never asked her parents to allow her to go to school with her brothers.

Some women are banned from schools. For instance, girls under the Taliban rule in Afghanistan are not allowed to be educated past the age of 12. There are certain schools that females attend in secrecy. The females arrive in twos or threes, heavily veiled, to receive an education. It is very dangerous to do so because everyone faces jail time, even if they are only children (Shah 2). This is enough to keep others away.

The gender gap between girls and boys is decreasing (only for primary school), except in South Asia and South Africa, where there is still a discrepancy in the completion rate (Anonymous 6). More boys than girls finish school throughout the world. Even though there are almost an equal number of boys and girls enrolled, the problem is that not all of the girls complete their education because of the restrictions.

Cultural restrictions are placed upon education for a variety of reasons, justifiable or not. Society's gender roles play a major part in restricting women from being educated. According to gender roles, men are the breadwinners and females are supposed to be in charge of the homestead. The women do the cooking, cleaning, and taking care of the children. When my mother lived in India, she had her bachelor's degree in nursing, and she was the head R.N of the hospital where she worked. When she came to America, she had an arranged marriage with my father. She wanted to take the nursing exam here, so that she could practice. But my grandmother and eldest uncle refused to let her. They said it was more important for her to stay home and take care of my brother and myself. They wanted her to follow the gender roles.

Many patriarchal societies view sending women to school as an "unwise investment" for families with low incomes and limited resources (Anonymous 7). There is not enough money to provide education to both the girls and boys. It is more pertinent for the moneymakers of the family to receive a better education, while the females are educated in the household chores (Metres 9). Male dominance is thought be another reason (Longman 6). So as to fulfill the gender roles and maintain the male dominance in the relationships, women are kept from being educated because having an education is empowering.

Protection is another reason that women are not educated. Many strict Islamic countries frown upon coeducation and there is a lack of women educators. It is frowned upon, but nothing is done to change the system for the better. For instance, in Afghanistan, when the women were removed from the job market, many of the schools had to shut down. This led to a deprivation of education for both girls and boys. The Taliban promised that proper schools for females would be set up when the war was over and the economy was stable (Shah 2). In countries such as Yemen, there are very few female teachers available because their families do not approve of them either taking trains by themselves to work or living apart from them (Longman 7). Females are not allowed to have male teachers, so as to protect them from predators (Longman 5). This, in conjunction with there being a shortage of women educators, leads to a lack of education.

There are many adverse effects that come from the cultural restrictions that are placed upon education. Women make up a great amount of the population. They should be able to help the economy. "According to a governmental women's committee: 'One of the factors leading to the poverty circle is the insufficient contribution of woman to economic development'" (Shah 4). Many economies suffer because not all of their population is working to its full potential. Some women, such as those from Yemen, believe that they can only work in the fields and give birth to too many children. Also because there is such a high fertility rate, it adds to the growing problems that countries like Yemen face in providing primary education for both the boys and girls (Longman 12).

Women feel the only way they can be productive is by producing children, and in order to not be divorced by their husbands, have many children. This has many detrimental effects on these women. Their bodies are not always fully developed and ready to give birth. They are not allowed to see male doctors, so if there are not any female doctors available, then they are not allowed to see any doctor. They generally suffer from malnutrition and at times die from giving birth. They sometimes eat less to have lighter babies, so that it is easier to give birth to them (Longman 8). Many times this leads to death during childbirth.

There are many benefits of education that should cause there to be action against restrictions on education. Women are said to be able to live healthier lives. They are smart about prenatal and delivery services during pregnancy.

Having an increased amount of educated women decreases the fertility rate of the nation because the women marry later in life. They live longer because they do not have to face an increase in their mortality rate from the constant life-threatening childbirths and can, therefore, look after the health of their kids. In poor households, it is shown that when a woman dies, her children face an increased mortality rate for the next two years and have a decreased nutritional intake (Anonymous 6). Thus, being educated means that the women will live longer, and they will continue to take care of those that will eventually work for the nation that they are living in.

The economy does better having educated women. Since women make up a good chunk of most populations, if they were all educated it would help to further a nation's growth. Everyone would be able to work jobs that would help to better the economy. When the fertility rate of women is decreased, the strain on the country to provide education for both boys and girls is less severe and, in turn, the remaining and existing population can be educated (Longman 12).

There are solutions to these restrictions. In certain Jewish sects, such as the Antwerp Jews, they are very orthodox, but some women are educated. These women had rebelled against the traditions and the things that are expected of them. Women that are educated rebelled against their norms and some still married Orthodox Jewish men (Longman 8). Some women refused to let the norms or standards of society stop them from getting what they want. They adjust around their higher education and balance both. Some of them had married men who did not mind educated women (Longman 9).

There are solutions in which the women do not have to rebel, solutions that have been deemed effective and proven to work. Many of these solutions have been set forth by a woman, Geeta Rao Gupta, president of the International Center for Research on Women. The school fees need to be reduced because they always work against the girls. There should be more schools built closer to home or safer transportation to and from school, so that parents will allow their daughters to attend those. The schools themselves should have running water and toilets. The curriculum should be girl-friendly and girl-related (Anonymous 11). These solutions would increase the number of women actually receiving education in countries.

For nations that do not endorse coeducation, schools should be built for girls especially because the Quran says that all children are born equal and should be given equal treatment (Longman 55). If schools were built within the confines of communities, more women of Islamic religions would be able to work as teachers, providing education to young children. This would prevent the excuse that males could possibly prey upon young women. Also, the families of the women educators would feel more at ease knowing that they were safer because they did not have to take dangerous train rides every day or live by themselves. These solutions could dramatically improve the lives of many women and the nations themselves.

Despite all of the solutions offered, girls continue to be deprived of education. In some situations, boys are also being deprived of their education, because women are not allowed to teach. The question is: why have the problems not been fixed? The solutions are straightforward and they seem simple. I believe that implementing these solutions would mean that the way of life for many individuals would change. The cultural restrictions that are placed on education have been around for centuries. These changes may challenge the authority and power that many men in these cultures have. It is difficult for some to accept that women are their equals. The problems can be fixed. The gender roles and way of life are changing. There are orthodox men that are marrying educated women. If women begin to fight for themselves and are supported by their families, I believe these changes can occur. The changes would benefit the cultures as a whole, and I believe the people of the nations will eventually begin to see that and allow the changes to occur.

Works Cited

"Interview with Geeta Rao Gupta, International Center for Research on Women." Harvard Educational Review 78.4 (2008): 577-588. Research Library Core, *ProQuest*. Web. 29 Oct. 2009.

Longman, C. "Sacrificing the Career or the Family? Orthodox Jewish Women between Secular Work and the Sacred Home." *The European Journal of Women's Studies* 15.3 (2008): 223. Women's Interest Module, ProQuest. Web. 29 Oct. 2009.

Metres, Katherine M. "Women's Affairs: Despite Illustrious Past, Yemeni Women Suffer Discrimination." *The Washington Report on Middle East Affairs* XVI.1 (1997): 31. Multicultural Module, *ProQuest*. Web. 29 Oct. 2009.

Shah, Saira. "Nightmare World: Afghanistan's Women." *The World Today* 57.8-9 (2001): 25+. *Academic OneFile*. Web. 29 Oct. 2009.

UNESCO Institute for Statistics (UIS). 2004. *Global Education Digest 2004*. Montreal: UIS.

Publishing Group
Essays

Introduction

Researching, thinking, and writing are at the core of the College of Arts and Sciences. No matter what field they're in, students must be able to research, to find and evaluate the best evidence and information on a topic. They must be able to think, to formulate original ideas and take a fresh approach to a problem or question. And, of course, they must be able to write—excellent research and thought must be communicated to others to have value. After all of their reading and thinking about the work of others, students must make their own contributions to the field by writing.

The constant exposure to accomplished works published in their field of study can intimidate students when they sit down to write. Or inspire them. It may do both as students struggle to bring their own vision to the subjects they study and find the right words. Fortunately, this struggle often yields remarkable writing. The following works, selected from student submissions to the third-annual Drexel Publishing Group writing contest, exemplify a firm grasp of subject matter and a facility with language.

This volume of *The 33rd* marks the first publication of the winners of the Zelda *Provenzano* Endowed STEM Writing Award, a contest created to honor the memory of the late Zelda Provenzano, who loved teaching writing at Drexel and had a passion for science and technology. The award encourages Drexel students to write about science, technology, engineering, and math. This category attracted intriguing submissions, as did the Humanities, Social Sciences, and Graduate Student Essay categories.

The essays in this section of *The 33rd* cover a host of subjects from a range of disciplines in the arts and sciences, including the history of tuberculosis treatment; the importance of the single lens microscope and the man who invented it; the role of violence in the American Civil Rights movement; the benefits of a close reading of a lyric poem; and the use of the word "like" and how a focus on grammar can ruin a date. The topics are as diverse as the students who wrote about them, but the essays all demonstrate originality and boldness as well as great skill in researching, thinking, and writing.

Robert Meyer

Death by Grammar

A little more than three years ago, I went on a blind date that ended spectacularly poorly. It began well; she was tall and pretty, as my friend had promised, but more than that she was friendly, intelligent and easy to talk to. As I later came to discover, she was also somewhat over-sensitive, theatrical, and violent. Understand, dear reader, that by telling you this, I'm not trying to detract from her good qualities; I only wish to create a fuller picture and offer some possible explanation for that night's catastrophic sequence of events.

To be fair, my own honest yet blunt nature had previously been mistaken for insensitivity, which was most certainly the case that night. Anyway, I consider *how* the date ended (with an ashtray being hurled at my head), to be much less shocking then *why* the date ended. You see, despite our mutually positive first impressions and immediate rapport, as the evening progressed, I found myself becoming increasingly distracted. The substance of her conversation, which had initially captivated and impressed me, fell silent as it became overshadowed by the style of her speech. I struggled through the rest of dinner to remain focused on the person and not the persona but, as the hours passed, I decided that I had to say something: "Do you realize that you use the word 'like,' on average, at least ten times a minute?"

They hardly seemed like fighting words but tell that to the glass ashtray I witnessed explode into a cloud of sand against her living room wall. Regardless of her overreaction, I can now understand why her instinct was to take offense. The fact is that most people, even frequent users of *like*, associate this pattern of speech with only negative stereotypes.

Even though the expanded use of *like* is a relatively recent phenomenon, over the past thirty years a large number of studies have been done on the topic by researchers in the fields of pragmatics, discourse analysis, and sociolinguistics. While originally, experts tended to dismiss *like* as meaningless vocal filler (like 'um' or 'uh') attributed to teenage and pre-teenage girls, this usage of *like* has since been reclassified as a discourse marker. Far from being meaningless, these markers (sometimes referred to as "nonstandard *like*") have been further classified into two distinct forms known as focuser *like* and quotative *like*.

Quotative *like* is easily described. Primarily found in informal storytelling, *"like,"* coupled with a form of *"be,"* introduces either a direct or paraphrased quote or may be used to relate an internal dialogue. For example: "He was like, 'can I borrow your shoes?' and I'm like, 'Is this guy serious?'"

Focuser *like* is by far the more common application of nonstandard *like*. San Diego State University professor and Harvard Ph.D. Robert Underhill asserts that *"Like* is neither random nor mindless. Instead, it functions with great reliability as a marker of new information and focus" (Underhill 234). Very basically, focuser *like* is used to call attention to, or highlight, some upcoming part of a speech. For example: "We went to, like, the craziest party ever!"

Furthermore, I would propose the addition of a subcategory to focuser *like* that I will refer to as: approximator *like*. Perhaps the most grammatically correct and socially acceptable form of focuser *like*, approximator *like* is used to disclose an upcoming estimation to the audience. For instance: "He was, like, six feet tall" or "It was like four o'clock."

Admittedly, my blind date can only be viewed as an extreme example, in terms of both her overreaction as well as the frequency with which she said *"like."* The fact is, while most of us say *like* in casual conversation, myself included, hardly any of us use it as much as she did. And, since *like* has both use and meaning, why should *like*-speak be so universally discounted and looked down upon?

In 1995, Jennifer Dailey-O'Cain Ph.D. of the University of Alberta, Canada, conducted a study aimed at identifying contemporary attitudes toward *like*-speak. To this end she employed surveys, which asked for direct opinions, as well as an ingenious set of matched-guise tests designed to reveal people's true and unconscious feelings. She would play for her test subjects two recordings of the same speaker: one version was peppered with *likes* and the other version had its *likes* digitally removed. She would tell her subjects that they were listening to excerpts from two different speakers and then ask them for their perception of each one.

Dr. Dailey-O'Cain proved that while almost all of the overt opinions expressed by her panel were strongly negative toward *like*, unconsciously most people felt that the matched-guise speakers sounded more attractive, cheerful, and friendly when they used *like*. Also, "When the younger speakers used *like*, they were perceived as more interesting than when they did not" (Dailey-O'Cain 73). So, who among us wouldn't want to seem more attractive, friendly and interesting? I, for one, most certainly would. But, like, wait a minute; it's not all good news.

The study also reaffirmed some of the public's negative impressions toward *like* users. For one, *like*-speak only made young people sound more interesting; older people were perceived as less interesting, less intelligent, and less mature. Also, speakers of all ages were regarded as less educated when they said *like*.

Dr. Dailey-O'Cain writes, "Some informants also mentioned that they feel [*like*] distracts from the message of the speaker and interferes with communication" (Dailey-O'Cain 70); my horrific date experience corroborates this belief. Since focuser like is used to highlight an upcoming part of a discourse, its use is fairly analogous with physically highlighting words or passages in a text book. As most students come to realize early in their scholastic careers, underlining every word in a book is a lot like underlining nothing at all.

Since young people's priorities are more aligned with being perceived as attractive and friendly than well-educated and mature, it is understandable that this method of speech is so popular among high school and college-aged individuals. However, the inescapable truth is that, as we age, our priorities will shift and eventually it will become more important to us that we be taken seriously, especially in professional interactions.

If a pattern of speech is repeated habitually over a course of years it becomes less a simple word choice and more a dialect. According to Michael and Susan Osborn, professors at the University of Memphis and authors of the textbook *Public Speaking,* if a person's dialect is different from that of his or her audience, they "may be seen as uneducated or socially inept" (Osborn and Osborn 318).

But is this really such a problem? Why not just use focuser *like* informally when we are around friends but not on those occasions where it feels inappropriate? Unfortunately, it is not clear that that's possible. If a person has relied on focuser and quotative *like* to add interest to most of their informal discourse, this dialect can become like a crutch not easily laid down.

While waiting for the elevator at Drexel University's Matheson Hall, I was passed by a student who was leading a group of high school seniors and their parents on a tour of our campus. If ever there were a time to sound well-educated, this was it. Obviously, by what she was saying, she meant to portray herself and our school in the best possible light. So, when asked by a parent, "What percentage of classes is taught by teaching assistants?" she proudly replied: "None. Some courses may have T.A.s assigned to the individual sections but the professor still, like, teaches the lecture."

Works Cited

Dailey-O'Cain, Jennifer. "The Sociolinguistic Distribution of and Attitudes Toward Focuser Like and Quotative Like." *Journal of Sociolinguistics* 4.1 (2000): 60-80.

Osborn, Michael and Suzanne Osborn. *Public Speaking.* 5th ed. Boston: Houghton Mifflin, 2000. Print.

Underhill, Robert. "Like Is, Like, Focus." *American Speech* 63.3 (1988): 234-46. JSTOR. Web. 24 Feb. 2010.

Nahjan Amer Nordin

Through the Reader

I grew up in a house that was akin to a bookstore for a home, seemingly endless rows of books filling both the upper and lower floors. My fondest memories of childhood were not ones that involved cartoon characters or comic superheroes but rather, ordinary characters that came alive in the books I had read: the Peter and Jane series, Enid Blyton's colorful stories, Sweet Valley and The Babysitters Club series, among others. Perhaps all these were reasons an accidental encounter with a particular novel, dare I say, changed my life.

It took place when I was nine years old. My eldest brother, 22 years old then, had one day come home with a box full of books, all randomly bought because they were cheap at a book fair. The novel was one of his great finds. It was not a novel I was allowed to read—he clearly felt I was too young to be reading such material. I, however, was intrigued. The minute he looked away, I picked it up and hid away to read it. I remembered feeling excited, as if I had pulled off a risky tryst. When I look back at it now, I still don't quite understand why and what had pulled me to the novel so strongly, yet at that time I felt enlightened. It told the story of a young man of fifteen, who met, befriended, fell in love, and shortly after, lost his love, a woman twice his age. Germany in World War II was the setting and clearly, as the story progressed, while his love for her continued to dominate the narrative, a more haunting issue was brought to the forefront. I finished the book with a grappling feeling.

Still, the strangest fact was that the book remained a mystery to me for close to ten years. Perhaps my eldest brother misplaced the book, perhaps he simply gave it away. Just as easily as I had found it, I had lost it. Having read it in secret that one time—the only time—and being so young, neither the author's name nor the title caught my attention. All I remembered was the storyline, the characters and most of all, the writing style. I remembered that the novel was German-translated, but that was all I knew. In the nine years of not knowing, I tried searching for it, although I never knew how or where to begin.

Nevertheless, strange as it may sound, the novel was so significant because it gave me a sense of purpose. It made me write. The writing style of the author captured me so greatly that over the years, I tried to emulate that same style; melancholic narrative with glimpses of the past and heavily laden with emotions. My writing process began with creating stories of my own. I took it a step further by publishing them on writing websites. It was only a short stint, but while at it, I had also managed to read some amazing pieces and along the way learned plenty about different writing styles. Since then, my life has been greatly focused on writing.

At home, I shared a journal with my eldest sister. It wasn't long before she gave it up, but I kept writing. Two years and four journals later, I switched to an online journal, otherwise known as blogging. In high school, I took writing seriously by participating in essay-writing competitions. I had never won a grand prize, but my personal victory was receiving *Highly Commended* for an essay submitted to the Commonwealth essay-writing competition. I joined the school's editorial board and moved up to the position of editor. I learned about article and report writing as well as editing. This led my eldest brother, a then-psychiatrist-in-the-making, to employ me as an unofficial editor of his graduate thesis paper. I kept at this for two years before he offered me another job, translating a psychiatry-related book from English to Malay. Yet, all the while, whether it was writing for personal pleasure, meeting deadlines for articles or getting paid for editing, I kept remembering that particular literary piece that had brought me there.

Looking back, I realized that for the longest time, I had defined myself as a writer. If people asked "What are you?" I would reply without hesitation that I am a writer. Although it took me longer to realize this, I now know that it gave me not only a sense of purpose, but also an identity. It made me feel that I had a special way with words–a talent, skill. Naturally, I gained confidence from this; it became both my pride and best trait. Nevertheless, even early on, I understood that having genuine passion for writing was hardly significant. Writing, in truth, was simply a form of expression shared by so many people that it could scarcely be considered as noteworthy. Sometimes I do wonder if I will come to regret not choosing to pursue journalism or creative writing as a major and instead choosing to let it remain merely as a passion. Yet whenever I think back to how I had gotten into it—the wonder of a novel—I still feel that it wasn't just mere coincidence. It was fate. Writing was my destiny. It will always stay with me.

I was seventeen when I encountered the movie, completely by chance. It told the story of a young man of fifteen who met, befriended, fell in love, and shortly after, lost his love, a woman twice his age. The setting was Germany during World War II. During their rendezvous, he would read her classic literature. This seemingly insignificant action turned out to play a central role many years later, an explanation of a greater issue. It had a tragic ending, one I knew vividly. I read the storyline once, twice. I could feel my heart palpitating deep in my chest. This was it. It had been turned into a movie! It took me nine years, but I had finally discovered it: *The Reader* by Bernhard Schlink. Now, I have my own copy. I purchased it at a book fair, too.

Katrina Gaudier

Operation Oppression

On August 28, 1963, Dr. Martin Luther King, Jr. delivered his famous "I Have a Dream" speech (Williams 203). This speech has arguably become the most recognizable event of the Civil Rights Movement and its speaker the figurehead. However, it is crucial to understand and recognize the events that preceded and followed as well as the countless men, women, and children involved in the struggle. The American Civil Rights Movement was much more than one man and one speech; it was a reaction to decades of strife. An entire community united in a battle to break down barriers. To do so took determination and resilience as blacks faced violence not only propelled by racial prejudices but also by gender and sexual propriety.

Violence, because of its multiple manifestations, significantly contributed to the tone of the Civil Rights Movement. It affected everyone from the victims to the observers to the doers. It had the power to teach people things, to oppress people, but also to immobilize the oppressed. This is why it played such a large role in the Civil Rights Movement; it was everywhere, but it was so multifaceted that people displayed it and responded to it in many ways.

Physical violence was the most direct and obvious form of oppression. It took the form of lynchings, bombings, and beatings. Demonstrators throughout the movement, whether they were sitting-in at lunch counters, registering to vote, or taking "freedom rides" through the South, were the victims of this sort of oppression. Even though the discrimination was the cause of the violent acts, there was no discrimination used in deciding who could be injured or killed. Leaders and children alike were brutally murdered and similar oppressive tactics were practiced against them as well. Although not alone in his racist quest, Birmingham Police Chief Bull Connor was responsible for much of the violence in his city. At one point in the movement, children took to demonstrating in the streets because many of the working adults could not afford to be arrested. In response, he ordered his firefighters to turn their hoses on the children. The hoses were equipped "with 100 pounds of pressure per square inch, the water hit with enough force to rip the bark off trees." He watched as the "children were knocked down by the streams, slammed into curbs and over parked cars" (Williams 190).

The police chief showed no regard for these children or their families, but he showed a terrifyingly strong commitment to his racism when he continued on despite the public eye being directly upon him. He and his city were on display for the entire country to judge as the images of the children shocked many Americans, including President Kennedy. However, Connor was not deterred by the negative attention or his monikers, "The Walking Id of Birmingham" and the "Dark Spirit of Birmingham" (4 Little Girls). In fact, he did not even stop at the hoses; he ordered his police attack dogs to "subdue" the children as well (Williams 190).

Robert Chambliss or "Dynamite Bob" was another pathological racist from Birmingham. He was responsible for countless acts of racial terrorism, but he was not held accountable until he bombed the Sixteenth Street Baptist Church in 1963. Chambliss killed four innocent young girls: Cynthia Wesley, Addie Mae Collins, Carole Roberts, and Denise McNair. As tragic as that is in itself, Chambliss' act took physical violence to a new level. He sparked a new type of fear because the church, especially this one, was supposed to be a safe haven during these hard times (4 Little Girls).

The Sixteenth Street Baptist Church was a significant landmark for the Civil Rights Movement; demonstrators were trained there, the SCLC called meetings there, and it was a general rallying point for activist activities in the area. Its significance was largely why it was a target, but also why the reaction to its bombing became a display of the transformative powers of violence. The bombing of the church and the loss of the children invoked an even stronger sense of community within the Civil Rights Movement. After leaders contemplated their options, they decided to use that energy towards a campaign for voting rights. Although already found in the Constitution, these rights were still being violated, especially in the South. It would take careful strategy and planning, but that had worked in past campaigns.

The battle against school segregation was one of those instances. Meticulous planning pioneered by Charles Hamilton Houston and continued by men like Thurgood Marshall was what ultimately led to the favored *Brown v. Board of Education* ruling. While these men suffered for their cause and were forever moving targets for white supremacists and segregationists, the children who braved the schools following the ruling were the ultimate targets. Melba Patillo Beals wrote about her experiences along with the other eight students who toughed out a tortuous year at Central High School in Little Rock, Arkansas. They entered the school despite the prediction of Little Rock Governor Orval Faubus that "Blood [would] run the streets if Negro pupils should attempt to enter Central High School." Once there, Melba was threatened by lynch mobs, attacked with dynamite in the stairwells, and injured by acid sprayed in her eyes. Melba used her faith and psychological support from her Grandma India to battle through the year in Central High. It also helped that, for a period of time, President Eisenhower was forced to send troops to protect the students. Her guard Danny and a surprising sympathizer, a white boy named Link, also helped her on the inside (Beals).

Despite the constant threat and acts of physical violence, the other students and the white community also taunted the black students through representational violence. When Minnigean Brown succumbed to her torturers and retaliated, she was expelled from the school. "One down, eight to go" became the mantra of the segregationists. Everywhere the students went, they saw signs and buttons printed with the line; it was a constant, additional reminder that their lives and well being were always in danger (Beals). While the nine students made it out of the Little Rock school alive and became heroes in the eyes of many, other children of the movement did not face the same fate.

Emmett Till was one of the most unfortunate. He became a different sort of symbol when he was brutally murdered by two men (neither of whom were found guilty) while visiting family in Mississippi. He was originally from Chicago and his mother, Mamie Bradley, prepped him for what he would face in the South. But, she did not realize that he would not return to her nor did he seem to completely recognize the severity of the situation. Emmett did not know that something as insignificant as a whistle or a wink would lead to his death.

Roy Bryant and J.W. Milam held differing opinions. They claimed they were forced to make an example out of the young boy because of the disrespect he showed them. They said that when they picked him up at Mose Wright's house in the middle of the night, they had only intended to scare him. It was not until Till refused to beg for mercy that they *had* to kill him (Williams 42). Milam shared his viewpoint with a journalist after he was acquitted: "What else could we do? He was hopeless. I'm no bully; I never hurt a nigger in my life. I like my niggers in their place. I know how to work 'em. But I just decided it was time a few people got put on notice" (Williams 43). The way they killed Till grabbed people's attention—the castrated body was found down the Tallahatchie River attached with barbed wire to a cotton gin fan with a bullet in the skull, one eye gouged out, and a crushed forehead.

Just as Milam and Bryant transformed Till into a symbol for what Mississippians were capable of, two of Emmett's relatives came to represent a different sort of strength. Mose Wright became the first black man to testify against white people; he had the courage to stand up against his oppressor, despite looming consequences, in the pursuit of justice. Juan Williams said that Wright's individual act of courage, like the acts of so many unknown citizens, "was just as important to the movement as the charismatic leadership of people like Martin Luther King, Jr." (Williams 57). They showed the power of transforming oppression into action and progress, and they inspired others to do the same.

Mamie Bradley was also a "nobody" who emerged from the situation and found herself in the spotlight for several reasons. The first was because of the decision she made to have an open-casket funeral for Emmett. She wanted to show the entire world what had happened to her son. While she was admired for her bravery in that respect, she was also constantly undermined based on gender propriety. This was a very sensitive and complicated issue because the way she was portrayed not only spoke to the character of her as a mother and a woman, but it was also directly tied to her effectiveness as a leader in the movement. Throughout the case and during the years following, Bradley struggled with maintaining the balance between being a good mother and public figure because she had to appear as feminine, but not overly sexual; strong, but not too independent; and devastated, but not too weak, all at the same time. Often, especially for being a single mother, she was portrayed in a harsh light. She was also accused of using her son's death for both money and publicity (Fedelstein). Gender propriety was major cause of these problems.

The many conflicting and confusing expectations were placed on Bradley solely because she was a black woman. They interfered with how effective she and other women could be in fighting in the movement. It was difficult to be heard under the constraints of a society that wanted its women to be "proper." Bradley was also not the only woman who faced these issues. In addition to the relatively better-known leaders such as Ella Baker, Rosa Parks, and Diane Neal, there were "hundreds of local, often 'unknown' black women leaders and activists" (Harley 175). They were pushed aside at the time and continued to be, made evident by the lack of representation and misrepresentation in the history books.

Fannie Lou Hamer was a different sort of leader. Like Bradley, she faced much personal hardship and devaluation before she became active in the movement and during the time she devoted to it. More than what she suffered herself, Hamer also pulled inspiration from abuse her forefathers had suffered. For example, she learned that her maternal grandmother had given birth to 23 children, but only three of them were fathered by black men. This was a prime example of both the devaluation of black women and the severe effects of sexual abuse. While Hamer did not birth any children, nor did she lose a son like Bradley, it was due to no decision of her own. Hamer was given a hysterectomy without her consent as part of the 1964 sterilization bill, which was "the legislature's pathetic attempt to repress the movement by scaring local folk, especially women" (Lee 161). Another sexual-based assault she faced was during the time she spent imprisoned in Winona, Mississippi.

There, she was beaten and exposed. She also witnessed the beatings of a fellow black prisoner in which his genitals were almost burned. Hamer took the experiences with her; she was not ashamed to share them with whoever needed inspiration (Lee 151-153).

In addition to the sexual hardship Hamer faced, she was also a victim of extreme poverty. Hamer and her community suffered from a type of violence, called tropic, which stems from extreme poverty, oppression and a severe lack of civil rights. The leaders of SNCC came to her community to help show them that voting rights could eventually make a difference in their quality of life. Hamer agreed with the student group. Together, they organized what became known as Freedom Summer. While the event was successful in many respects, it also uncovered an issue that had never before surfaced in the Civil Rights Movement.

The controversial aspect of Freedom Summer was the decision to involve about 1,000 volunteers from the North, a majority of whom were white students (Lee 157). The students grew to be almost more of a problem than they were worth for Hamer and SNCC. The female activists were the biggest problem as their behavior and involvement with young black men was perceived as reckless. Despite Hamer's warnings, they remained naïve to racial tension and southern mores. She and others feared that the "clear violation of southern race-sex taboos was just begging for a violent reaction that would stifle the movement" (Lee 158). White women were revered as "prized possessions" that needed to be protected from black men in southern society. Black women, however, were never treated as such, under any circumstances. This caused tension in itself during the project.

The naïveté of the white activists was also problematic; they volunteered to fight for what they believed to be a worthy cause, but they would never truly be able to understand the plight of the others they were fighting alongside of. So, while Freedom Summer presented a chance for both racial groups, white liberals and blacks, to work side by side, it exposed a possible weakness in the outside volunteers. Blacks began to question the motives of the whites and whether they could be trusted to stick to the same ideals, never having been oppressed themselves (Williams 248).

Gloria Richardson was no stranger to oppression, but responded to in a different way than most leaders. Like many of the female leaders, little is known of her, but she was one of the more controversial characters of the movement. Richardson also did not act in accordance to gender roles. However sparse or misconceived the information available about her is, it is still clear that she was a strong woman who very much held to her beliefs and opinions. Often called a "marginalized figure," "gun-toting militant," and "feminist icon,"

Richardson emerged as a leader of the Cambridge Movement and an example of the effects of tropic violence (Harley 174). The citizens of Cambridge, Maryland felt a similar feeling to those in the poorest towns in Mississippi and Richardson realized that "there was no simple solution to their sense of economic and political powerlessness." (Harley 179). Her leadership style and political agenda revolved around the needs and attitude of the working class. Another important aspect of her style was that she did not adhere to the nonviolence ideal of the Civil Rights Movement. This caused a rift to form between her and leaders like Martin Luther King, Jr.

King found himself in many difficult situations during the movement that he came to represent. Some resented him for his popularity while others continued to sing his praises. Bayard Rustin was close to King until social pressures forced a betrayal on King's part. Rustin was a skilled organizer and speaker, but he was also openly gay. When Strom Thurmond threatened to start a scandal based on falsehoods that King was sexually involved with Rustin, King folded and denounced his comrade (Brother Outsider). Rustin's personal interactions within and outside the movement demonstrated how sexuality was also an issue in the search for civil rights. His experiences illustrated a whole different sort of sexual injustice.

Rustin's entire political career can be examined as social commentary. On one hand, it may be surprising to many that Rustin was accepted within the movement at all. Nevertheless, he was still pushed to the sidelines and did not receive the credit he deserved for the work he put in. The March on Washington was an example of how Rustin's work was not always considered. That day in August of 1963 was transformed into one of the largest and most successful events during the movement. It essentially came together because of the organizing and planning of Rustin and A. Phillip Randolph (Williams 198). However, most still associate the march with King's aforementioned speech; they do not first think of the man who was responsible for it happening.

In addition to the hard work of the individuals, there was also another considerable mode through which violence influenced the movement. Violence, in all forms, incited reaction. Because the reactions of the oppressed had equal influential powers, the doctrine of nonviolence became one of the most central aspects of the movement. Racists resorted to all types of violent oppression; this forced the oppressed to react to the violence, but the way they did so was their decision. In almost all instances, they chose the nonviolent path. This was no coincidence, as the leaders made it a point to spread the ideology, through pamphlets and conferences, so that it weaved in and out of every project and campaign. In some ways, it gave black people a sense of power over their oppressors, and it also forced cooperation and patience within the community of activism.

The American Civil Rights Movement posed many different threats to the lives and well being of many American men, women, and children. However, not acting meant the continuation of unjust practices that plagued African-American lives. Much blood and many tears were shed in the process, but so many people were able to find strength in each other and through their faith. Through overcoming obstacles thrown at them, whether they were violent, racial, gender-based, or sexual, individuals and communities became heroes. They rose as symbols of hope through adversity, and it was through them that the Civil Rights Movement came to be. Because, in the words of Juan Williams, "Indignity suffered alone is debilitating; indignity shared can transform into power" (Williams 60).

Works Cited

4 Little Girls. Dir. Spike Lee. 1997. DVD. HBO Documentary.

Brother Outsider. Dirs. Nancy D. Kates and Bennet Singer. 2003. DVD.

Beals, Melba Patillo. *Warriors Don't Cry*. Abridged. New York: Simon Pulse, 1995. Print.

Fedelstein, Ruth. "I Wanted the Whole World to See: Race, Gender,and Constructions of Motherhoodin the Death of Emmett Till." *Nor June Cleaver: Women and Gender in Postwar America* 1945-1960. Ed. Joanne Meyerowitz. Philadelphia: Temple University Press, 1994.

Harley, Shannon. "Chronicle of a Death Foretold." *Sisters in the Struggle: African American Women in the Civil Rights-Black Power Movement*. Ed. Bettye Collier-Thomas and V.P. Franklin. New York: New York University Press, 2001. Print.

Lee, Chana Kai. "Anger, Memory, and Personal Power: Fannie Lou Hamer and Civil Rights Leadership." *Sisters in the Struggle: African American Women in the Civil Rights-Black Power Movement*. Ed. Bettye Collier-Thomas and V.P. Franklin. New York: New York University Press, 2001. Print.

Williams, Juan. *Eyes on the Prize America's Civil Rights Years 1945-1965*. Penguin Books, 1987. Print.

Joshua Dylan Stevenson

Explication as Zen

Introduction

There is something musty in the phrase *explication de texte*. The eyes glaze, the snores erupt. Explications are as exciting as those other tried and true pedagogical standbys, which no one past eighth grade would expect to have visited on them: diagramming sentences, completing a geometric proof, or counting the angels on a pinpoint. Stuffy, scholastic; petty, pedantic; maybe even irritating and irredeemable. Who would, given the tools of global modernity, super-fast Internet research, the excitement of theoretical speculation, all of these sexy 21st century toys, who would turn to the *explication de texte* to read anything? But close reading does not punish; it rewards. Explication is the basis by which all great readers come to their interpretations of texts.

The poem

For this exercise I have chosen a short eight-line lyric by Aleksandr Blok. A Russian symbolist poet, Blok is considered one of the great Russian poets, although not generally well-known outside of Russia. This period of Russian literature, often called the Silver Age, saw many tumultuous developments, from the apocalyptic and decadent to the strict and formal, flourish. Blok, being the most important symbolist, attracted the ire of a variety of critics, even Trotsky, who devotes a chapter of his *Literature and Revolution* to Blok. Luckily for us, Trotsky is not a good reader of lyric poetry and his prediction that Blok's lyrics would fade into obscurity has proven unfulfilled. Blok composed the following lyric in 1912, the time leading up to the Bolshevik Revolution and World War I. I provide this poem in several versions for ease of reference: the original Russian, a transcription, and a plain translation.

Ночь, улица, фонарь, аптека,

Бессмысленный и тусклый свет.

Живи еще хоть четверть века—

Все будет так. Исхода нет.

Умрешь—начнешь опять сначала

И повторится все, как встарь:

Ночь, ледяная рябь канала,

Аптека, улица, фонарь.

Noch', ulitsa, fonar', aptyeka,

Byessmyslyennyj I tusklyj svyet.

Zhivi yeshchye hot' chyetvyert' vyeka—

Vsye budyet tak. Ishoda nyet.

Umryesh'—nachnyesh' opyat' snachala

I povtoritsya vsye, kak vstar':

Noch', lyedyanaya ryab' kanala,

Aptyeka, ulitsa, fonar'.

Noch', ulitsa, fonar', aptyeka,

Byessmyslyennyj I tusklyj svyet.

Zhivi yeshchye hot' chyetvyert' vyeka—

Vsye budyet tak. Ishoda nyet.

Umryesh'—nachnyesh' opyat' snachala

I povtoritsya vsye, kak vstar':

Noch', lyedyanaya ryab' kanala,

Aptyeka, ulitsa, fonar'.

Night, street, lamp, drugstore,

A meaningless and dim light,

Live another quarter of a century—

It will be this way. There is no exit.

You will die—you will begin again from the beginning

And everything will repeat itself as of old:

Night, the icy ripples of the canal,

Drugstore, street, the lamp.

One of the beautiful attributes of this poem is its simplicity. The majority of nouns appear in the nominative. The verbs are simple; there are no gerunds or participles. The poem uses ordinary words to extraordinary effects.

Structure and stricture

The poem reinforces the idea of completeness in several ways. For example, the first five words cycle through the five vowels of the Russian language. Furthermore, the words that begin the poem also end the poem. And the poet's arsenal of literary and sound devices is well-represented. For example, alliteration plays an important part in line six, literally repeating the sounds of the word *povtoritsya* in the next two words.

The meter of the poem is iambic tetrameter, a common Russian meter. The initial spondee, the two heavy stresses of *noch'* and *ulitsa* give an immediate ponderous feeling to the poem, as if to announce that serious subject matter. When the images of the first stanza reappear at the end, beginning in line seven, the poem relents a little with the trochee, a heavy stress followed by a light stress, again a slightly ponderous feel against the general pattern overwhelmingly represented, the iamb, a light stress followed by a heavy stress. Overall, the repeated iambs give the poem a metrical regularity and also reinforce the ideas of repetition and the inexorable in the poem.

On the level of verbal construction, the first stanzas contains only imperfective verbs, while the second only contains perfective verbs, closing in the sense of completion. In this poem, the first stanza contains three verbs (*zhivi, budyet, nyet*), all imperfective, which means they connote incompletion or habitual action; the second stanza contains three verbs (*umryesh, nachnyesh, povtoritsya*), all perfective, which connote completed actions. The poem thus moves from the open in the first stanza to the closed in the second stanza.

In each of these ways, through alliteration, sound, meter and verbal aspect, we see how the poem reinforces itself. The poem in this case is like a tight argument, where the sense of the poem, its meaning, encodes itself in the more literal sense of the poem, its physical quality. The strictures of this poem lie within its structures.

Breaking the cycle: paronomasia

Even a beginning reader will immediately see a complication with this lyric. The poem says "everything will repeat itself, as of old." But things do not repeat themselves exactly. The list of things in the first stanza does reappear, but they are not in order. "Night, street, lamp, drugstore" now becomes "Night... drugstore, street, lamp." We have reached a point of dissonance. Even more, the list now contains an extra element, which is all the more striking because it is not a simple nominative noun as the rest, but a more complex string of words. This noun phrase is nearly baroque compared to the rest of the poem. Is it possible the poem is tricking us and does not actually mean what it says?

Certain disciplines avoid ambiguity as much as possible. The sciences define terms carefully. Philosophers devote thousands of pages to defining categories. Literature, however, since it builds with words, cannot avoid the ambiguities inherent in words. Nabokov, one of our more linguistically talented authors, wrote: "Paronomasia is a kind of verbal plague, a contagious sickness in the world of words." One can see at this the image of Doctors of Letters rushing to save the text from this disease. However, wordplay and punning are not scandals; they are useful tools to mean two things at once and add depth to his writing. However, we resist homophony and paronomasia, because we prefer simple answers. The explication revels in the text's ambiguity, its two faces and about faces. The poem must always be reread and reinterpreted against itself.

The first point to note in this rereading is the Russian word *svyet*. All languages have homonyms. It would seem inconceivable for clear communication that homonyms should exist. Speakers should desire a discrete word for every discrete concept, without using the same word twice. Given the number of sounds available to a language, homonyms are strictly unnecessary. Light can mean both "weightless" and "the perception of brightness." The Russian *svyet* is similar. To be sure, the primary meaning is "light" in the latter sense, the amount of brightness. However, it also means "the world." Thus, the poem indicates that the world described in line one is itself meaningless and dim. The word *byessmyslyennyj* also needs to be reread. The root here *smysl* means not only meaning, but corresponds to the English "thought," and turned into verbal form colloquially means "to understand." Thus, this world, and also this light, is thoughtless, meaningless, even incomprehensible. At this point the poem dares us to interpret it, to makes sense of it. It is fair to say a world comprised only of night, a street, a lamp and a drugstore is actually all of those things: a barren landscape. But the poem does more than comment on the poem-world; it comments back on itself, becoming self-referential. Let us not go so far to say that all poems require this treatment. This poem, however, does.

Another interesting point is the word *opyat'*. This word simply means *again*. It has no homonyms. It does however contain another word inside of it that may have an interesting parallel in the poem. Inside the word is *pyat'*, the Russian word for five. Just as the first stanza has only one number word, *chyetvyert*, "a quarter" and hence four, the only connection the second stanza has with numbers is this hidden five. The number of terms in the first line is four, which would explain, besides obvious metrical considerations, why the poet uses the word *chyetvyert'*, reinforcing the four terms of line one, and then when things "begin again (*opyat'*)" they appear now as five (*pyat'*) in lines seven and eight. The poem prepares us for the change.

Finally, in the realm of double readings there is the word *povtoritsya*. Again, this word simply means "it will repeat itself." However, this word also can contain a double meaning. The word *povtorit'* means "repeat", but also "revise," as when schoolchildren are told to repeat work in order to improve. Now our reading reinforces the poem's surprise: that the cycle breaks and revises itself.

Finally, in all this dissonance the addition in line seven stands apart. The "icy ripples of the canal" contain their own contradiction. Ripples would seem to reinforce the cyclical meanings of the poem described. However, they are ice, frozen, incapable of movement. They are thus both repetitions and singular, incapable of repeating themselves at all. The addition literally crystallizes the struggle of the poem.

Life and Death

We seem to be at an impasse now. Let us read the poem one more time to incorporate the dichotomy we have until now failed to consider: life and death. The first stanza contains the command *zhivi*, "live!" The second stanza contains the pithy *umryesh'*, "you will die." In the first stanza where life appears, there is also the meaningless, the thoughtless: the antithesis of what we expect life to be. There is no escape in living. On the other hand, the second stanza, where death appears, there is the new beginning, the end of a lone light on a dark street on a cold night. The poem does not claim to either solve problems of meanings or life and death: it provokes us into a concomitant state of dissonance which we must solve ourselves. This is why Trotsky is terribly wrong about Blok's lyric poems: they will continue to live on because they encode the struggles of life and death, meaning and experience in creative ways.

Close reading seeks to enliven the text, not to reduce it to the sum of its parts and certainly not to solve the poem as if it were an equation. The *explication de texte* should be revived in the manner of Blok's poem, a struggle for the the living reader searching for meaning in texts unfairly presumed dead.

Abhishek Yeleswarapu

I Hope Your Brain and Vertebral Discs Feel Better

Biomedical engineering is a field that never sleeps. Whether the clock hits 7 a.m. in New York, Zurich, or Tokyo, pioneering research is constantly happening at a frenetic pace. From developing less-painful chemotherapy procedures to research in the Illinois labs of Gatorade to improve athlete performance, the world of biomedical engineering affects us in countless ways every single minute of our lives. My decision to join the ranks of this discipline, and furthermore, to join the BS/MS program at Drexel University, was by no means an easy one, but rather a tumultuous personal emotional rollercoaster for me and all those around me.

It was day one for me at CAF Capital Management LLC, a hedge fund located in the heart of Manhattan, and I was at the top of the world. I had not completed high school, wasn't even 18 years old, and already I was enjoying the lifestyle of the rich and famous, complete from the salary all the way to the 5th Avenue apartment. I had been chosen for a two-month internship/ competition at one of the elite hedge funds in the city, and despite the financial ruins surrounding us, CAF had ploughed through the debris and selected six interns from different corners of the nation for their program. The six of us were from completely different backgrounds, with the common denominator being that we all had our sights set on the ultimate prize offered by the firm: a 12-month contract given to the intern who outperformed the others, both in the written exams and the portfolio challenge. In the Wall Street world, it goes without saying that a guaranteed contract of employment for any length of time is unheard of in the best of times, let alone the fact that we were in the middle of a financial system meltdown. And I, a 17-year-old, without even a high school diploma, was in the middle of a competition for this contract, along with five college graduates, the youngest of whom was still five years my senior. The stakes were high.

Handing me the keys to my 51st-floor office, the managing director of the fund, a man by the name of John Carzinski, spoke to me for the first and only time during my tenure at CAF, "I don't know why the hell they selected you, but I'll tell you one thing, they must've seen something, 'cause they're rarely wrong. And you'd better do one hell of a job, or you're screwed." And with that, I was off to the races. For just over six weeks, there was not a single instance where I logged less than 110 hours for the week. I was clocking just short of

16 hours a day, getting back to the apartment, reading my textbooks for the examinations that would greet me the next day, and just praying that I would be able to squeeze in a few hours of sleep somewhere. It was brutal, but I loved every second of it. A month and a half of it, and any rational human being would be sick and tired of the daily grind, but I was getting more and more into the competition with each passing day. And I wasn't doing badly either; I was averaging over a 94% on my examinations, and was in second place in the portfolio challenge, with a six week return on investment of almost 76.3%, just 4.2% behind the leader, an OSU economics graduate. I was in this competition, and I was in it to win. And then came the phone call.

Ironic, isn't it, that problems have the peculiar tendency to strike just when everything seems to be going right? My mother had suffered an automobile accident with a drunk driver, and I had to get back to New Jersey immediately, as she was in critical condition. But I was so close, with only 12 days to go, and I had the chance of a lifetime. On the other hand, my mother was in critical condition at the hospital, and there was only one thing that was for certain: I had to make a decision, and quick.

Two and a half hours later, I found myself outside the emergency room at Somerset Medical Center. This was not the way I had anticipated meeting my family for the first time in six weeks. Four nerve-wracking hours later, the head orthopedic surgeon at the facility came out, and from the moment I saw his grim expression, I knew that something was wrong. He addressed my father, "Mr. Yeleswarapu, I am really sorry, but we cannot do this surgery. Your wife has a congenital brain condition that we found during our scans, and after much consultation with my colleagues, we came to the decision that operating would be too dangerous. That being said, she will most likely be okay, but she will need to be on bed rest for quite a long time." Those words echoed in my head for days, to the point where I began to wonder whether I was going crazy.

And so began my next journey in life, away from all the glitz and glamour of my Wall Street life. My mother was in the hospital for the next seven weeks, recuperating from her injuries. In the meantime, I went back to the city the next day, got my stuff from my apartment, and just sent one email to Mr. Carzinski: "My mother met with an accident yesterday. I cannot continue with this, as I have to be back with my family. I am sorry for letting you all down." I never received a response from him. I did, however, receive a generic card from the office, the type that they print and send around Christmas time, telling me to "feel better." And at that moment, it struck me: these people weren't humans; they were robots, devoid of all human emotions. And I definitely wasn't about to join their ranks. But I cried. Why? Even I don't know. I think it had to do with the fact that I had given up so much, so quickly. It wasn't by any means easy, but it was for sure the right thing to do, at least in my mind.

Four months later, when it came time to apply to colleges, I looked over my draft of my application essay to the Wharton School of Business, which I had written back in my freshman year of high school, and with no sense of regret whatsoever, I clicked delete. I still applied to my dream school, the University of Pennsylvania, but rather to the College of Engineering.

Unfortunately, due to complications with my financial aid application, it was out of my reach and I had to revert to my Plan B. And so I joined the BS/MS in Biomedical Engineering: Devices and Imaging program at Drexel University, in order to be able to do more research into emerging technologies in the field of orthopedic surgery. With a fantastic collection of faculty and history of being involved in cutting-edge research, Drexel is a first-rate engineering research school, along with unique and different graduates, due to its innovative co-op education system.

I am at Drexel with a purpose. I didn't choose some random field one day and decide to just go with it because it sounded cool. Unfortunate events in my life changed everything and made me take a different perspective on life, one that I could never have imagined myself following. But by working on these emerging medical technologies, I hope to make my impact on the lives of people around the world, and help them live their lives just a little bit better. I'm not going to be naïve and say that I want to create a machine that cures any disease instantaneously, as I too know my boundaries. But if I can help to create something such as what Professor Onaral has done—in her case a handheld CAT scanner to help aid in the early detection of internal brain injuries—then that will make me content.

I cannot be the surgeon who has to make the split-second decisions that dictate whether someone survives or not, but rather I can be the person in the background, ensuring that that surgeon has all the technology that he or she needs to do that surgery well. I can be the person developing the new medical technologies for the progressing world. I can be me, and Drexel can help me be it.

Robert Meyer

From Madoff to Picard

First, lure in investment capital with the promise of above-average returns, do nothing with the money, and then lie about the performance. Market your fake track record to keep redemptions low while continually attracting new victims and then hope that it will last forever. The structure of a Ponzi scheme is very simple.

One would assume that the job of the trustee appointed to oversee the liquidation of an exposed scheme would be almost as simple and straightforward. Just take the money that exists and distribute it to the victims proportionately based on what they lost. However, in the aftermath of Bernard Madoff's $65 billion Ponzi, nothing is straightforward. While understanding that dismantling the world's largest anything is bound to be challenging, court-appointed trustee Irving Picard seems to be making the process more painful than it needs to be. In fact, the man with the potential to be the victims' best advocate has already been named in at least two class-action lawsuits filed by former Madoff investors.

Despite being confirmed as a disinterested party by the courts, a new conflict of interests has manifested itself as a direct result of Mr. Picard's appointment to trustee. His actions in connection with this case demonstrate that his allegiance lies not with the victims but with his employer, the Securities Investor Protection Corporation (SIPC).

Despite its 40-year history, most Americans have never heard of the Securities Investor Protection Corporation. In 1970, following a rash of broker-dealer mergers, insolvencies, and bankruptcies, Congress passed the Securities Investor Protection Act (SIPA) in an effort to shore up confidence in the industry. The act provided standardized procedures for liquidating a failed broker-dealer and created SIPC, a non-profit, non-government membership corporation. The company acts like an insurer for securities account holders, much the same way that the FDIC protects the account balances of bank customers. In his testimony before congress, Stephen P. Harbeck, the president and CEO of SIPC for the past six years, explains:

> To the extent securities or cash is missing from customer
> accounts, SIPC may use its [fund], within limits, to restore

> customer accounts to the appropriate account balances...
> The fund is supported by assessments on SIPC member
> firms and its assets currently total $1.6 billion... SIPC
> may advance up to $500,000 per customer on account of
> missing securities, of which up to $100,000 may be based
> upon a claim for cash. (Harbeck, 111th Cong)

The statutes also provide for a $1 billion line of credit with the United States Treasury, giving SIPC a maximum total of $2.6 billion with which to satisfy customer claims. According to SIPC's website, over the 38 years prior to December 2008, it has performed 321 liquidations and paid out a total of $520 million (SIPC). Since the company's resources are now five times this amount, it would appear that SIPC is more than adequately funded, but never before has it been faced with a scheme as large as Madoff's.

Pursuant to SIPA, a few days following the discovery of fraud at Bernard L. Madoff Investment Securities (BLMIS), Irving Picard was named the trustee in charge of the liquidation. His appointment could have been seen as a forgone conclusion in light of his extensive working history with SIPC. Journalist and Madoff victim Robert Chew said that "Picard is considered the superstar of SIPA trustees, having handled the largest cases SIPC has managed... [He] has served as trustee in more brokerage firm liquidations than anyone else in the U.S." (Chew).

If this long professional relationship is not enough reason to suspect Mr. Picard of bias in favor of his employer, then just consider his potential paycheck. According to Adam Shapiro of *Fox Business News*, the trustee's first fee request was filed in August 2009 and totaled $759,000 for himself and $14.6 million for his lawyers, Baker & Hostetler (Shapiro). If you take this as his standard rate for eight months of work, then Mr. Picard will surely net millions based on the likelihood that this liquidation will continue for several more years.

Diana Henriques of the *New York Times* reported that, in that same fee request, Irving Picard claimed that because these administrative expenses are paid directly out of the SIPC Fund and not from Madoff assets, "[these] expenses will have 'absolutely no impact' on the amount victims ultimately receive" (Henriques B4). While this might be true for the average-sized liquidation, in the case of the Madoff Ponzi the size and number of customer claims may threaten to bankrupt SIPC itself. Since Mr. Picard is paid out of the same fund which provides the $500,000 SIPC advances, it is in his best interest not to approve so many claims as to fully deplete the fund.

SIPC's stated goal is to quickly return missing customer assets following the closure of a brokerage firm, but the men and women working for SIPC have an obvious and overriding goal to stay in business. According to Eric Konigsberg, a journalist for the *New York Times,* "In all, about 8,800 claims have been filed, and even conservative estimates place the total number of Madoff victims in the tens of thousands" (Konigsberg). Assuming that there are 10,000 victims, if each one were advanced the full $500,000 in SIPC protection, the bill would come to $5 billion, almost twice what SIPC has available.

There just is not enough money to be fair to everyone. So, Mr. Picard must find a way to dramatically reduce both the number and the amount of eligible claims. To the extent that the trustee can influence how the numbers are interpreted, it is in his best interest to calculate the amount of money lost to be as low as possible and the number of victims to be as few as possible. By doing so, not only would he rescue SIPC from insolvency but he would make the amount of assets that he is able to recover appear to be a higher percentage of total losses.

To this end and to the detriment of Madoff victims as a whole, Mr. Picard has interpreted the definitions of "net equity" and "BLMIS customer" in such a way as to create four broad and overlapping classifications of victims. They are: direct investors, indirect investors, net winners, and net losers. Incredibly, while these classifications allow for victims to be treated differently, no class is treated especially well when compared to their situations.

The first broad distinction made between Madoff victims involves classifying them as either direct or indirect investors. The indirect group placed money into hedge funds or other feeder funds which in turn invested in BLMIS. Due to a lack of transparency regarding the strategies and operations of these funds, some investors did not know where their money was placed until news of the fraud broke. The losses suffered by indirect investors can be every bit as devastating as those of Madoff's direct clients, but "indirects" do not qualify for SIPC protection. So, not only are they ineligible to receive the $500,000 SPIC advance, they will also not be given a pro rata share of whatever assets Mr. Picard is able to secure.

These investors must adopt a DIY approach to recovering their losses. Their only recourse is to hire legal representation and attempt to sue whomever they can. According to attorney Eric M. Rosenberg, the list of potential targets includes: advisers and lenders to Mr. Madoff (such as BLMIS's small outside accounting firm), parties who contributed to recommending the investment, the Securities and Exchange Commission, and parties through whom the investment was made (Rosenberg). Success is not guaranteed for a few reasons. Not only do the lawsuits suggested by Mr. Rosenberg vary in their level of difficulty (suing the government is especially challenging), but with so many victims going after the same defendants it is likely that insolvency and bankruptcy will prevent full or even partial restitutions from being obtained.

The most obvious target for litigation would be the large feeder funds that the "indirects" invested in. Madoff whistle-blower Harry Markopolos testified before Congress, professing the culpability of these fund managers:

> [Ask] yourself, how can [Bernard Madoff's] performance
> be that perfectly smooth and in only the up direction
> when markets go down as well as up? Then ask yourself
> what the managers of these feeder funds were thinking
> as they performed due diligence or even if they were
> thinking while they performed due diligence. Yes, BM
> was a "no-brainer" investment but only in the sense
> that you had to have no brains whatsoever to invest into
> such an unbelievable performance record that bears no
> resemblance to any other investment managers' track
> record throughout recorded human history. (Markopolos,
> 111th Cong)

Indirect investors certainly have a strong case but Irving Picard is already suing several large feeder funds, trying to claw back over $10 billion in net winnings. So, these funds could be bankrupted before the "indirects" get their bite at the apple.

Those individuals and organizations that placed money not through an intermediary but directly into BLMIS are known as direct investors and are the only victims possibly eligible for SIPC protection. As mentioned before, if approved by the trustee (although most are not), members of this investor group can receive up to $500,000 advanced by SIPC. However, as business journalist Stephen Foley points out, it is important to realize that this statutory maximum payout "has been fixed at [this] level since 1978 and eroded in value by inflation ever since" (Foley).

According to the website MeasuringWorth.com, based on the consumer price index, this amount should be worth $1,650,590.31 in today's dollars. This means that less than one third of the amount of coverage intended by the Securities Investor Protection Act is actually being given out by SIPC.

More importantly, direct investor losses are being calculated based not on their November 2008 account balances, but on the "money in, money out" definition of net equity being used by the trustee. This makes Mr. Picard look better because the recovery he is able to make on behalf of victims will appear to be a higher percentage. Stephen Foley explains, "Mr. Picard has calculated the net losses from the Madoff fraud not at $65bn but at $13bn or so, being the amount of cash that victims actually put with the fraudster minus the amount of cash they took out over the years" (Foley). Using this new lower number, if the trustee wins the $10 billion in feeder fund claw-backs, an almost full recovery of investor losses becomes technically possible.

However, this approach fails to take into account the value of time lost, i.e., large opportunity costs, inflation, and the compounded interest that was forfeited. The trustee's narrow definition of equity means that the victims themselves will collectively be entitled to far less SIPC coverage. Also, the net equity issue serves to further segregate direct investors into two new subgroups: net winners and net losers.

Those investors who have withdrawn more from their BLMIS accounts than they have deposited are classified as net winners and will not receive any SIPC money or portion of recovered assets. In fact, they may instead become the source of additional recovered assets to be shared among the net losers.

Net winners, despite what the name implies, are not necessarily better off than any other class of victims. Investigative journalist Joe Nocera describes the situation of a woman "who put in, say, $1 million and over a 15-year period withdrew $1.2 million. On that person's November 2008 statement—the last one before the fraud was exposed—she probably still had a very healthy balance, maybe $500,000 or more [...] To her, that money is real" (Nocera). It is Picard's view that this woman lost nothing and instead owes the investor pool $200,000. The decision whether or not to sue her for a recovery is solely within the trustee's discretion. Obviously, if her BLMIS account represented her life savings, Mr. Picard wouldn't waste time litigating a bankrupt investor. Even though the details of this example are hypothetical, it is important to realize that there are net winners who have lost everything and, by the current plan, will receive nothing.

Net losers, by comparison, are the only victims that stand to receive any restitution from SIPC, although one hesitates to refer to them as the lucky ones. Their losses are still underestimated by Picard and, according to Mr. Nocera, they are still required to return any funds that they withdrew within the final 90 days of the scheme (Nocera). This can in no way be seen as preferential treatment.

Irving Picard's accomplishments can be seen in the running totals which appear at the bottom of his website, MadoffTrustee.com. As of November 12th, the number of claims determined was 2,913. This represents only a third of the reported 8,800 claims filed. Of these 2,913, more than 45% were denied outright, presumably based mainly on net winner determinations. So, the number of allowed claims is only 1,590 (MadoffTrustee.com). However, don't think that these victims completely escaped Mr. Picard. The total SIPC coverage committed to this remaining 18% of customer claims, again according to his website, is exactly $545,610,157.02 (MadoffTrustee.com). While this figure is already greater than the total amount of money that SIPC dispensed in all of its previous liquidations, it is still not as large as it could have been. 1,590 multiplied times $500,000 is $795 million. So, cumulatively these claims were paid out for only two-thirds of the maximum coverage.

When compared to the possible $5 billion in liability that SIPC was facing, Mr. Picard has done brilliantly. In light of this success, it is not surprising that both he and his fellow colleagues are being generously compensated. According to Ms. Henriques of the *New York Times*, "As of Oct. 31, SIPC had spent $557.6 million on the Madoff liquidation, $94.2 million of which was for administrative expenses" (Henriques B4). This means that less than 5/6 of every dollar paid out actually made it to the victims.

If fairness is taken to mean that everyone is treated the same, then Bernard Madoff was the last person to treat these victims fairly. He stole indiscriminately from his customers. Be they young or old, hedge fund or charity, wealthy celebrity or retired pensioner, their money was universally accepted. Irving Picard may be, and is, called many things by the Madoff victims but "fair" is not one of them. He has splintered them into different groups and sub-groups which are entitled to varying levels of protection and consideration. He has used his power to protect his employer and his own paycheck at the expense of those whom he was selected to help. It is understandable that some victims, as Mr. Nocera reports, feel "that Mr. Picard and SIPC have treated them almost as badly as Mr. Madoff" (Nocera).

Works Cited

Assessing the Madoff Ponzi and the Need for Regulatory Reform, 111th Cong. (2009) (testimony of Stephen P. Harbeck). Web. 5 Nov. 2009. <http://www.house.gov/apps/list/hearing/financialsvcs_demharbeck010509.pdf>.

Assessing the Madoff Ponzi Scheme and Regulatory Failures, 111th Cong. (2009) (testimony of Harry Markopolos). Web. 5 Nov. 2009. < http://financialservices.house.gov/markopolos020409.pdf>.

Chew, Robert. "Irving Picard at Center of Post-Madoff Storm." Time.com. 30 May 2009. Web. 3 Nov. 2009. <http://www.time.com/time/business/article/0,8599,1901593,00.html>.

Foley, Stephen. "The Hunt for Madoff's Money; Getting the Fraudster Jailed for Life was just the Start of a Long Battle for Justice for Bernard Madoff's Victims. Stephen Foley Reports on the Investigation into the Missing Millions." *The Independent (London)* July 1 2009, sec. BUSINESS: 36. *LexisNexis*. Web. 5 Nov. 2009.

Henriques, Diana B. "Rising Tab in Unwinding of Madoff Assets." *New York Times* 24 Nov. 2009, Business sec.: B4. Print.

Konigsberg, Eric. "Investors Compete for a Piece of the Madoff Pie." *New York Times* 29 June 2009, Business sec. DealBook. New York Times. Web. 12 Nov. 2009.

"Measuring Worth—Relative Value of US Dollars." *Measuring Worth.com*. Web. 5 Nov. 2009. <http://www.measuringworth.com/uscompare/>.

Nocera, Joe. "Ire at Madoff Swings Toward the Referee." *New York Times* July 4 2009, sec. B; Business/Financial Desk; TALKING BUSINESS: 1. LexisNexis. Web. 5 Nov. 2009.

Rosenberg, Eric M. "Another View: Advice on Lawyers for Madoff Victims—DealBook Blog—NYTimes.com." DealBook. Ed. Andrew R. Sorkin. *New York Times*, 15 Jan. 2009. Web. 11 Nov. 2009. <http://dealbook.blogs.nytimes.com/2009/01/15/another-view-advice-on-lawyers-for-madoff-investors/>.

Shapiro, Adam. *Fox Business Video: Madoff Bankruptcy Trustee Will Seek "Clawbacks" Going Back Six Years*. Fox Business. FBN, 19 Feb. 2009. SecuritiesDocket.com. Securities Docket. Web. 2 Nov. 2009. <http://www.securitiesdocket.com/2009/02/19/fox-business-news-video-madoff-bankruptcy-trustee-will-seek-clawbacks-going-back-six-years/>.

SIPC—Securities Investor Protection Corporation. Web. 6 Nov. 2009. <http://www.sipc.org>.

Ammar Shahid

In Defense of Islam

As the war on terror has progressed, it has become increasingly common to see headlines by major news outlets similarly titled: "Taliban Claims Responsibility for Suicide Blast." Conjuring up foreign words such as Muslim and *Jihad*, it should come as no surprise that with the influx of such negative articles, many people have a tainted view on Islam, sometimes going as far as to think that the religion itself is opposed to peace and modernization. The truth of the matter, however, is that despite the claims made by terrorists carrying out such atrocities as suicide bombings, their actions are in blatant violation of the basic tenets of Islam. As will be further discussed in this paper, this is most notably the case when one compares the true concept of *Jihad* to the terrorists' understanding of it.

To begin our discussion, let us first outline what Islam, Muslim, and *Jihad* mean. A Muslim is a religious person who submits their will to Islam. Islam, which comes from the Arabic word *salaam* (defined as peace), is a term used for someone who submits to the will of God. Muslims believe that all the prophets and people who submit their will to God's divine decrees are Muslims. In fact, it is required for a Muslim to believe this. Moreover, Muslims believe in all of the divine scriptures, such as the Bible, the Torah, and the Psalms of David. However, they believe that through time, these scriptures have become corrupted due to human intervention (Masters). Therefore, Muslims only base their rulings on the Quran, which is believed to be the last book revealed to mankind directly from God. Because of this, Muslims take everything from the Quran to be the divine truth and will continue to do so until the end of time. As a result, Muslims dissect and interpret every verse of the Quran for its meaning. However, sometimes verses are left ambiguous. This is believed to have been done on purpose, under the assumption that the verses in question are meant to pertain to multiple instances or events, and need further clarification to be understood fully. This clarification often comes from the sayings of Muhammad, which have over the years been collected in large volumes of books and are collectively referred to as *hadiths*. These *hadiths* provide insight into the Quran as well as into many other daily activities. If, after consulting both these sources doubt still remains on a matter, then Muslims turn to scholars who have studied Islam extensively. Generally, a group of scholars will debate and interpret the Quranic verses to derive rulings for the entire Muslim community. In their interpretations, they consider the context of the revelation, the place where it was revealed, and who specifically it was meant to address (i.e. a whole nation, specific nation, or a certain individual). For example, the Quran commands Muslims to pray when it says, "Truly, those who believe and do righteous deeds, and perform Salah [prayer], and give Zakah, they will have their reward with their Lord. On them shall be no fear, nor shall they grieve" (Al Qur'an 2:277). This verse clearly mandates that Muslims must pray, but no clear description is given to how the prayers should be done in this verse or in any other place in the Quran. Only by looking at the *hadiths* do Muslims receive guidelines for the correct way to pray. It is critical to understand the above points because it is here where many radical Muslims err in their ways and consequently end up with warped interpretations of their everyday duties. Often a radical Muslim's twisted worldview is reflected in their literal interpretation of verses in the Quran and disregard for *hadiths*, the time and place of revelation, and the intended audience.

Most people today are not opposed to the beliefs and values of a Muslim. Rather, many people are outraged by the manner in which some Muslims try to spread their beliefs. Specifically, people feel animosity towards many Muslims because of *Jihad*. *Jihad*, by Western media, is generally defined as "Holy War." However, this definition is not accurate. The word *Jihad* in Arabic comes from the root word *jahada*, which means struggling or striving to do "what is right." The Arabic word for "holy war" would be *harb-u-muqadasah*, which is surprisingly not found anywhere in the Quran (Islamic Concept). The struggle to do "what's right" is required for every Muslim. About *Jihad*, the Quran says, "Those who believe, fight in the cause of Allah (God), and those who reject faith, fight in the cause of Evil; so fight ye against the friends of Satan: Feeble indeed is the cunning of Satan" (Al-Qur'an 4:76). *Jihad* should be done to free the oppressed; ultimately, this would allow the individual to choose a path they so desire. *Jihad* can come in a variety of forms. Intellectual *Jihad* is concerned with forbidding evil actions and commanding good ones, economic *Jihad* is related to the struggle to improve one's family life through just means, and physical *Jihad* deals with having to ward off an unjust oppressor (Islamic Concept). In all these instances, physical *Jihad* is the last resort and should only be utilized when all other means of solving the conflict have failed. According to the Quran, "If the enemy incline towards peace, do thou (also) incline towards peace, and trust in Allah: for He is One that heareth and knoweth (all things)" (Al-Qur'an 8:61). Thus, as can be seen, the Quran stresses the importance of peaceful resolutions that will cause the least harm to the involved parties.

Furthermore in cases where physical *Jihad* must be undertaken, very stringent conditions are placed by the Quran on Muslims regulating conditions for warfare and the manner in which war must be conducted. During warfare,

Muslims are only allowed to engage with the opposing force's military and must leave all civilians and innocent bystanders alone. In an authentic *hadith* narrated in *Sahih Al Bukhari*, Abû Dâwûd relates from Anas b. Mâlik that Allah's Messenger would say the following words to his troops before sending them to war: "Go forward in the name of Allah. Do not kill an elderly person, nor a small child, nor a woman, and do not exceed the bounds," showing that it is prohibited to harm people not participating in the war (Islamic Concept). Additionally, when Muslims are dealing with the enemy during war they are in no way, shape, or form allowed to humiliate the enemy. About this matter, the Quran says, "O ye who believe! stand out firmly for Allah, as witnesses to fair dealing, and let not the hatred of others to you make you swerve to wrong and depart from justice. Be just: that is next to piety: and fear Allah. For Allah is well-acquainted with all that ye do" (Al-Qur'an 5:8). Based on the teachings from the Quran, for Muslims, war does not provide an excuse to treat others inhumanely, and prohibits acts of mutilation and torture.

Moreover, if an enemy wants to engage in peace talks, then war activities should cease and all attention should be turned to establishing a peaceful resolution to the war. This is detailed in the Quran when it is written, "Tell those who believe, to forgive those who do not look forward to the days of Allah: It is for Him to recompense (for good or ill) each people according to what they have earned" (Al-Qur'an 45:14), showing the fact that forgiving is more rewarding and better in the eyes of God for a Muslim than killing someone (Islamic Concept).

Lastly, one of the most important limiting facets when dealing with physical *Jihad* in warfare is that according to Muslim belief, it is prohibited to force someone to convert to Islam as in the Quran it says, "Let there be no compulsion in religion" (Al-Qur'an 2:256). Therefore, *Jihad* cannot be undertaken for the purpose of converting non-Muslims. The purpose of physical *Jihad* can only be to either eliminate poverty and oppression or to bring about the "good" of something.

Comparing these universally accepted conditions by Muslim authority for Jihad to the radical Islamic groups, it should become increasingly clear that there is a great conflict between these two ideologies. Two great problems arise in the terrorist's implementation of Islam. The first problem lies in the terrorist's goal, or their cause for *Jihad*. Al Qaeda and other terrorists groups claim they are implementing *Jihad* to create a pure Islamic state ruled by Islamic laws derived from the Quran. They believe that they are carrying out God's will by doing this and that the most effective way of accomplishing this is by eliminating the opposing religions. This belief opposes the very goal of *Jihad*, which is to free the oppressed individual. Forcing conversions of non-Muslims to Islam unwillingly would cause forced converts to be oppressed, as they are prohibited from making their own decisions. Oftentimes to justify their twisted claims, radical groups will take verse out of context, thus altering the actual meaning of the verses (Haleem).

As an example, a commonly misused verse by Islamic extremists to justify their eradication of "unbelievers" occurs in chapter 2 of the Quran and says, "And slays them wherever ye catch them, and turn them out from where they have turned you out. Such is a reward of those who suppress faith" (Al Qur'an 2:191). But they fail to look at that verse in context of the revelation. Looking at the verses which follow the verse outlined above, it will become increasingly clear that the previous verse is not commanding the mass slaughter of non-Muslims. Case in point, the verses immediately after verse 191 advise Muslims to show "no hostility except to those who practice oppression" (Al Qur'an 2:193), but to stop: "If they cease, [since] God is Oft-Forgiving, Most Merciful" (Al Qur'an 2-192). Analytically looking at the reason and time when this verse was revealed also provides insight into the actual meaning of the verse. This verse was revealed during the battle for Medina, when Muslims were fighting against all the polytheists of Arabia. Due to the overwhelming amount of troops, the Muslims formed a pact with the nearby Jewish tribes for protection and aid. However, the Jews turned on the Muslims during the middle of battle, allowing the polytheists into the town. It is believed that these verses were, in turn, revealed to Muhammad at this time, telling the Muslims to kill all the Jews they had formerly aligned with (who broke their pact) (Haleem). While there are many more verses Islamic terrorists will point to in an attempt to justify their claims about eradicating the non-Muslims, these claims follow the same general pattern of inaccurately singling out phrases and words from the Quran in order to provide justification for their politically motivated ideas (Kepel Viii).

A second main problem with the terrorist's *Jihad* lies in their method of implementation. One of the most commonly used tools by Muslims terrorists is the suicide bombing of towns, villages, and markets. The belief here is that this is an effective way to scare off their enemies. Some groups also believe that this martyrdom will lead them straight to heaven, based on the Quranic verse that says, "Allah hath purchased of the believers their persons and their goods; for theirs (in return) is the garden (of Paradise): they fight in His cause, and slay and are slain: a promise binding on Him in truth, through the Law, the Gospel, and the Qur'an: and who is more faithful to his covenant than Allah? Then rejoice in the bargain which ye have concluded: that is the achievement supreme" (Al Qur'an 9:111). This verse shows that God is guaranteeing heaven for the person who dies fighting for the cause of God. Terrorist groups utilize this verse to persuade naïve Muslims to terrorize innocent people by suicide bombing areas to further their terrorist goals. Conversely, this ill-founded belief contradicts what the *hadith* and Quran say about what is permissible during warfare. Killing oneself for the "greater good," as these people claim, will not lead to heaven because suicide is strictly forbidden by Islam in various places. About suicide, the Quran says, "O ye who believe!...[do not] kill yourselves, for truly Allah has been to you Most Merciful. If any do that in rancour and injustice, soon shall We cast him into the Fire..." (Qur'an 4:29-30). Islam never preaches anywhere that a sin should be committed, even if it is incurred in attempt for a better cause. The fact that these terrorist groups are attacking innocent people is also committing a grave sin as the Quran explicitly says, "The blame is only against those who oppress men with wrongdoing and insolently transgress beyond bounds through the land, defying right and justice. For such there will be a chastisement grievous (in the Hereafter)" (Al Qur'an 42:42). Instead of tackling their problems with their respective governments head-on, these terrorist groups are trying to elicit an armed response from the government in order to paint themselves as the victims and call others to their cause. As quoted earlier from the Quran, "Truly Allah loves not the transgressors." Thus, by trying to instigate a war, the Jihadist groups are violating the strict boundaries of warfare established by the Quran.

Another un-Islamic aspect of the Muslim terrorist is that they more often than not refuse to hold peace talks with their purported enemies. These groups believe that by fraternizing with them (generally the Western nations) they will be going against divine decree. However, this belief is unwarranted and disproved by examining the history of Muslims around the world. Muslims have frequently lived cooperatively with non-Muslims throughout the course of history. During the prophet's time in Medina and Mecca, many Jews and Christians were allowed to live under Muslim rule and received protection, as long as they paid the *Jizya*, or poll tax, similar to the way the countries work now by paying tax to the government so we don't have to serve in the military (Bostom 157). Muslims lived in Spain for over 700 years and ruled a large portion of India for an extensive period of time, never forcing the mass conversion of any of these groups, which helps to explain why such areas are still religiously diverse (Bostom 589).

Like Christianity and Judaism, Islam is a monotheistic religion which focuses on adhering to God's will. For Muslims who follow Islam, the basis for such information comes from the Quran and the *hadith* of the prophet Muhammad. Given the ambiguous nature of some verses in the Quran, in recent times terrorists have taken to altering the meaning of such verses or refusing to take into account the context of others to further their own agendas. The resulting tension from these terrorist attacks fueled by radical Islamic beliefs has cumulated in some confusion about who the real enemy in the War on Terror is. Thus, it must be stated, that in the War on Terror the enemy is not those who follow Islam, but it is rather the terrorists who veil their political and personal motives behind the religion of Islam (Kepel). Only by eradicating this veil and educating the masses can terrorist Islam truly be defeated. By diminishing the followers of radical Islam, it will allow us to finally destroy the terrorist groups and create a peaceful world that all the religions strive for.

Works Cited

Bostom, Andrew G., ed. *The Legacy of Jihad. Amherst.* NY: Prometheus, 2005. Print

Haleem, Abdel. "Introduction." *The Qur'an. Oxford Islamic Studies Online.* 08-Mar-2010. <http://www.oxfordislamicstudies.com/article/book/islam-9780192831934/islam-9780192831934-miscMatter-6?astart=1&asize=20>.

"Islamic Concept of Jihad, Holy War?" *Your Resource for Accurate and Authentic Information about Islam.* Web. 09 Mar. 2010. <http://www.whyislam.org/SocialOrder/Jihad/IslamicConceptofJihadHolyWar/tabid/115/Default.aspx>

Huda. "Suicide Bombers in Islam." *About.com.* Web. 08 Mar. 2010. <http://islam.about.com/cs/currentevents/a/suicide_bomb.htm>.

Kepel, Gilles. *Jihad: The Trail of Political Islam.* United Kingdom: I.B Tauris & Co. Ltd, 2006. Online.

Masters, Daniel, AbdurRahman Squires, and I. Kafka. "A Brief Introduction to Islam" (Part
    I of II). *The Religion of Islam.* Web. 08 Mar. 2010. <http://www.islamreligion.com/articles/1333/>.

The Qur'an: Translation. Trans. Abdullah Yusuf Ali. Elmhurst: Tahrike, 2000. Print

Katherine Devanney

Mental Illness on College Campuses: A Problem and a Solution

For many, the college years are times of tremendous growth and happiness. But for others, they are a rocky period, marred by mental illness ranging from mild depression to the most dangerous of disorders. For these students, problems may be compounded by the broken system of mental health services at many universities and colleges throughout the country. Despite the overwhelming challenges faced by college students, problems in communication combined with insufficient funding in college counseling centers have allowed millions of American college students to go without the help they need, sometimes leading to extreme violence.

It's no secret that college students today face tremendous challenges, especially while adjusting to independent living and college life. But perhaps the largest challenge faced by the young adult is the struggle with identity (Kadison and DiGeronimo 8). For the first time, the student has to make all the decisions regarding his or her life. Living with students from so many cultures can make a young adult question the values he or she was raised with, which can in turn lead to internal conflict or conflict with family members (11).

And lastly, it is important to consider the additional challenges faced by international and minority students. Despite the best efforts of universities and colleges, discrimination, especially of Black and Hispanic students, still occurs on college campuses, which not only places undue pressure on the student but also causes him to question if he even belongs in college at all (Kadison and DiGeronimo 50-51). Likewise, Asian students face labels such as "The Brain" and often face demanding parental expectations to succeed at all costs (57).

With all of the demands of college life, it is no wonder that so many students face problems throughout their higher education. For many of the students suffering, their problems are usually mild and a quick trip home can resolve ongoing depression. But for others, untreated mental illness can destroy a student's life, and the lives of those around him or her.

Consider the tragic case of Seung-Hui Cho at Virginia Tech. Although Cho had written about wanting to "repeat Columbine" since the eighth grade

(Flynn and Heitzmann 480), Virginia Tech was blindsided by his rampage on April 16, 2007. Furthermore, it was not until altercations involving other students that Cho's condition was brought to the attention of the mental health team at Virginia Tech at all (480).

Isolated from nearly everyone at school, Cho focused his limited social attention on a handful of female students, who found his attraction "weird or threatening while projecting self-hatred" (480). It was after this incident was brought to the police that Cho sent a text message to his roommate, indicating that he was suicidal, which then led to Cho's involuntary hospitalization (480-481).

A little over a year later, Cho murdered 32 students in what appears to be a delusional, paranoid rampage (481). In a video sent to NBC before the second half of his shooting spree, Cho appears to blame the world for driving him to what he is doing, and perhaps, in twisted irony, he is correct. Could Virginia Tech have actually failed in addressing Cho's problems? As with most colleges, the answer is yes.

In a survey of college counseling center directors asked what the biggest challenges faced today is, the most overwhelming response was simple: money (Kadison and DiGeronimo, 156-157). But while money is certainly an issue in preventative, routine psychological care, there is no way to put a price tag on the true cost of the life lost at Virginia Tech. Immediately following the massacre, walk-in counseling hours were established for over ten hours a day, including weekends for grieving students, and more than 1,000 students were seen in the first week alone (Flynn and Heitzmann 483).

With numbers like these, one has to wonder how much money the University actually saved with clearly sub-par mental health services. Although Virginia Tech may not have realized the need for expanding and improving its counseling services, other colleges and universities should look to this as an example; funding may be tight when making an annual budget, but isn't it better to spend a little bit of money each year in preventing these crises than waiting until one happens and pouring thousands of dollars into fixing the situation then?

Besides finances, the other major problem facing colleges trying to help unstable students is the privacy and confidentiality clauses regarding mental health care. HIPPA laws prevent mental health professionals from notifying anyone else about the potential threat an individual poses. Unless that person directly states that he or she is suicidal or homicidal, nothing can be done.

One possible solution is that of a threat assessment approach, recommended before Congress during a hearing on "Best Practices for Making College Campuses Safe." In his statement, Dr. Dewey Cornell goes into specific detail about the threat of overcompensating for such disasters by showing that a campus is only expected to have a murder once every 265 years. However, Dr. Cornell is also quick to point out the importance of prevention, rather than crisis response.

But before even beginning to plan a strategy for preventing violence, one needs to consider the role a college even plays in caring for its students. After all, it is a business—an institution created to teach its students, not babysit them into adulthood. "Colleges and universities," some administrators say, "are not residential treatment centers for students with unstable mental health problems" (Kadison and DiGeronimo 155).

But then there are those who argue that the more that a school helps students manage their mental health, the more they will achieve, thus making the school look better. Although it would require additional funding and staffing, ideas such as locating the counseling center in a common area to make it more accessible, offering more immediate appointments and telephone consultations, and offering more evening and drop-in hours (177-178), would drastically increase the number of students seen, making it harder for students like Seung-Hui Cho to fall through the cracks.

One model that shows promise is a program at Johns Hopkins, where every student who visits the counseling center is given a questionnaire, which can identify those most at risk of suicide. Those determined to be a significant risk are placed on a "suicide tracking" list, which is then reviewed weekly by a panel of psychologists (179). By following students on the list individually, psychologists are able to make sure that the students are not only going to treatment as recommended, but that their treatment protocols are working for the individual. Furthermore, any dramatic change in the behavior would trigger additional evaluation, which could help prevent a tragedy like Virginia Tech.

So while there will always be many college students with mental health problems, there are equally many options for colleges to help them. By implementing more hours and more staff, students who want and need help will be better able to receive it in a timely manner. With better funding to college counseling centers, students will be able to get the help they need, averting tragedies like the Virginia Tech massacre.

Works Cited

Flynn, Christopher and Dennis Heitzmann. "Tragedy at Virginia Tech: Trauma and Its Aftermath." *The Counseling Psychologist* 36.3 (2008): 479-489.

Kadison, Richard and Theresa Foy DiGeronimo. *College of the Overwhelmed: The Campus Mental Health Crisis and What to Do About It*. San Francisco, CA: Jossey-Bass, 2004.

United States. House of Representatives. Committee on Education and Labor. *Best Practices for Making College Campuses Safe*. 110th Cong., 1st sess. Washington: GPO, 2007. Print.

Alison Grant

Equalizing Opportunities for Differing Anatomies: The Inequality of Reproduction

Introduction

"The fact is that women have been trapped. Reproduction is used, consciously or not, as a means to control women, to limit their options and to make them subordinate to men. In many societies a serious approach to reproductive health has to have this perspective in mind. We must seek to liberate women."

Dr. Nafis Sadik
Executive Director, UN Population Fund

Throughout the world, women are discriminated against based on gender. Healthcare for women and healthcare that is gender specific for women are not equal to that available for men worldwide. That is why there is a need to address reproductive rights. They pertain primarily to women and thus have been overlooked and inadequately dealt with. According to the United Nations, reproductive rights include "the right to reproductive health ... for men and women; reproductive decision-making, including voluntary choice in marriage, family formation and determination of the number, timing and spacing of one's children and the right to have access to the information and means needed to exercise voluntary choice; equality and equity for men and women, to enable individuals to make free and informed choices in all spheres of life, free from discrimination based on gender; and sexual and reproductive security, including freedom from sexual violence and coercion, and the right to privacy" (UNFPA). There are three main issues with reproductive rights that will be addressed in this paper: reproductive health, contraception and the right to choose not to conceive, and the right to conceive.

Reproductive Health

One third of all illnesses in women in developing countries ages 15-44 are related to pregnancy, childbirth, abortion, reproductive tract infections, or HIV/AIDS ("The Right to Reproductive and Sexual Health"). Currently 16,000 women die each day during pregnancy and childbirth with 99% of these deaths occurring in developing countries, and more than half in sub-Saharan Africa ("The Right to Reproductive and Sexual Health"). Fifty-one percent of pregnant women suffer from iron-deficiency anemia ("The Right to Reproductive and Sexual Health"). There is a clear need for better maternal healthcare for women worldwide and most improvements would be low-cost. As Muhmoud Fahtalla from the World Health Organization said:

> Pregnancy-related deaths...are often the ultimate tragic
> outcome of the cumulative denial of women's human
> rights. Women are not dying because of untreatable
> diseases. They are dying because societies have yet to
> make a decision that their lives are worth saving.
> (Grimes 1917)

While there are women's reproductive rights issues throughout the world, the problems are larger in developing countries because the lack of healthcare for women results in many preventable deaths. Less than two-thirds of women in developing countries have assistance from a skilled health worker during birth, and only 34% of women in eastern Africa (WHO). While women in developed countries frequently have at least four prenatal visits, only 12% of women in Ethiopia even receive one (WHO). Women have about ten times the risk of a maternal death in developing countries versus developed countries (WHO).

Another problem with maternal health is cultural presumptions about pregnancy. Women are oftentimes deferred treatment because social customs dictate they should not be pregnant. Or, possibly, social customs and/or laws dictate they shouldn't have had an abortion (Grimes). While these women need attention, they must wait indefinitely for no reason other than stigma.

Even in developed countries, like the U.S., women are discriminated against by healthcare policies. In medical trials to study diseases, new procedures, and drugs, women have frequently been excluded over the years, causing most medical knowledge to be based around men's health. Additionally, women have been discriminated against by health insurance in the U.S.

Contraception and Women's Right not to be Pregnant

In the nineteenth century, there were activists in the U.S. who promoted "Voluntary Motherhood." These women supported the idea that no woman's sole existence should be based on her role as a mother (Gordon). As Elizabeth Cady Stanton asked, "Must the heyday of her [a woman's] existence be wholly devoted to the one animal function of bearing children?" These women fully supported the ideas now being presented about a woman's right to decide whether or not to have children and a woman's right to decide when to start and how to space them. However, these women only advocated for a woman's right to refuse her husband and did not support birth control (Gordon).

Contraception would increase men's sexual freedom, not women's, because "Man is a man whether he is faithful to his wife or not," but women had two categories: "wife or prostitute" (Gordon 16).

Eventually, activists began to promote contraception as well. They began to accept the idea of female sexuality (Gordon), and they believed women should have not just the right to avoid pregnancy, but also the right to "say yes ... to sex, inside and outside of marriage" (Siegel 820). While contraception has become more accepted today than it was a hundred years ago, the lack of acceptance of abortion is detrimental to women's health.

Abortion

Currently 72 countries in the world prohibit abortion or allow it only to save the mother's life (Grimes). This accounts for over 25% of the world's population. Other countries have requirements of receiving a family member's permission, counseling, or allowing abortion only to preserve mental or physical health (Abdullaeva). With the extremity of these abortions laws, 19-20 million abortions occur worldwide each year by individuals without the proper skills and/or in environments that are not to medical standards, causing an estimated 68,000 deaths and millions of complications (Grimes). Estimates claim that about 20-50% of women who have an unsafe abortion are hospitalized, and many (20-40%) suffer from long-term effects such as infertility (Grimes).

The majority (97%) of these unsafe abortions occur in developing countries, with over half occurring in Asia (Grimes). However, when comparing the ratio of abortions to women, South America has the most, with 34 out of every 1000 women, compared to Asia's 13 out of every 1000 women (Grimes). Nonetheless, Africa has the highest death rate from unsafe abortions (709 out of every 1000), proving that there is not one specific area of the world adversely affected by unsafe abortions, but that all developing countries suffer from laws against abortions.

In 2001, there was an abortion case, *KL v. Peru. KL* was carrying a fetus with anencephaly, a disease where the child will be born without a scalp, cerebellum, or either brain hemisphere. In 25% of these cases, the child dies during delivery. In 50% of the cases, the child dies within a few minutes to one day. And in the final 25% of cases, the child dies within 10 days (Jaquier). KL was told by her doctor of her fetus' condition and the risks it would bring to her health. KL went through a series of tests to verify what this doctor said; however, when it came time to actually have an abortion, no doctor would do it. Peruvian law states that doctors can go to jail for up to three months if the child who would have been born would suffer mental or physical defects.

KL was forced to bring the child to term and breast feed her until she finally passed after four days. The case was brought before the ICCPR Human Rights Committee and they ruled that denying access to legal abortions violates women's most basic human rights (KL v. Peru). However, this does not change the physical, economic, and moreover, mental ramifications KL experienced.

Legalization of abortion does not increase the rate of abortion; it simply brings the unsafe abortions out into the public and provides women with better care in these medical proceedings (Grimes). In fact, the Netherlands has unrestricted access to free abortions and contraception and one of the lowest rates of abortion in the world (Grimes). Nonetheless, other countries are making legislation to limit women's access to abortions. In 1997, Poland eliminated the exceptions for women with social and economic reasons. In 1998, El Salvador made abortion illegal with none of the usual exceptions such as rape, fetal impairment, and the mother's health (Grimes).

In fact, even the U.S. is attempting to limit access to abortions with the Stupak-Pitts amendment to the healthcare reform bill. Researchers from the George Washington University Medical Center "conclude that the treatment exclusions required under the Stupak/Pitts Amendment will have an industry-wide effect, eliminating coverage of medically indicated abortions over time for *all* women, not only those whose coverage is derived through a health insurance exchange" (Rosenbaum et al). The Stupak-Pitts amendment states:

> No funds authorized or appropriated by this Act . . . may
> be used to pay for any abortion or to cover any part of
> the costs of any health plan that includes coverage of
> abortion, except in the case . . . that would, as certified by
> a physician, place the woman in danger of death unless an
> abortion is performed . . . or unless the pregnancy is the
> result of an act of rape or incest.

With a majority of Americans using some funds from this Healthcare Reform, this would virtually eliminate abortion access in the U.S. No plan with abortion coverage can accept even one subsidized customer and no public funds can be spent on plans covering abortions even if abortion is paid for entirely by private premiums.

Rights to Pregnancy

Reproductive rights are not only a battle for women to control when they become pregnant, but also a battle for the ability to become pregnant. Some women are discriminated against and the oppressors try to keep them from reproducing. These women must fight for their rights to reproduce, contrary to what most feminists think reproductive rights are campaigning for.

Sterilization

Throughout the world there have been many cases of women being sterilized for eugenics. Most know about sterilization during the Nazi regime; however, they were not the first and even after the destruction in Nazi Germany and the reprimanding of many practices, other places still carried out sterilization. The U.S. had forcibly sterilized 64,000 persons by 1965 under state eugenics laws (Scott). In 1966, 26 states in the U.S. had eugenics sterilization laws (Scott). These sterilizations were aimed at the mentally disabled, mentally ill, epileptic, and criminal populations (Scott).

Now, even with most eugenics laws repealed, disabled women are still seen as "'asexual' or 'defective' and undesirable as sexual partners and mothers" (Kallianes and Rubenfeld 204). In some cases they are still forced into sterilization or into getting an abortion, but overall disabled women are discriminated against in many parts of reproductive health. They are usually not provided sex education because of their "asexuality" and therefore are not knowledgeable about diseases and contraception (Kallianes and Rubenfeld). Also oftentimes they are directly told they should not have children because they could not possibly be a "good mother" and the child could "suffer psychological damages as a result of having a disabled parent" (Kallianes and Rubenfeld 209). While some believe disabled women do not have children because they are physically incapable, it is usually because of social barriers (Kallianes and Rubenfeld).

Other acts of sterilization around the world have usually been against minorities and indigenous peoples. In the '70s and '80s the Slovakian government targeted Roma (gypsy) women for sterilization. Although this coercion is said to have stopped with the fall of communism, the practice is believed to persist. Robert Fico who ran for parliament in 2002 promised to "actively effect the irresponsible growth of the Roman[i] population" ("Coerced Sterilization" 2). No other political candidates, NGOs, or public leaders (besides the Roma) criticized his statement. In 2003, a report that interviewed 230 Roma women found a pattern of forced and coerced sterilization with 110 sterilizations after 1990 ("Coerced Sterilization"). Clearly, there is still a bias against the Roma people and an attempt to eliminate their reproduction.

Another case of sterilization was in Peru, during the Fujimori presidency. Sterilization increased from 10,000 in 1996 to 110,000 in 1997 (Johansen), with more than 200,000 people overall being sterilized (BBC News). They would offer incentives of food and clothes to rural women to convince them to be sterilized and gave monetary bonuses to doctors and nurses for every sterilization they performed. Many women, who could not read or speak Spanish, were told to sign forms waiving their rights to sue for malpractice (Johansen) and then received little after care (BBC News).

Conclusion and Steps Forward for Women's Rights

Contraception has been important in releasing women from the sole role of mother and housewife. Contraception allows women to plan childbirth, giving them the capacity to do more with their lives. The ability to choose if, when, and how often to have children, provides women with the ability to receive an education and start a career. But while many who argue for women's reproductive rights are fighting for ways to allow women to choose options other than pregnancy, it should be remembered that the concept of reproductive rights inherently includes the right of women to pregnancy, which some women have to fight for as well.

Reproductive healthcare is gender oriented because of biological differences between males and females. With a male-priority thought process and cultural systems in many societies, maternal healthcare has been inadequately addressed. As was stated previously, a majority of maternal deaths happen in African countries. In November 2005, the Protocol on the Rights of Women in Africa was implemented, which should improve maternal and reproductive healthcare for women in Africa.

The protocol provides women the right to an abortion when pregnancy results from rape or incest, or endangers the health of the mother, in every state that ratifies it. This is important, because, again, Africa has the highest rate of deaths from unsafe abortions. Providing women with some access to legal abortions should help lower this rate. The protocol also establishes and strengthens existing prenatal, delivery, and postnatal health service. As was stated earlier, women in Africa currently have very little access to maternal and pregnancy healthcare.

States that ratify the protocol have to prohibit female genital mutilation, and provide women with the right to family planning education and choice of contraception, and the right to self protection from STIs, which includes the right to knowledge of a partner's health status. As of 2008, 23 states have ratified this protocol including Ghana, South Africa, Rwanda, Zambia, Nigeria, and Burkina Faso. Hopefully over time we will see improvements in women's reproductive health in Africa due to this protocol.

This is one example of an effort to better women's reproductive rights in an area which currently suffers the most deaths from a lack of women's reproductive healthcare. Efforts like this and much more should be taken throughout the world to continue to better women's status. While we can see in developing countries women's reproductive rights are negatively correlated with female death rates and this is a major concern in these parts, it is also clear that women's reproductive rights help better women's status in society. We must step further than lowering maternal deaths, and allow women a choice in pregnancy. This will give them more access to resources outside of the home, such as education and jobs, to become autonomous individuals and further women's rights efforts in many spheres.

Works Cited

Abdullaeva, Mehribon. "Abortion Around the World—Overview." *NOW Foundation, Inc.* Web. 11 Nov. 2009. <http://www.nowfoundation.org/issues reproductive/050808-abortion_worldwide. html>.

"BBC NEWS | Americas | Mass sterilisation scandal shocks Peru." BBC NEWS | *News Front Page.* Web. 10 Dec. 2009. <http://news.bbc.co.uk/2/hi/americas/2148793.stm>.

Coerced Sterilization of Romani Women in Slovakia. Rep. The Commission on Security and Cooperation in Europe, Mar. 2003. Web. Nov. 11. <www.csce.gov/index.cfm?FuseAction=Files.Download&FileStore_id=667>.

Gordon, Linda. "Voluntary Motherhood; The Beginnings of Feminist Birth Control Ideas in the United States." *Feminist Studies* 1.3-4 (1973): 5-22. Print.

Grimes, David A., Janie Benson, Susheela Singh, Marianna Romero, Bela Ganatra, Friday E. Okonofua, and Iqbal H. Shah. "Unsafe Abortion: The Preventable Pandemic." Lancet 368 (2006): 1908-919. Print.

Jaquier, Monika. "FAQ about Anencephaly." *Anencephalie-info - Bienvenue.* Web. 11 Nov. 2009. <http://www.anencephalie-info.org/e/faq.php>.

Johansen, Bruce E. "Stolen Wombs, Indigenous Women Most At Risk." *Rat haus reality, ratical branch.* Web. 11 Nov. 2009. <http://www.ratical.org/ratville/stolenWombs.html>.

Kallianes, Virginia and Phyllis Rubenfeld. "Disabled Women and Reproductive Rights." *Disability and Society* 12.2 (1997): 203-21. Print.

KL v. Peru. ICCPR UN Human Rights Committee. 24 Oct. 2005.

Rosenbaum, Sara, Lara Cartwright-Smith, Ross Margulies, Susan Wood, and D. R. Mauery. *An Analysis of the Implications of the Stupak/Pitts Amendment for Coverage of Medically Indicated Abortions. George Washington University Medical Center.* School of Public Health and Health Services, 16 Nov. 2009. Web. 9 Dec. 2009.

Siegel, Reva B. "Sex Equality Arguments for Reproductive Rights: Their Critical Basis and Evolving Constitutional Expression." *Emory Law Journal* 56.4 (2007): 815-42. Print.

Scott, Elizabeth S. "Sterilization of Mentally Retarded Persons: Reproductive Rights and Family Privacy." *Duke Law Journal* 1986.5 (Nov 1986): 806-65. Print.

"The Right to Reproductive and Sexual Health." *Welcome to the United Nations: It's Your World.* Web. 11 Dec. 2009. <http://www.un.org/ecosocdev/geninfo/women/womrepro.htm>.

UNFPA—*United Nations Population Fund.* Web. 8 Dec. 2009. <http://www.unfpa.org/public/>.

"WHO | Maternal mortality." Web. 11 Nov. 2009. <http://www.who.int/making_pregnancy_safer/topics/maternal_mortality/en/index.html>.

Katrina Gaudier

Racial Identity

In our society, the term "race" has come to carry a negative connotation because of many people's attitudes and actions towards others of different races. In short, "race" is thought of negatively because racism is negative. However, racism has been prevalent throughout the history of our country and, unfortunately, can still be found today. Our race makes up a large part of who we are as individuals, and stereotypes and ignorance should not be able to hinder our self-expression and self-appreciation. Racial identity greatly influenced the writers of the Harlem Renaissance. In fact, it is partly why their writing is so powerful and has been influential for so many years. Langston Hughes and his poetry especially speaks to me, and it has helped shaped my views on racial identity. It has been said that, "Through his poetry...he promoted equality, condemned racism and injustice, and celebrated African American culture, humor, and spirituality."[1] That sense of pride he has in his culture and background has definitely influenced me and the way that I think about my own racial identity and how I relate to others.

The Harlem Renaissance celebrated black culture and the writers connected to the movement expressed great pride their heritage. Langston Hughes was one of the most influential writers of the Harlem Renaissance. His versatile writing gained so much popularity because of its accessibility and versatility. That was beneficial because he wished for it "to capture the dominant oral and improvisatory traditions of black culture in written form." He incorporated those traditions by modeling his poetic stanzas around the style of jazz music and used everyday vocabulary from black speech. He did this so he could use his poetry to share his culture with America. He was very much involved in politics and took a stand for racial justice. He wanted change, and that desire showed through in poems like "I, Too." In that particular poem, he looks back at the past to when "They sent me to eat in the kitchen" because he is "the darker brother." However, he also looks to the future in the next stanza and talks about "tomorrow" when "I'll be at the table" and "They'll see how beautiful I am" because "I, too am America."[2] He is anticipating a time when nobody is discriminated against because of the color of his or her skin. Even though there have been major improvements made since then because of people like Hughes, racism is never really going to completely disappear.

---

[1] http://www.americaslibrary.gov/cgi-bin/page.cgi/aa/hughes
[2] Hughes, Langston. Collection of poems. Baym 2026-2037

I grew up in Irvine, California. It is almost the center of Orange County and has been named one of the "Safest Cities in the United States."[3] Any outsider can clearly see how it is almost indescribably different from Philadelphia. However, one who lived there and went to school there would be able to tell you differences you would not find on any census or website. I did exactly that and when I sat in class I heard the other kids talk about the "stupid Asian kid" who ran into them because "their eyes were closed," or about how they would not eat lunch behind the classrooms because of the "dumb FOBs who couldn't speak English." On top of that, every time I *earned* a good grade on a test or an assignment, I had the pleasure of hearing, "That's what you're supposed to do because you're Asian." For my entire high school experience, I despised the fact that I was Asian and that I made up part of that 30% of Irvine's population.[4] I hated who I was simply because of the stereotypes others made and the judgments they passed on me based solely on the color of my skin.

I should have realized back then that I could not let other people's ignorant opinions have such an effect on me. I was a person, just like them. I should have been able to express myself just like Hughes did in his poem, "Theme for English B," when he said,

> *"Well, I like to eat, sleep, drink, and be in love.*
> *I like to work, read, learn, and understand life.*
> *I like a pipe for a Christmas present,*
> *or records—Bessie, bop, or Bach.*
> *I guess being colored doesn't make me NOT like*
> *the same things other folks like who are other races.*
> *So will my page be colored that I write?*
> *Being me, it will not be white.*
> *But it will be*
> *a part of you, instructor.*
> *You are white —*
> *yet a part of me, as I am a part of you.*
> *That's American."* [2]

We live in America, and part of American culture is that it is a melting pot of so many cultures that people have brought here. Nonetheless, rather than embrace that quality, people choose to ignore it.

I left Irvine for the first time last year when I came to Drexel. Philadelphia provided me with a whole new living environment that I had never experienced before. I was still Filipino and still a minority, but since I have been in Philadelphia, I have not been made to feel bad about that fact. It is not that

[3] http://www.cityofirvine.org/depts/default.asp
[4] http://www.idcide.com/citydata/ca/irvine.htm

I have forgotten the fact that I am colored, nor has it been the case that I am not sometimes treated differently because of it. The difference is that I am not always on the defensive about it. I feel like I have had time to look back and reflect on how I was treated before versus how I am treated now. That reflection has made me realize that my skin color can really be looked at as more of a blessing than a curse. It gives me the ability to share things about my background, my culture, and myself with others in America, like Hughes did. I am not looking to have any sort of grand impact, but I do like having something unique about me to share with others.

One more benefit that I have discovered is that many extra opportunities have been presented to me because of my race. I have received recognition because of what I have accomplished as a minority. Several opportunities to attend events have also been opened up to me because of my race. Before my change in attitude, I do not think I would have even thought about attending them because I felt so terribly about who I was. Now, however, I take full advantage of all of the opportunities I am given because we all have to keep in our minds that:

> "Freedom will not come
> Today, this year
> Nor ever
> Through compromise and fear."[2]

With those lines, Hughes conveys a strong message that we cannot ever be afraid to take action. I will admit that the fact that I like having extra opportunities because I am a minority sounds a little hypocritical coming from someone who opposes any type of prejudice. However, since I have no control over what I am offered, it only makes sense to take advantage of them.

Langston Hughes sends such a strong message for racial equality though his poetry. It paints such a powerful picture of what his people have been through in the past that has helped shape what their culture is today. He speaks to encourage the American people to embrace all of our differences and not discriminate because those differences are largely what make our country unique. Everyone should be able to feel proud of his or her race and appreciate it for himself or herself. Hughes did because he embraced that "[his] soul has grown deep like the rivers."[2] It knows so much because he has embraced his culture and is proud of it.

Works Cited

Baym, Nini., ed. *Norton Anthology of American Literature Seventh Ed Volume D.* New York: 2007.

City of Irvine. 28 February 2008. < http://www.idcide.com/citydata/ca/irvine.htm>

Hughes, Langston. *Collection of Poems.* Baym 2026-2037

Langston Hughes. 28 Februrary 2008. *The Library of Congress.* 28 February 2008. <http://www.americaslibrary.gov/cgi-bin/page.cgi/aa/hughes>

Public Safety. 1 March 2010. City of Irvine Website. <http://www.cityofirvine.org/depts/default.asp>

Clinton Burkhart

Mesenchymal Stem Cells and Their Role in Myelogenous Leukemias: Causes and Treatments

Abstract

Mesenchymal stem cells (MSCs) play a critical role in causing the fatal myelogenous leukemias, but they also play a significant role in understanding the diseases and their treatment. Acute myeloid leukemia (AML) and chronic myeloid leukemia (CML) are both myeloproliferative diseases (MPDs), or diseases of the bone marrow in which excess cells are produced. In these mentioned conditions, the cells produced in excess are cancerous white blood cells. While the uncontrolled proliferation of MSCs is thought to be the cause of AML and CML, they are also the best target for the study and treatment of these diseases. Human myeloid leukemias were used to develop the polyclonal tumor model. This model stated that although tumors are often monoclonal in origin, they very rarely consist of a homogenous cell type, instead consisting of a heterogeneous mixture of cells (Nitta et al., 2009).

The treatment of human myeloid leukemias is also heavily influenced by MSCs. MSC treatments of AML allow for a lower dose of chemotherapy, such that MSCs can be transplanted, or even re-infused, into the bone marrow of a patient and thus, greatly enhancing the effectiveness of treatment. Regarding current AML and CML medications, the drug Acadesine has recently been found to be an effective anti-leukemia agent in CML patients. The study of K562 cells (the first line of myeloid leukemia cells to be immortalized in culture) has shown great promise in treating myeloid leukemias; specifically, during clinical trials, MSCs were found to inhibit K562 cell expansion, which allowed the cells to survive harsher conditions, thereby promoting K562 survival and chemotherapeutic resistance.

Introduction

Mesenchymal stem cells (MSCs) have been found to be the cause of human myeloid leukemias, and most recently scientists have begun to show that these cells may also help combat the deadly diseases. Acute myeloid leukemia (AML) is characterized by the rapid growth of abnormal white blood cells. The symptoms of the disease are caused by the replacement of normal bone marrow with leukemia cells, which lowers red cell, platelet, and normal white cell counts, while greatly increasing the amount of cancerous white blood cells *in vivo*. This disease affects 1.2% of adults, and while rare, it is very dangerous.

Chronic myeloid leukemia (CML) is characterized by the unregulated growth of myeloid cells in the bone marrow. This condition, in turn, increases the proliferation of granulocytes (neutrophils, eosinophils, and basophils) and their progenitors. This disease has been associated with the genetic reciprocal translocation between chromosomes nine and 22; more specifically, chromosome nine became elongated as the translocated chromosome 22 attaches to chromosome nine, thereby extending it (also known as the Philadelphia chromosome). Testing for this specific chromosomal elongation is a fairly accurate indication of CML, as 95% of patients with CML have this genetic mutation.

CML was once thought to be curable when the drug Imatinib, or more commonly known as Gleevec, was introduced. Imatinib was capable of destroying CML cells with surprising efficiency; the drug's efficacy stemmed from its capability to bind to the active site of the phospho-tyrosine kinases (PTKs), preventing the PTKs from cleaving adenosine triphosphate molecules (ATP), or high-energy molecules within the body. Eventually, however, due to the mutagenic nature of cancer stem cells (CSCs), the cancer was able to mutate and develop a resistance to Imatinib. Similarly, the drug Acadesine has been found to kill CML cells in a way that Imatinib was not able to, thereby allowing doctors to treat resistant strains of CML (Robert et al., 2009).

Mesenchymal Stem Cells as Methods for Treatment

Mesenchymal stem cells are also used as direct treatments for cancers. In adults with AML, the regeneration of neutrophils was studied with and without the transplantation of MSCs. In this study, AML patients that were in the first complete remission were studied to determine the factors affecting neutrophil recovery after irradiation. Patients that received a transplant of MSCs, referred to as bone marrow-derived stem cell transplantation (BMSCT) in this study, were found to have a higher rate of neutrophil regeneration, and a higher probability of neutrophil regeneration with an increase in dose of MSCs (Kozlowska-Skrzypczak et al., 2009). The most important finding in the study was not the regeneration of neutrophils, but the quality of the neutrophils regenerated. This finding is especially important for patients suffering from AML, whose neutrophils were devastated by the disease, leading to the proliferation of abnormal white blood cells; accordingly, the re-growth of non-precarcinogenic cells is important for the complete remission of the disease.

In K562 cells, the regulation of growth and apoptosis were studied in leukemia cells that were first immortalized in culture from a CML patient (Wei et al., 2009). Regarding the methods performed, K562 cells were exposed to both MSCs and a PI3K (Phosphoinositide Kinase-3) inhibitor molecule. It was found that the K562 cells, when exposed to MSCs, displayed both retarded growth and apoptosis; whereas, following exposure to the PI3K inhibitor, apoptosis occurred at a greater rate (Wei et al., 2009). These results illustrate that if MSCs are exposed to leukemia stem cells (LSCs), although they do retard the proliferation and growth rates, they also increase the survival rate of the LSCs; this increase, in turn, then allows the leukemia cells to survive chemotherapeutic treatments, promoting the progression of drug resistant myeloid leukemias. However, when the PI3K pathway was inhibited in the K562 cells, the cells displayed an increase in apoptotic behavior. This finding suggests that PI3K may control apoptotic pathways within the cancerous leukemia cells. Such a finding presents the possibility of a target possible drug design to increase apoptosis in LSCs, which could prevent the recurrence of cancer.

Another cellular signaling pathway that was studied was the p53 pathway. Normally the p53 pathway controls two things: apoptosis and DNA repair. The p53 gene is important for the survival of cancers because of its role as a tumor suppressor gene. The main function of p53 is to assess DNA damage and decide whether the DNA can be repaired; if the DNA is too damaged to be repaired, p53 initiates the apoptotic signal cascade. In studies performed on AML cells, the activation of p53 greatly increased the rate of apoptosis signaling pathways. In human myeloid leukemias, especially AML, the myelogenous leukemia cells were able to recruit stromal blast cells, like myofibroblasts, and convert them into myeloblasts (Tashiro et al., 2009). In AML, these new myeloblasts enhance the production of abnormal white blood cells, leading to the progression of the disease. Significantly in this study, the activation of p53 led to the apoptosis of the myeloblast cells, even while they were still part of the tumor-associated stroma (Carter et al., 2009). The identification of p53 as a possible target for treatment of AML could lead to a future treatment of the disease.

In recent studies, MSCs have been used to treat graft-versus-host disease (GVHD). In GVHD, which is a common complication of bone marrow transplantations, the recipient's immune system marks the donor cells as foreign and attacks the donor cells. The patients in this study, that had leukemia and were unable to generate healthy blood cells of their own, received unrelated donations of MSCs along with bone marrow. Normally, patients with GVHD reject the donor marrow and their leukemia therefore persists. With the injection of MSCs, however, into their bone marrow along with the new marrow, it was found that the recipient did not reject the marrow.

It was observed in this study that the ratio of the helper T-lymphocytes Th1 and Th2 fluctuated significantly. Usually the Th2 cells, which are responsible for the destruction of foreign cells, are present at increased levels in patients with GVHD; however, with the added injection of MSCs, the concentration of Th1 cells increased while the concentration of Th2 cells decreased. An increase in the acceptance rate of donor cells by the host immune system was observed following this decrease in immune response (Zhou et al., 2009).

Discussion

The impact of mesenchymal stem cells on the study and treatment of cancer, and especially on myelogenous leukemias, is significant. MSCs are thought to be the causative agents in AML and CML and are integral to understanding the disease and early treatments. MSCs that proliferate uncontrollably and produce abnormal white blood cells are the cause of the symptoms of both AML and CML. Both varieties of myelogenous leukemia were at one point treated with Imatinib. The eventual resistance of the myeloid leukemias to Imatinib led to both a greater understanding of the disease and to studies that could produce valuable treatments to not only myeloid leukemias, but all cancers. The study of K562 cells, which were isolated from a patient with CML, led to the heterogeneous tumor model and better screening and treatment options for all cancers (Nitta et al., 2009).

A drug that looks fairly promising to treat patients that possess Imatinib-resistant strains of myeloid leukemias is Acadesine. Acadesine has an anti-leukemic effect on cells that have become resistant to Imatinib. Imatinib resistance was characterized by the binding mutation of the Imatinib molecule, whereby it bound a different amino acid, thereby preventing it from binding to the phospho-tyrosine kinase enzymes. This disability to bind to the phospho-tyrosine kinase enzymes, in turn, allowed the leukemia to proliferate (Robert et al., 2009).

The targeting of PI3K and p53 signaling pathways was studied in order to enhance the apoptosis of leukemia cells. PI3K, when active, inhibits apoptosis, and p53, when active, signals apoptosis. In the first study, when PI3K was inactivated, the cells displayed an increase in apoptotic behavior (Wei et al., 2009). In the second study when p53 was activated, apoptotic activity was observed to increase (Carter et al., 2009). *In vivo*, p53 is a tumor suppressor gene responsible for the regulation of the cell cycle and DNA repair. In order for cancer to survive *in vivo* it must either directly inhibit p53 or a random somatic mutation must cause an inactivation in the gene, prohibiting it from functioning. This is the case of the Philadelphia gene in CML. In CML, testing for a mutation in the Philadelphia gene is a fairly definitive test for CML, as

95% of patients with CML have a reciprocal translocation in the nine and 22 chromosomes (Robert et al., 2009)

Mesenchymal stem cells can also be used as treatments themselves. In some studies MSCs were found to increase both the rate of neutrophil regeneration and the quality of neutrophils regenerated. This increase in neutrophil regeneration quality is important for patients with human myeloid leukemias in order to reduce the reoccurrence of the cancer (Kozlowska-Skrzypczak et al., 2009). MSCs were also used to treat GVHD, in which patients reject marrow transplants when their immune system recognizes donor cells as invasive and therefore, initiates attack. MSCs were found to decrease the immune response of the host, thereby reestablishing the proper T-lymphocyte balance and allowing the host to accept the donation (Zhou et al., 2009).

Future of MSCs in Myeloid Leukemia and Cancer Treatments

The future of MSCs in the treatment of myeloid leukemias and cancers is very promising. The drug Acadesine shows the most promise in the treatment of drug-resistant strains of leukemias. Strains of AML and CML that have evolved a resistance to Imatinib, which was once thought of as a cure for the disease, are dangerous and require treatment. Acadesine provides some hope for patients with resistant strains of the disease. Future research may aid in elucidating the factors that allow Acadesine its anti-leukemic properties and perhaps an even more effective drug may emerge from such research.

The targeting of cellular signaling pathways also shows great promise. The studies outlined in the review discuss p53 and PI3K pathways that when inhibited and activated, respectively, enhance cellular apoptotic signals. Targeting both of these pathways, separately, showed promise in causing apoptotic death of the myeloid leukemia cells. In the future, research may be performed on both of these pathways and may perhaps lead to the development of a drug that affects both of these pathways simultaneously, which would cause an even greater degree of apoptosis in myeloid cells.

Mesenchymal stem cells can also be used to help regenerate newer and better neutrophils in patients that are unable to make normal blood cells of their own. While such research may not cure the disease, it would certainly improve the quality of life for patients with AML and CML. Future research with MSCs could also improve the acceptance of bone marrow transplants, which would be beneficial for many diseases, especially for patients that have undergone full body irradiation during the course of cancer treatment.

Works Cited

Basak, G. W., & Carrier, E. (2009). Search for multiple myeloma stem cells—the long and winding road. *Biology of Blood and Marrow Transplantation: Journal of the American Society for Blood and Marrow Transplantation, 16*(5), 587-594.

Bereshchenko, O., Mancini, E., Moore, S., Bilbao, D., Mansson, R., Luc, S., et al. (2009). Hematopoietic stem cell expansion precedes the generation of committed myeloid leukemia-initiating cells in C/EBPalpha mutant AML. *Cancer Cell, 16*(5), 390-400.

Carter, B. Z., Mak, D. H., Schober, W. D., Koller, E., Pinilla, C., Vassilev, L. T., et al. (2009). Simultaneous activation of p53 and inhibition of XIAP enhance the activation of apoptosis signaling pathways in AML. *Blood, 115*(2), 306-14.

Kim, M., Madlambayan, G. J., Rahman, M. M., Smallwood, S. E., Meacham, A. M., Hosaka, K., et al. (2009). Myxoma virus targets primary human leukemic stem and progenitor cells while sparing normal hematopoietic stem and progenitor cells. *Leukemia, 23*(12), 2313-2317.

Kozlowska-Skrzypczak, M., Gil, L., & Komarnicki, M. (2009). Factors affecting neutrophil recovery after autologous bone marrow-derived stem cell transplantation in patients with acute myeloid leukemia. *Transplantation Proceedings, 41*(9), 3868-3872.

Li, J. M., Southerland, L. T., Lu, Y., Darlak, K. A., Giver, C. R., McMillin, D. W., et al. (2009). Activation, immune polarization, and graft-versus-leukemia activity of donor T cells are regulated by specific subsets of donor bone marrow antigen-presenting cells in allogeneic hemopoietic stem cell transplantation. *Journal of Immunology, 183*, 7799-7809.

Maier, P., Spier, I., Laufs, S., Veldwijk, M. R., Fruehauf, S., Wenz, F., et al. (2009). Chemoprotection of human hematopoietic stem cells by simultaneous lentiviral overexpression of multidrug resistance 1 and O(6)-methylguanine-DNA methyltransferase (P140K). *Gene Therapy, 17*(3), 389-399.

Nitta, E., & Suda, T. (2009). Cancer stem cell concepts--lesson from leukemia. *Nippon Rinsho: Japanese Journal of Clinical Medicine, 67*(10), 1863-1867.

Robert, G., Ben Sahra, I., Puissant, A., Colosetti, P., Belhacene, N., Gounon, P., et al. (2009). Acadesine kills chronic myelogenous leukemia (CML) cells through PKC-dependent induction of autophagic cell death. *PloS One, 4*(11), e7889.

Tashiro, H., Mizutani-Noguchi, M., Shirasaki, R., & Shirafuji, N. (2009). Acute myelogenous leukemia cells with the MLL-ELL translocation convert morphologically and functionally into adherent myofibroblasts. *Biochemical and Biophysical Research Communications, 391*(1), 592-597.

Wang, A., Alimova, I. N., Luo, P., Jong, A., Triche, T. J., & Wu, L. (2009). Loss of CAK phosphorylation of RAR{alpha} mediates transcriptional control of retinoid-induced cancer cell differentiation. *FASEB Journal, 24,* 833-843.

Wei, Z., Chen, N., Guo, H., Wang, X., Xu, F., Ren, Q., et al. (2009). Bone marrow mesenchymal stem cells from leukemia patients inhibit growth and apoptosis in serum-deprived K562 cells. *Journal of Experimental & Clinical Cancer Research, 28*(1), 1-7.

Yi, J., Chen, J., Sun, J., & Wei, H. L. (2009). The relationship between multi-drug resistance and proportion of leukemia stem cells and expression of drug transporters in drug-resistant leukemia K562/ADM cells. *Zhonghua Yi Xue Za Zhi,* 89(25), 1741-1744.

Zhou, H., Guo, M., Bian, C., Sun, Z., Yang, Z., Zeng, Y., et al. (2009). Efficacy of bone marrow-derived mesenchymal stem cells in the treatment for sclerodermatous chronic graft-versus-host disease: a clinical report of four patients. *Biology of Blood and Marrow Transplantation, 16*(3), 403-412.

Giby George

Comprehending the Complexity of Surgical Complications

Introduction

Assuming that physicians, specifically in the instance of surgery, honestly disclose to the patient the full nature of any complication encountered during the surgical procedure, the decision of whether to understand and forgive the physician, if the complication had arisen due to the physician's fault, or charge the physician with malpractice, remains up to the patient. Because of this possibility of malpractice, surgeons often refrain from revealing to the patient any complication that may have arisen during surgery. Regardless of the prospect of a malpractice suit, however, physicians must make sure to disclose to the patient the full nature of any complication that may have been encountered, while also considering the patient's emotional and mental state, as doctoring is as much a delineation of the humanities as it is a sub-domain of science.

Following physician-patient disclosure of the complication encountered, patients can either choose to forgive the physician, thereby realizing how fundamentally human the practice of doctoring actually is, or file a malpractice suit against the physician, should the patient feel that a complication had occurred due to "physician negligence." This complexity surrounding the very nature of complications and physician-patient disclosure has become increasingly compelling to me after having worked in the operating room (OR) for the past year as a perioperative surgical assistant. Using primarily my experience from the OR, this paper will explore the delicate balance between physician-patient disclosure and patient response, ultimately concluding with three case studies with each followed by a small number of reflective questions.

(1) Patient Response to Disclosure of Complication: Malpractice

Regarding surgical malpractice suits, research supports the claim that full mutual disclosure regarding complications and thus improved physician-patient communication lessens the probability of the patient filing a malpractice suit against a physician. For instance, as cited in a 1994 patient satisfaction study, it was found that 70% of all litigation cases were related to poor physician-patient communication (Beckman et al. 1367). It can be said then that since patients are equally as important as physicians are in the practice of doctoring, patients have the same right as physicians to be informed of any complications that may have arisen during the course of treatment. Additionally, in the instance of surgery, when deciding whether to reveal to or conceal from the patient a complication that may have arisen during surgery, physicians should consider that patients have full access to their medical record and thus, the record of the surgery performed. Therefore, regardless of whether or not the surgeon chooses to reveal the nature of any complication that may have arisen during surgery, the patient may eventually find out about such a complication by means of his or her medical records (Adedeji et al. 734). Potential malpractice suits can thus be avoided to some extent through full physician-patient disclosure, such that the patient is informed by the physician of any complication that might have been encountered.

Definition of a Justified Surgical Malpractice Suit

The question then becomes: what constitutes a justified malpractice suit against a physician? As defined by Dr. Patricia M. Danzon, chairperson of the Health Care Systems Department in the University of Pennsylvania's Wharton School of Business, a malpractice suit, initiated by the patient against a physician, may be justified in the instance of "physician negligence." She further delineates:

> To establish a cause of action under a negligence rule of
> liability, the plaintiff must show that a duty of care existed;
> that the defendant failed to conform to the required
> standard of care, either by his acts or by failure to act; that
> the plaintiff sustained damages; and that the breach of
> duty was the proximate cause of the damages. (1)

However, since this definition is entirely subjective, a malpractice suit may be initiated against a physician in any instance in which the patient feels that the physician neglected his or her duties. Certainly, if a patient is not informed by a physician of a complication that had arisen during surgery and, perhaps even worse, the patient experiences additional complications as a result of this original complication that was not revealed, malpractice, according to Dr. Danzon, is justifiable. However, if a patient had been informed by the physician of a complication that been encountered during surgery, then the decision of whether or not to instigate a malpractice suit against the physician is highly dependent upon the patient's interpretation of the clause "physician negligence."

(2) Patient Response to Disclosure of Complication: Loss of Trust in Doctoring

As mentioned earlier, the practice of doctoring, categorized under the domain of science, is an area of continuous trial-and-error learning and is thus imperfect. Dr. Atul Gawande, a general surgeon practicing currently at Brigham and Women's Hospital in Boston, MA, and associate professor of surgery instructing presently at Harvard Medical School, notes in his book *Complications: A Surgeon's Notes on an Imperfect Science* the tendency for many individuals, especially patients, to characterize the practice of doctoring as infallible and error-free. He states:

> We look for medicine to be an orderly field of knowledge
> and procedure. But it is not. It is an imperfect science, an
> enterprise of constantly changing knowledge, uncertain
> information, fallible individuals, and at the same time lives
> on the line. There is science in what we do, yes, but also
> habit, intuition, and sometimes plain old guessing. (7)

It is therefore ultimately up to patients whether they choose to realize that the practice of doctoring is governed by physicians that are human and therefore, subject to human error. With regard to surgery, should a physician encounter a complication then, whether it be attributed to human error or simply a complication due to the nature of the surgery, and should the physician reveal such a complication to the patient, the patient may choose to either understand the underlying human nature of the practice of doctoring or resort to filing a malpractice suit against the physician.

Introduction to Case Studies

As mentioned prior, from having worked in the OR for over a year, I have witnessed many surgical procedures involving such complications. Three actual OR cases will be reviewed here that require the reader to serve as the patient and therefore, decide whether in each instance, it would be reasonable to understand the nature of the complication encountered and therefore, forgive the physician, or whether legal action should be initiated against the physician. I use pseudonyms for all of those that were involved with the actual cases, including the patients and the OR team members, in order to safeguard the identities of these individuals. Additionally, each case may be preceded by the surgeon's qualifications and/or past surgical history. After each case summary, a few questions may follow, asking essentially what course of action should be taken by the patient.

(1) Case Study

Sean O'Connor, a 66-year-old male, arrived in the OR for an emergency total hip replacement due to severe femoral head fracture, visualized by x-ray, as a result of a weather-related slip-and-fall accident. He had no relevant medical/surgical history that would have suggested the possibility of any potential complications, with the exception of mild hypertension. It should be noted that the surgeon, a graduate of the New York University School of Medicine, having done residency and fellowship work at Thomas Jefferson Hospital, Cooper University Hospital, among other prestigious hospitals, was more than equipped to perform such a surgery. Regarding the case, the surgery progressed uneventfully without any complications until the surgeon announced to the circulating nurse that he had accidentally "nicked" the femoral artery and therefore, required vascular surgical intervention at once. The circulating nurse immediately notified the on-call vascular surgeon, who replied that he would arrive within the next few minutes. Upon his arrival, the vascular surgeon proceeded to repair the punctured femoral artery without any additional complications. It was recorded that the patient lost approximately 1.5 L of blood as a result of this complication and thus, required a unit of packed-red blood cell (PRBC) transfusion. Following the repair of the femoral artery, the orthopedic surgeon continued with the total hip replacement, which proceeded to completion without any further incidents. After the surgery, the orthopedic surgeon honestly informed the patient and his family that vascular intervention and a blood transfusion had been required during the procedure because he had accidentally punctured the femoral artery.

In this instance, taking into account that the physician had fully disclosed the nature of the complication encountered during surgery and the intervention that had been required, how should the patient respond? Would forgiveness on the patient's part be too much to ask in this situation? Or, would a malpractice suit initiated by the patient against the physician be the only way to justify the additional harm inflicted? If the patient pursued a malpractice suit, how would "physician negligence" be defined in this instance? Should the physician's qualifications and credentials be a factor when making such a decision? And lastly, are there any additional factors that should be taken into account prior to making such a decision?

(2) Case Study

Catherine Field, a 47-year-old female, had been scheduled for an elective total abdominal hysterectomy/bilateral salpingo-oophorectomy, in which her uterus, adjacent fallopian tubes, and ovaries were to be surgically removed due to the presence of uterine cancer. She had no other relevant medical/ surgical history aside from the aforementioned uterine cancer. The surgeon for this case was highly experienced in performing such surgeries, as he routinely performs similar procedures. Moreover, it should also be noted that he has had consistently high success and patient satisfaction rates. Regarding the case, the procedure progressed uneventfully until completion without any complications. As the OB-Gyn surgeon was closing, or suturing, the abdominal incision, he was informed by the scrub nurse of a discrepancy in the lap sponge count. After multiple sponge recounts, the surgeon decided to call for x-ray assistance to determine whether the lap sponge had accidentally been left inside the patient's abdominal cavity. Based on the x-ray results, it was concluded that the missing lap sponge had indeed been left inside the patient's abdominal cavity. The surgeon immediately re-opened the patient's abdomen and retrieved the misplaced lap sponge. Following the completion of the surgery, the surgeon informed both the patient and her family that x-ray had been called in and that he had needed to partially re-open her abdomen due to a discrepancy in the lap sponge count.

Similar to the previous case study, is forgiveness on the patient's part feasible in this situation or would a malpractice suit be the only option? Would a malpractice suit against the physician be justified, especially considering that the physician had admitted his human error to the patient? Going further with the potential malpractice suit, how would "physician negligence" be characterized in this instance? If it were mentioned that following this case, the surgeon performed four identical procedures without any similar complications, should this fact be taken into consideration by the patient when deciding whether to initiate a malpractice suit against the physician? Finally, are there additional considerations that should be taken into account prior to arriving at a suitable conclusion?

3) Case Study

Gordon Campbell, a 58-year-old male, had been scheduled for an elective nasal polyp removal surgery performed under general anesthesia. He had significant cardiac history, including hypertension, coronary artery disease, and high cholesterol; his past surgical history included coronary balloon angioplasty, in which an occluded blood vessel is re-opened with the assistance of a small, balloon-like medical device. The complication that was encountered during this specific instance was a result of an anesthetic induction rather than a product of the actual surgical procedure. Prior to further discussing the case, it should be noted that both the anesthesiologist and nurse anesthetist were more-than-qualified to perform such a procedure. Collectively having more than fifteen years of practice, the anesthesiologist, a graduate of the Thomas Jefferson University College of Medicine, and the nurse anesthetist, a graduate of the University of Pennsylvania's Nurse Anesthesia program, had never encountered a similar complication in the past. During anesthetic induction, the patient was medicated with a standard dose of Fentanyl intravenously (IV). Fentanyl is a narcotic drug commonly used for induction of general anesthesia, especially for patients with significant cardiac history. Among others, one of the rare side effects of this drug includes chest wall/ jaw rigidity, in which the chest wall and jaw muscles are unusually stiff and rigid, thereby complicating respiration (Barash, Cullen, and Stoelting 528). This condition is further exacerbated in older patients, especially if the drug had been administered too quickly. In noting the patient's chest-wall rigidity and recognizing that the drug might have been pushed too quickly, the nurse anesthetist and the anesthesiologist immediately called for more assistance to manage the airway of the patient, such that adequate ventilation could be maintained. One of the anesthesiologists that had arrived felt it best to deliver a dose of Narcan (Naloxone), a drug that is capable of reversing the effects of Fentanyl, to the patient. Due to the reversing effects of this drug, it was observed that the patient's chest wall/jaw rigidity had been successfully resolved; however, because of the total reversing effects of Narcan, an additional dose of the original narcotic (Fentanyl) was needed to once again sedate the patient. The better option in the face of this complication, as opposed to administering a drug that completely reversed the effects of the sedative, would have been to administer a muscle relaxer, such as Succinylcholine, to the patient in order to relax the chest muscles, thereby keeping the patient asleep while alleviating the difficulty of respiration. Following this initial complication, however, the surgery progressed to completion uneventfully. After the procedure, the anesthesiologist and nurse anesthetist both disclosed to the patient and his family members the full nature of the complication that had been encountered during surgery.

In this final instance, how should the patient respond? By understanding the nature of the complication and ultimately forgiving the physician, or resolving to file a malpractice suit against the physician? If malpractice, how would "physician negligence" be defined if the physician had certainly been honest and forthright with both the patient and his family? Should the anesthesiologist's and nurse anesthetist's qualifications and credentials be taken into account when making such a decision? Are there are any other aspects of the situation that should be considered prior to deciding whether to initiate a malpractice suit or forgive the physician?

Conclusion

As evidenced by each of these case studies, the complexity behind complications is often overwhelming, such that patients themselves do not often know whether they ought to forgive the physician or seek recompense from the physician by filing a malpractice suit in the instance of established "physician negligence." The sensitive nature of this issue as well as its many facets must all be considered prior to arriving at a suitable conclusion. Regardless of the ultimate outcome, as discussed, physicians must be sure to fully disclose the nature of any complication encountered during surgery. Patients, however, are faced with the decision of whether to understand the complication that had arisen and ultimately forgive the physician, thereby acknowledging the underlying human nature of the practice of doctoring, or seek compensation for the harm committed by the physician by filing a malpractice suit against the physician. Ultimately though, if the practice of doctoring is to continue to survive and evolve, patients should attempt to understand that since it is categorized under the imperfect domain of science, in most instances, complications may be somewhat inevitable in the practice of doctoring, suggesting that forgiveness may be the best way to move forward.

Works Cited

Adedeji, Simisade, Daniel K. Sokol, Thomas Palser, and Martin McKneally. "Ethics of Surgical Complications." *World Journal of Surgery* 33 (2009): 732-737.

Barash, Paul, Bruce F. Cullen, and Robert K. Stoelting. *Handbook of Clinical Anesthesia*. 5th ed. Philadelphia: Lippincott Williams & Wilkins, 2001.

Beckman, Howard, Kathryn M. Markakis, Anthony L. Suchman, and Richard M. Frankel. "The Doctor-Patient Relationship and Malpractice: Lessons from Plaintiff Depositions." *Archives of Internal Medicine* 154.12 (1994): 1365-1370.

Danzon, Patricia. *Medical Malpractice: Theory, Evidence, and Public Policy*. Boston: Harvard University Press, 1985.

Gawande, Atul. *Complications: A Surgeon's Notes on an Imperfect Science*. New York: Henry Holt & Co., 2003.

Nikul Patel

The Birth of a Science: Leeuwenhoek and the Single Lens Microscope

Optical instruments, such as glass spectacles, existed as early as the latter half of the thirteenth century. One of the earliest accepted optical instruments was comprised of a combination of the already popular concave and convex glasses. Some found that when these glasses were placed at specific angles relative to each other to create a two-spectacle system, magnified images of distant objects could be obtained. At the same time, around the late 1500s, the use of this same two-spectacle system led to the discovery of how the type of lenses used and the relative spacing of those lenses could influence the level of magnification and resolution of a nearby object. It eventually came to be understood that by placing a weak positive lens and a strong negative lens a certain distance apart from each other, a nearby object could be magnified and viewed clearly (Ford 19). In fact, this initial setup led to the development of the first compound microscope, which was claimed to have been invented by the Dutch Zacharias Janssen. Constructed with a single long brass tube two inches in diameter, with the lenses placed at one end and the eyepiece at the other, this early compound microscope was able to magnify objects up to nine times (Allen 2). After the first compound microscope was introduced, others were able to make slight modifications to Janssen's original design to develop microscopes with magnifications of nearly fifty times (Ford 19).

These more advanced compound microscopes quickly gained popularity throughout Europe. One of those individuals who would find interest in the new microscope and would perform several notable experiments with it was Robert Hooke, who before then, was best known for his study of springs. In the year 1665, after performing a handful of experiments with the compound microscope, Hooke published his findings in what would become one of the most influential books in the history of the microscope. In his book, titled *Micrographia,* Hooke describes the appearance of fine shavings of a bottle-cork and attempts to elucidate how the cork's microscopic structure may give a clue about its physical composition. Through his observations, Hooke also discusses the peculiar presence of small, cell-like structures within each cork shaving, which led scientists of that time to question whether everything, including humans, were made up of these "tiny structures" (Ford 19). Although these and other pioneering observations with the compound microscope at that time, including Hooke's coining of the term "cell," could all be found in

Micrographia, it was not until a few years after the book was published that a Dutch draper would create his own microscope and see things, on the microscopic level, that no one else, including scientists like Hooke, had even dreamt of seeing.

Born on October 24, 1632 in the Dutch town of Delft, Antony van Leeuwenhoek came from a rather humble background. His childhood was not easy, as both his father and eventually his stepfather passed away before he turned 14. Then at about the age of 16, Leeuwenhoek left the countryside and traveled to Amsterdam, where he learned the business of a linen-draper (Ford 26). Eventually, in 1654, Leeuwenhoek returned to his native town of Delft where he would live for the rest of his life. Shortly after purchasing property, at about the age of twenty-seven, he was appointed to the post of Chamberlain to the Sheriffs of Delft, where he worked as a civil caretaker. Records show that Leeuwenhoek also worked as a surveyor around 1669 as well as a financial advisor in 1676 (Ford 27).

There has been much speculation as to when and how Leeuwenhoek received his initial introduction to microscopy and his subsequent development of the new single lens microscope. The most commonly accepted theory is that Leeuwenhoek read Hooke's *Micrographia* and became fascinated with Hooke's microscopic findings. More specifically, as a traveling draper, Leeuwenhoek was shown Hooke's illustrations (in *Micrographia*) of the microscopic characteristics of fabrics, which he too found to be quite interesting (Ford 40). In fact, in the preface of his book, Hooke discusses a different kind of microscope which he, at that time, preferred not to use, the type of microscope that Leeuwenhoek would eventually come to perfect. He writes, "If one of these lenses be fixed [...] against a needle hole pricked through a thin plate metal, and an object be placed very near be looked at through it, it will both magnify and make some objects more distinct than any of the large microscopes" (Ford 40). Indeed, Hooke's *Micrographia* served as one of the catalysts that would lead Leeuwenhoek on a journey to more fully understand how lenses worked and to eventually make significant contributions to the field of microscopy.

In order to develop an improved microscope, compared to the microscope used by Hooke and others, which would have better magnification and resolution, Leeuwenhoek was burdened with the task of designing new lenses that would be able to meet these specific requirements. Unlike the spheroidal lenses that were used in the earlier compound microscopes, Leeuwenhoek was able to develop a more parabolic-shaped lens through a process similar to glass blowing. From this process, he was able to create lenses that were much flatter and that were able to provide a wider field of view than was possible from the earlier ground, spheroidal lenses (Ford 63). These flatter lenses, unlike the ones employed in the early compound microscopes, allowed for greater magnification compared to the earlier models (Steenblik et al., 3). Leeuwenhoek then had to take on the task of creating the base of the actual microscope. Although Leeuwenhoek would construct several hundred microscopes during his time, all of his microscopes would follow a general assembly theme. In assembling his microscopes, Leeuwenhoek would first connect two metallic plates around one of his lens. Then he would send a long screw up from the bottom of the microscope to support a stage block, which would contain a single focusing screw. The focusing screw would project through the block and push against one of the plates when screwed in place, moving the block away from the lens. Through the focusing screw, the object being studied could then be brought into focus. A third screw with a blunt end would be placed on top of the stage block to act as a post in which the specimen being studied could be placed. A small handle would then be connected to the side of the screw so that the specimen-holder could be rotated when desired (Ford 64). This new microscope design, also known as Leeuwenhoek's first single lens microscope, would be able to produce magnifications of up to 200x compared to the outdated compound microscope, which could, at best, produce magnifications of only 50x. Leeuwenhoek's single lens microscope would undoubtedly revolutionize the field of science and ultimately help usher in a new area of scientific research and study—microbiology.

In August 1674, while he was traveling in a boat across a small lake, Leeuwenhoek noticed that in certain locations, the bottom of the lake appeared "marshy or boggy." Inspired by Hooke's insistence in *Micrographia* that no seeds could be found from the sporangia of the mildew fungus and his desire to prove him wrong, Leeuwenhoek collected some of the water and returned home. Using one of his newly created microscopes, he proceeded to closely examine the fungus-containing water and to his astonishment, he saw several microscopic creatures moving about in the sample. What Leeuwenhoek saw in the water that day were several distinct microorganisms, or "animalcules," according to Leeuwenhoek, all of which had never been seen before. Making note of the appearance of these organisms Leeuwenhoek writes in one of his journals, "...I could see two tiny limbs near the head, and two little fins at the rear end of the body." He goes on further to write, "These animalcules had different colours, some being whitish and transparent, other with green and glittering little scales..." (Ford 77).

Impressed with what he had found, Leeuwenhoek continued to study these tiny organisms, particularly the bell-shaped *Vorticella*, making note of its shape, movements, and feeding behaviors. He not only focused his attention on these microorganisms, but he eventually shifted his attention to other organisms found in different water samples from the lake, from the eel worm to the anopheline mosquito. In fact, Leeuwenhoek is credited for describing the different postures adopted by the anopheline mosquito, a mosquito known to carry and transmit malaria. More specifically, the posture that Leeuwenhoek observed in these types of mosquitoes helped to serve as an indicator for the presence of the malaria virus in the mosquitoes, a finding that proved important during the repeated attempts to eradicate malaria during the early parts of the 20th century.

Furthermore, Leeuwenhoek showed that the freshwater rotifer could survive temporary desiccation, providing a means by which future microbiologists could obtain and preserve different rotifers for scientific research (Ford 80). His other contributions to the growing field of microbiology included his discovery and subsequent studies of flukes, along with his proposition that certain diseases could be transmitted through microscopic organisms later referred to as parasites. Leeuwenhoek also studied conception through observations of spermatozoa of rabbits and dogs as well as the shape and structure of red blood cells (Ford 86). These significant discoveries by Leeuwenhoek were on the microscopic scale and proved beneficial in the subsequent development and growth of the field of microbiology.

Although many of the experiments and studies performed by Leeuwenhoek through the use of the single lens microscope may seem unimportant now, the things that he was able to see and the eventual conclusions that he was able to make were, at that time, groundbreaking. Leeuwenhoek is not only credited with the invention of the single lens microscope but he is also credited for the discovery of red blood cells, bacteria, free-living parasites, and rotifers, among other things (Ford 49). Indeed, all of the experiments performed by Leeuwenhoek would have been difficult and all of his subsequent discoveries would have taken longer to come to fruition without the newly developed single lens microscope. The single lens microscope not only ushered in a new era of scientific research and experimentation, but it also came to redefine the way people viewed the world around them.

Works Cited

Allen, R.M. *The Microscope*. New York: D. Van Norstrand Company, Inc., 1940.

Ford, Brian J. *Single Lens: The Story of the Simple Microscope*. New York: Harper & Row Publishers, 1985. Print.

Steenblik, Richard A., et al. "Lenses and Uses, Including Microscopes." US: Patent 6847480. 25 January 2005.

Donna Kapes

Innovations at the End of Life: POLST

Abstract

Healthcare is facing numerous obstacles in the appropriate delivery of care. Nowhere is this more apparent than in the realm of administering effective end-of-life care, as currently healthcare falls far short of consistently providing such care. With the use of Physician Orders for Life Sustaining Treatment (POLST), which are legal physician orders that clearly communicate patients' end of life decisions and are valid across the continuum of home, nursing home, ambulance, and hospital settings, this can be accomplished. These brightly colored one-page orders are specifically geared to those with life expectancies of less than two years. Patient and primary care provider, either physician or nurse practitioner, discuss and then decide on what medical interventions the patient wants at the end of life. Unlike traditional advance directives, this innovative health care advance has proven to effectively enforce the treatment that the patient wants at this crucial time and honors end-of-life decisions.

Innovations at the End of Life: POLST

An aged patient brought in by ambulance to the emergency department is mostly unresponsive, moans when an invasive procedure is attempted, but is unable to verbalize the quality of care she wants at the end of life. Working in the emergency department can prove to be vexing and ethically challenging when providing aggressive care to a patient at the end of life. In order to limit treatment in the state of Pennsylvania, a physician signed "Do Not Resuscitate" (DNR) order is necessary, which can be difficult to obtain, and even if obtained, typically it is only after aggressive treatment has already begun, either by emergency medical personnel or upon presentations to the emergency department.

The Problem with End of Life Care

The traditional way of managing patients with chronic or terminal disease toward the end of life has proven to be largely ineffective in honoring patients' wishes (Cohen-Mansfield and Lipson, 2008). Morrell, Brown, Qi, Drabiak, and Helft (2008) found that, after over 20 years, the established use of advance directives still has no measurable impact on honoring patients' end-of-life care decisions. Indeed, Covinsky et al. (2000) showed that patients with advance directives were no more likely than patients without advance directives to have preferences for or against cardiopulmonary resuscitation (CPR) documented in the medical record or to have DNR orders written among those who preferred not to have such invasive procedures. Although older people prefer to die in the surroundings in which they live, those wishes are consistently not honored (Fried et al., 1999). This leads to frustration on the part of healthcare providers as they seek to maintain a balance between aggressive end-of-life care and providing comfort to those who are near death. The need, therefore, exists for innovation in providing effective end of life care that honors patients' wishes.

As 20% of Americans die following treatment in an intensive care unit (ICU) and the rate of ICU use at the end of life increases significantly with age as well as the number of coexisting chronic illnesses, use of the ICU at the end of life must be addressed (Angus et. al., 2009). In an attempt to understand how ICU nursing directors and physicians perceive end-of-life care issues, Nelson et al. (2006) sent out mailings to almost 600 ICU nursing directors and physicians with an amazing 78% return response rate. The high level of returns may indicate a heightened level of concern regarding the lack of adequate end-of-life care. Nelson et al. showed that nationally, ICU directors perceive that there are important barriers to end-of-life care in the ICU. Important barriers to end-of-life care identified included unrealistic patient or family expectations, inability of patients to participate in end-of-life discussions, and the lack of advance directives (Nelson et. al., 2006).

Nelson et al. (2006) demonstrated the need to implement a program so that patients and their families can discuss and make end-of-life decisions prior to being in an emergency situation that would cause admission to the ICU. Currently, the practice in most states, as well as in Pennsylvania, is to provide aggressive life saving treatment when a patient presents to the emergency department, as there are no physician orders valid across the continuum of care. This occurs even when a patient has a terminal illness or deteriorating life threatening condition which will result in death. While the emergency physician attempts to contact the patient's next of kin to discuss the emergent plan of care, due to critical time restraints, aggressive care is typically started, which may include intubation as well as other advanced life support means. This cycle then leads to the patient being admitted to the ICU where the ICU team then struggles with the next plan of care.

To address the need to effectively provide for end-of-life care that is consistent with the wishes of those involved, a few states have adopted the 'Physician Orders for Life Sustaining Treatment' (POLST) paradigm. This legal intervention is designed to improve the quality of care patients receive at the end of life, based on effective communication among the patient, family, and healthcare team, and is honored by health care professionals (POLST). Physician orders are written that are honored across the continuum of care for the patient, such as at home, nursing home, ambulance, and hospital settings, including the emergency department. The POLST paradigm is specifically aimed at those with a life expectancy of less than two years due to terminal illness or deteriorating chronic medical conditions. Since POLST are legally binding physician orders valid across the continuum, their use can provide the effective intervention needed for successful communications and increase the likelihood of a patient's end of life decisions being honored.

Review of the Literature on the Use of POLST

In the first major research done a few years after the adoption of the POLST paradigm in Oregon, Tolle, Tilden, Nelson, and Dunn (1998) showed that the use of POLST resulted in the respect of patients' wishes regarding end-of-life treatment as well as the patients receiving a high level of comfort care. As most of the patients (85%) that transferred into the hospital setting did so due to poor pain control, that then was the focus of the emergency department visit and not aggressive care, which many times leads to the infliction of more pain at the end of life (Tolle et. al., 1998). This sentinel work empowers the healthcare professional to be able to provide care that the patient wants and to relieve pain. Even in the 15% of hospitalizations that were for the purpose of extending life, the patient was still directing the course of treatment chosen (Tolle et. al., 1998).

The POLST program is used in Oregon nursing facilities to facilitate the carrying out of patient and family wishes regarding end of life care. Brummel-Smith, Carley, Hickman, and Tolle (2004) noted that a majority of individuals with DNR orders requested some other form of life-extending treatment. This validates that DNR does not mean "do not treat" and that POLST is a reliable vehicle to convey patients' end-of-life wishes into physician orders to ensure patient-driven care is provided. Brummel-Smith, Carley, Hickman, and Tolle provides credibility that the POLST paradigm empowers patients to make end-of-life decisions that they are comfortable with and not feel pressured to forego all treatment.

Patients feel empowered in directing their own end-of-life care. In a pilot study, undertaken only six months after the state of Washington introduced the POLST paradigm, Meyers, Moore, McGrory, Sparr, and Ahern (2004) revealed that all of the residents and legal surrogates expressed confidence that the POLST form accurately reflected stated wishes. Both the residents' and legal surrogates' wishes regarding directives as stated in the interviews universally concurred with their POLST directives. After only a few months following the introduction of POLST, nursing home residents and legal surrogates increased their knowledge base regarding levels of care that the resident wanted at the end of life and those wishes were respected with the use of POLST. Both the residents and legal surrogates expressed satisfaction in the increase in their end-of-life knowledge base and the ability to become empowered to make such decisions and feel comfortable that those decisions would be honored through the POLST paradigm as evidenced by the participants' end-of-life decisions being honored 90.5% of the time (Meyers et al., 2004). Lee, Brummel-Smith, Meyer, Drew, and London (2000) also demonstrated that with the use of the POLST paradigm, patients during the last two weeks of their lives were far more likely to have their end-of-life decisions honored with the use of POLST than with traditional advance directives. Hickman et al. (2009) noted that with the use of POLST in the hospice setting, patients' preferences for end-of-life treatment were honored an amazing 98% of the time.

Needs and Possibilities Inherent in End of Life Care

The need exists to examine current and past practices regarding respecting and implementing patients' end-of-life decisions. Patients' preference for the site of terminal care consistently is not the hospital setting (Fried et. al., 1999). Yet, nationally, over 20% of older patients die not only in the hospital setting, but in the intensive care unit after receiving aggressive, invasive treatment (Nelson et. al., 2006). As noted, intensive care physicians and staff recognize important barriers to optimal end-of-life care in this setting (Nelson et. al, 2006).

While the use of advance directives has been in effect for years, they have been largely unsuccessful. Those patients who come to the hospital with completed advance directives requesting no heroic measures be taken still have no measurable impact as Morrell, Brown, Qi, Drabiak, and Helft (2008) confirmed; although 22% of patients had an advance directive on their chart requesting no resuscitation, no DNR physician order accompanied that directive. Perkins (2007) describes a case study in which the primary care physician discussed traditional advance directives with a terminal patient and his wife. When the patient developed difficulty breathing, the wife called emergency services and the patient was brought to the emergency department. The wife brought the signed advance directives along and the emergency physician agreed to honor them and provide the patient with comfort measures only. However, when the patient's daughter arrived, she accused the physician of "murdering Daddy." Risk management was consulted and instructed the physician to begin aggressive management of the patient immediately, which included intubating the patient (Perkins, 2007). The patient died a few days later with his end of life decisions not honored.

In Oregon, the state that originated the POLST paradigm, about 50% of the population was dying in acute care hospitals in 1980, which was comparable to deaths across the United States (National Center for Health Statistics.) However, with the implementation of the POLST paradigm, by 1999, Tolle and Tilden (2002) stated that in-hospital deaths had dropped to 31% in Oregon, with some hospitals reporting in-hospital deaths at 22%. Tolle and Tilden asserted that more people at the end of life are having their decisions not to die in-hospital honored due to the use of the POLST paradigm. During that same time frame, nationally, about 56% of American deaths in hospitals were reported (Tolle and Tilden, 2002). Certainly, this shows that the POLST paradigm is effective in honoring a patient's end-of-life decisions regarding where the patient wants to die.

Although more research is needed to substantiate that as the POLST paradigm is utilized in more states that the same results continue, the research done is reliable and does offer enough evidence to justify the use of POLST in order to better honor patients' end-of-life decisions (Meier and Beresford, 2009). Hickman (2009) is awaiting publication of a study conducted in 139 hospice programs and 685 nursing homes in Oregon, West Virginia, and part of Wisconsin that is the first study to investigate the POLST paradigm across states in various settings. Unpublished findings are that the use of POLST helps ensure that patient preferences documented as treatment orders can be followed as well as having a wide range of treatments discussed (Tucker, 2008). Having the POLST paradigm be utilized across the continuum of care allows emergency medical technicians not to begin aggressive measures in the home or nursing home setting if that is in accordance with the patient's decisions (Schmidt et. al., 2004). Indeed, having the POLST orders when a patient presents to the emergency department of a hospital will be a great asset in planning that patient's care. Clearly, the use of the POLST paradigm results in a patient's end-of-life decisions being honored.

Innovation Proposal: Implementation of POLST

Unfortunately, incorporating the POLST paradigm into practice is beyond the scope of any individual. Dependent upon the types of laws in various states, either a regulatory or legislative approach must be utilized to implement the POLST paradigm (POLST). In states where a regulatory change is possible, such as in Oregon, once the POLST program was approved, additional changes to the paradigm could be made without a return to the legal process (POLST). Hickman, Sabatino, Moss, and Wehrle-Nester (2008) provide some insight into the laws that each state currently has and offers direction needed to implement POLST.

In 2006, under Pennsylvania Act 169, a committee was authorized to advise on the use of POLST. By the end of 2008, the committee returned with an endorsement of POLST; however, Pennsylvania Secretary of Health, Everette James, requested more input from conservative stakeholders and POLST remains stalled in the Pennsylvania Department of Health (K. Brody, personal communication, November 13, 2009). Therefore, letters from conservative stakeholders must be obtained and then submitted to the department for further consideration.

In practical terms, education on POLST must be done across the state of Pennsylvania, starting with healthcare providers. As emergency healthcare providers already share a frustration in providing aggressive treatment to patients at the end of life, without patient direction, providing education in this environment will help to build support for the POLST paradigm. Then education needs to be provided to the rest of the healthcare communities in the state. Utilizing posters, emails, and other correspondence alerting staff to the POLST paradigm and website will allow for easy access to information regarding its use.

Only after the healthcare population has been educated in the POLST paradigm should a public education program be mounted, as medical and nursing staff can then be utilized as a learning resource. By emphasizing the choices available with the POLST program as well as its effectiveness in implementing these choices, public support can be garnered. With the information needed to legally change Pennsylvania law, meeting with state legislators to educate them and seek their support will be necessary.

Utilizing the POLST paradigm has been shown to be significantly more effective in ensuring that a patient's end-of-life care decisions be honored as compared to traditional advance directives. The POLST form is a simple-to-read brightly colored one-page form, which specifically and clearly states what treatment the patient wants and is signed by a physician or nurse practitioner as well as the patient or family. Those living at home are encouraged to post the brightly colored POLST form on the refrigerator so that emergency personnel can easily access it if called to the home. POLST is in no way a glorified advance directive or DNR form but, instead, indicates explicitly what potentially life-prolonging interventions, as well as comfort measures, the patient and physician have agreed upon (Meier and Beresford, 2009). These POLST orders may include some level of comfort care or even aggressive care options based on the patient's decisions. Unlike traditional advance directives with little compliance, the POLST paradigm enjoys a significantly high rate of compliance (Hickman et. al., 2008). Also, unlike traditional advance directives, the POLST paradigm is not suitable for everyone. Indeed, POLST is appropriate only for those patients who have a terminal disease or advanced chronic illness with a limited life expectancy of less than two years (Meier and Beresford, 2009).

No information was uncovered that disputes the positive findings with the use of the POLST paradigm. Available studies have demonstrated that the use of POLST does not mean "do not treat" and that most patients do indeed want some form of treatment and successfully obtain that level of treatment desired. Patients and families have expressed satisfaction with the use of POLST. Through the use of the POLST paradigm, nursing and medical professions can accurately honor the patient's end-of-life decisions. Simply, the use of POLST increases the likelihood of a patient's end-of-life decisions being honored, and therefore, must be implemented.

Works Cited

American Nurses Association. (2001). Code of ethics for nurses with interpretive statements. *Silver Spring: ANA.*

Angus, D. C., Barnato A. E., Linde-Zwirble, W. T., Weissfeld, L. A., Watson, R. S., Rickert, T., et al. (2004). Use of intensive care at the end of life in the United States: An epidemiologic study. *Critical Care Medicine,* 32(3), 638-643.

Brummel-Smith, K., Carley, M. M., Hickman, S. E., & Tolle, S. W. (2004). Use of the physician orders for life-sustaining treatment program in Oregon nursing facilities: beyond resuscitation status. *Journal of the American Geriatrics Society,* 52(9), 1424-1429.

Cohen-Mansfield, J., & Lipson, S. (2008). Which advance directive matters? An analysis of end of life decisions made in nursing homes. *Research on Aging,* 30(1), 74-92.

Covinsky, K. E., Fuller, J. D., Yaffe, K., Johnston, C. B., Hamel, M. B., Lynn, J. et al. (2000). Communication and decision-making in seriously ill patients: findings of the SUPPORT project. *Journal of the American Geriatrics Society,* 48(5), S187-193.

Fried, T. R., Van Doorn, C., O'Leary, J. R., Tinetti, M. E., & Drickamer, M. A. (1999). Older persons' preferences for site of terminal care. *Annals of Internal Medicine,* 131(20), 109-112.

Hickman, S. E. (2009). Converting treatment wishes into orders at end of life: A multi-state study to evaluate the efficacy of the physician orders for life-sustaining treatment (POLST) program at ensuring the wishes of nursing home residents are honored at the end of life. RO1 NR 9784. *National Institute of Nursing Research.* Research submitted for publication.

Hickman, S. E., Nelson, C. A., Moss, A. H., Hammes, B., J., Terwilliger, A., Jackson, A., et al. (2009). Use of the physician orders for life-sustaining treatment (POLST) paradigm program in the hospice setting. *Journal of Palliative Medicine*, 12(2), 133-141.

Hickman, S. E., Sabatino, C. P., Moss, & Wehrle-Nester, J. (2008). The POLST (physician orders for life-sustaining treatment) paradigm to improve end of life care: Potential state legal barriers to implementation. *Journal of Law*, Medicine & Ethic, 1(36),

Lee, M. A., Brummel-Smith, K., Meyer, J., Drew, N., & London, M. R. (2000). Physician orders for life-sustaining treatment (POLST): Outcomes in a PACE program. *Journal of the American Geriatrics Society*, 48, 1219-1225.

Meier, D. & Beresford, L. (2009). POLST offers next stage in honoring patient preferences. *Journal of Palliative Medicine*, 12(4).

Meyers, J. L., Moore, C., McGrory, A., Sparr, J., & Ahern, M. (2004). Physician orders for life-sustaining treatment form: Honoring end of life directives for nursing home residents. *Journal of Gerontological Nursing*, 30(9), 37-46.

Morrell, E. D., Brown, B. P., Qi, R., Drabiak, K., Helft, P. R. (2008). The do-not-resuscitate order: Associations with advance directives, physician specialty, and documentation of discussion 15 years after the patient self-determination act. *Journal of Medical Ethics*, 34, 642-647.

National Center for Health Statistics: 1997 National Mortality followback survey. *Atlanta: Centers for Disease Control and Prevention*. www.cdc.gov/nchswww/about/major/nmfs/nmfs/htm

Nelson, J. E., Angus, D. C., Weissfeld, L. A., Puntillo, K. A., Danis, M., Deal, D., et al. (2006). End-of-life care for the critically ill: A national intensive care unit survey. *Critical Care Medicine*, 34(10), 2547-2553.

Perkins, H. S. (2007). Controlling death: The false promise of advance directives. *Annals of Internal Medicine*, 147(1), 51-57.

POLST. (2009). Physician orders for life-sustaining treatment paradigm. <http://www.ohsu.edu/polst/

Schmidt, T. A., Hickman, S. E., Tolle, S. W. & Brooks, H. S. (2004). The physician orders for life-sustaining treatment program: Oregon emergency medical technicians' practical experiences and attitudes. *Journal of the American Geriatrics Society*, 52(9), 1430-1434.

Seferian, E. G. & Afessa, B. (2006). Adult intensive care unit use at the end of
life: A population-based study. *Mayo Clinic Proceedings*, 81(7), 896-901

Tolle, S. W., & Tilden, V. P. (2002). Changing end-of-life planning: The Oregon
experience. *Journal of Palliative Medicine*, 5(2), 311- 317.

Tolle, S. W., & Tilden, V. P., Nelson, C. A., & Dunn, P.M. (1998). A prospective study of
the efficacy of the physician order form for life-sustaining treatment. *Journal of
the American Geriatrics Society*, 46(90), 1097–1102.

Tucker, M. E. (2008). Program improves implementation of advance
directives: Findings from a National Institute of Nursing Research on POLST.
Internal Medicine News, 41(24).

Angela Silverman

Review: *Living in the Shadow of Death*

Throughout the 19th and into the early 20th centuries, tuberculosis was the leading cause of death in the United States. Countless histories and case studies have been compiled that narrate the progression and treatment of the disease and the troubles and triumphs of medical doctors, treatment facilities, and the field of public health. Often overlooked and undervalued is the experience of the actual patient. Published in 1994, *Living in the Shadow of Death* was one of the first in-depth accounts of tuberculosis from the patient's perspective. In this compelling history of the disease, Sheila Rothman chronicles the deadliest period of the epidemic in the social context of the times and briefly explores the implications for similar epidemics today. She seeks to portray those suffering from tuberculosis as major players in the wider drama of medical history, while allowing them "the dignity of explaining in their own words how they lived life in the shadow of death" (9).

The book's appeal is due primarily to the sources utilized; information is drawn not from medical case files but from family archives of diaries, personal letters, and memoirs. Rothman termed these collections "narratives of illness," referring to the story of disease progression and its effects on every aspect of the patient's life, as gleaned from these illuminating personal sources (1). What she failed to anticipate was just how ambitious this project would be, for there is of course no one unifying story of the "typical" tuberculosis patient coming from such an eclectic population as that of the United States and a timeframe over a century in length. Rothman's chosen limits, while unavoidable and probably materialistically sound, are a bit unfortunate in regards to what they exclude. The first two sections of the book, which delve into the experience of the consumptive "invalid" in the first half of the 19th century, are limited to middle-to-upper-class white patients from New England. While this is undoubtedly due to the wider availability of sources from those with the ability to write and the resources to preserve or publish, the lack can be assumed to be substantial. The author herself expresses the hope that other researchers will examine the experiences of other populations more thoroughly (9). Meanwhile, the reader can only imagine the difference in experience between a wealthy white American and an impoverished, marginalized servant, African American, or recent immigrant.

Despite these limitations, Rothman does a laudable job portraying the experience of her chosen demographic. She has arranged the book into four parts: the first two elucidating the invalid experience in the early 1800s by gender, the third as the western states opened for exploration, and the last as time and treatment technologies progressed and radically changed the face of disease. Each part examines the social and technological framework of the time period and the role of disease therein.

The content seems to fall naturally into two major sections between the first three parts and the fourth, ultimately dividing the content between consumption and tuberculosis—the disease before the discovery of its pathogen, and after. Through most of the 19th century, the disease was not called tuberculosis but "consumption," characterized by the wasting effect it had upon its victims. Consumption was not well understood—it was thought to be hereditary and non-contagious, and sufferers were allowed full freedom to choose whether and how to seek treatment. In this section, the author describes physicians as "recommending" and "endorsing" salubrious regimens and climates and calls them "peripheral figures" in invalids' lives (7, 21, 59). She asserts that consumptive individuals were more than helpless victims of disease—they were "wary and sophisticated consumer[s] of medicine," willing to change doctors and regimens with which they were dissatisfied (105). In contrast, once the *Tubercle bacillus* bacteria was isolated as the cause of the disease, the balance of power shifted to heavily favor the physician over the patient. Rothman follows the progression of treatment from a highly individualized regimen including travel and outdoor exercise to one of universal confinement and strict regulation. "For many," she declares, "the only analogy to entering the sanatorium [...] was imprisonment" (229).

The first three parts of the book effectively depict the individual experience of living with consumption, lives necessarily rearranged in "pursuit of health" (45). Some of the most valuable content within this section lies in the contrast between prescribed treatments for men and women, and as time progressed. Consumptive men were told to work outdoors, to travel, to seek the most healthful climate for their constitution and to enjoy the vigor of the journey. Women, their lives revolving around household duties and "unwilling to allow medical regimens to override social and religious values," were allowed to remain in the home while doing their best to follow the proper dietary and exercise regimen (105). Between the first half of the century and the last, the major change in treatment was the substitution of curative climates—physicians began recommending relocation to the American West rather than sea voyages to exotic locales.

Stylistic contrast is created by the author's questionable choice to portray the male experience through a seemingly endless series of ultimately repetitive cases, and the female through the eyes of only one woman—the wealthy Deborah Vinal Fiske. She anticipates this criticism and includes an argument in support of her decision, which falls somewhat short of convincing (79). Nevertheless, Rothman achieves a concrete depiction of each gender's conflicts, emotions, and their lives through the lens of illness. The unifying theme is the uncertain nature of life in the face of such a mysterious disease. No one knew whether they would recover, "whether a remission might last for months, years, or decades" (7).

Men were forced to decide between following career aspirations for as long as they were able and abiding by common wisdom to protect their health by traveling and laboring outdoors. A slew of accounts of the different ways men attempted to resolve this conflict yields an engrossing view of the times, though it is eventually weighed down by the sheer number of cases reviewed. Women likewise had to decide whether to marry and have children, not knowing if they would be able to carry out the household duties or if they would soon leave their young children motherless. Rothman hits an emotional peak with a poignant account of Deborah raising her daughters to be polite, dutiful, and welcome in other people's homes—essentially, to be good orphans.

Compelling as the early accounts may be, the most relevant aspects of the book to modern life are delineated in the fourth and final section, which depicts the experience of patients of tuberculosis as a bacterial infection. Here, Rothman delves into historical records to examine how an increase in knowledge about the disease led to strict political measures, and the ways in which those measures stigmatized populations and violated individual rights. She uses letters, memoirs, and institutional newsletters to paint a bleak picture of life for those confined in sanatoriums, which became the standard treatment for tubercular patients in this period. In this setting, the patient became passive and the physician was no longer an advisor but a figure of unquestionable authority. Patients in these institutions were so isolated from the outside world that they felt "[t]he only real things were connected with the sanatorium" (235). They were bound by a "book of a thousand rules (more or less)," which Rothman believes existed to "serve the convenience of the staff" (231-2). The sanatorium is clearly portrayed as an institution we should not wish to revive.

In the epilogue, the author speaks briefly about the discovery of antibiotics and the hope it inspired for the total eradication of disease—optimism that was soon after shattered by the modern-day HIV epidemic and the resurgence of tuberculosis. She touches on the correlations between public health measures and possible abuses of power that existed in the early 20th century as well as the implications for present-day epidemics, but does not draw any conclusions or make recommendations beyond a plea to "remember that we are in a profound way affecting individual life chances and life choices" (252). This entreaty defines the ultimate goal of Rothman's book and the way in which it is most effective: to provide a voice for those who are most in danger of being marginalized and stripped of their rights—the innocent victims of disease.

Work Cited

Rothman, Sheila M. *Living in the Shadow of Death: Tuberculosis and the Social Experience of Illness in American History.* Baltimore: Johns Hopkins University Press, 1995. Print.

Week of
Writing

Introduction

Drexel University's fifth annual Week of Writing (WoW) was held in May of 2010. WoW is a weeklong celebration of writing with an emphasis on creative writing, sponsored by the Department of English and Philosophy, the College of Arts and Sciences, and Magnificent Minds. This past year's events included panel discussions about flash fiction, the evolution of the writing machine, the craft of stand-up, and poetry by Drexel faculty, as well as both a raucous story slam and open-mic extravaganza. WoW also featured multiple drop-in creative writing workshops and the *Painted Bride Quarterly* Book Fair for Literacy. And, once again, at the reading marathon, faculty and students read their own original creative writing back-to-back, a new reader every few minutes, as the audience came and went throughout the days.

Each year, the lead-up to the marathon is the WoW Writing Contest, used to determine which students will be invited to read at the event. The faculty judging panels determined the best fiction, poetry, creative nonfiction, humor, and opinion/editorial writing produced by Drexel students in 2010. Those winning students not only read at the WoW marathon and earned prizes, but also now have their writing published in the third volume of *The 33rd*.

Creative writing is among the most challenging fields. Even experienced authors who have been writing for years often struggle to find just the right word. As author Gene Fowler famously said, "Writing is easy. All you do is stare at a blank sheet of paper until drops of blood form on your forehead." The writers whose work appears in this section have stared at that blank sheet of paper, or that computer screen. Whether or not blood formed on their foreheads, they have struggled for the right words to touch their readers and bring their vision to life. The Week of Writing will continue to celebrate and reward their efforts.

Michael B. Harris-Peyton

Live Museum Display

These are the places they call Boundaries, Parks, and Reservations.
Vast useless emptiness, put to no work because no work is possible.

Near the road, old B.I.A. buildings have their gravel parking lots
So the whites can shed their guilt and marvel at baskets.

An unpaved road—the budget for asphalt is stretched this century—
Connects the highway to the place where they keep the attractions.

Remnants of a People packed in tin boxes the size of boxcars.
The one with the biggest tin box has a rancher hat and is almost snow.

On Thursday they drive forty miles to find a Wal-Mart in a shared truck.
On Friday they sell what they bought—white money is like stealing it all back,
slow.

On Monday everyone is here, and a baby cries because his mother is gone
And the house smells like cornmeal and Listerine and transmission fluid.

They could take a picture of the one boy with the green eyes who belongs
nowhere. Seeing it, the whites will say there has to be pain in pursuit of
beauty.

That boy, with his duct-tape sneakers, America shirt and red-muddy knees
Knows the smell of gunmetal and alcohol and wet red mud and an
aluminum house.

He will see no such thing for himself as pain in the pursuit of beauty;
He sees for himself already a gradual death in the pursuit of nothing.

Autumn Elliot

Polska

You probably think I'm one of those silly, emotional people that cries about
things they didn't previously take much interest in, like a bandwagon
supporter for mourning.

But I feel for this world so intensely and, unlike so many, I still have a deep,
boundless love and faith for people as people, as conglomerate of billions of
individuals, and an understood unit of one, like water molecules in
an ocean wave.

Sometimes it gets rough, sometimes white caps toss some about mercilessly,
while the wave feet cause the whole thing to crash over too close to land, and
everything seems to fall apart, everyone goes everywhere and the
cohesion seems lost.

and then,

sure enough,

everyone goes back to the same place,

to be part of the same thing.

I love people, I love different societies, and uniting differences, from
nationality to religion.

This is hurting a lot of people, and it destroyed something elaborate.

And for that,

My heart is broken.

Lauren Gatto

Night Wrath

That night,
the eggshell moon
with its gorgeous pallor
like the inside of an Oreo
hung like a cuticle,
jagged. Pieces had fallen
into perpetuity.
Stars grew bored
and careless, dropping bits
on the black
night pavement.
Beautiful
and broken.

That night,
my house held its hands
over its ears
as rage defiantly
spilled April's basket
of fresh slumber
while strangling
her quietness
until she whimpered.

That night,
I heard the other homes whisper,
how thankful they were
that the people
in their heated bellies
smiled
and never screamed.

That night,
shouting infected rooms
while anger
banged on doors

and soiled floors.
Lamp shades danced in the living room
to the aquarium requiem
of the pair of Japanese fighting fish.

That night,
little sisters slept
in cribs like ivory castles
resting on peaks of cumuli
above the thunderstorm.
Carnation pink curtains
moved to the night
and plush bunnies
resting on
pink icing throws
soothed April
as she trembled,
crouching in the closet.

I yelled
at the yelling,
so it wouldn't
peel castle paint
and tear
strawberry coverlets
and rearrange
dreams
pale as vanilla gardenia,
beautiful
not broken.

Carolynn McCormack

The Jersey Girl's Creed
After Allen Hoey

I believe in four leaf clovers and
wishing upon a shooting star.
I believe in the need to just keep going
even when you have no idea where you're headed
because you never know who or what you could
stumble upon.
I believe that the only thing better than the first snowfall,
is the way the first firework on the Fourth of July sparkles.
I believe in the wisdom of my mother
because if I had only listened to her the first time,
I would have fewer regrets.
I believe that the cure for anything is a cup
of Starbucks coffee and a conversation with
your best friend.
I believe in driving with the windows down and
the music blaring because you don't want to miss
that first smell of the bay that says you've made it
to the Jersey Shore.
I believe that red stockings can be extremely classy
if worn by a girl with the right attitude.
I believe that the best way to spend your life
is confidently—there is no reason to apologize for
who you are.
I believe that persistence is key,
but when you have to give up, let it go.
I believe that it is acceptable to make mistakes,
but I believe that I am never ever wrong.
And I believe that right now I am going
to pour myself a drink and bury my toes in the sand
because right now, this is the only place I need to be.

Emily Homrok

Critical

"'Newsome,' writes Anne Carlyle of the *Mahaiwe Review*, 'is apparently as new to her writing as the unfortunate readers of her debut novel, *Husband*. These poor, patient souls find themselves hurled closer and closer to Newsome's black hole of clichés, one tear-soaked breakup at a time. Do we *really* need to revisit those pimply high school years? Thank God I'm a woman, or I might be doomed to spend eternity as a character in Newsome's literary (?) hell. Or, maybe I'm completely wrong. Maybe Newsome is just some sort of revolutionary trying to teach us all why literacy is, in fact, a bad thing.'"

She reads the entire article—869 words, she counts, dragging her pointer finger deliberately as a child learning to read—aloud to Derry, who sits with the wide Chinese fans of his hands folded, looking at his wife. It is easy for Derry to look at people, because his eyes are enormous, bay windows, irrepressible as activists. Julia has small eyes, the color of things that spend their lives in slime and mud, like toads or worms or catfish. It is hard for her to look at people the way Derry can.

"How can you smile?" she demands, holding her obituary on her lap.

"You're cute when you're mad," Derry says, pressing a baker's finger into her chin.

It is moments like these that make her alone, make her pine for an evil man who can torch her, wrap her in Wendigo fire—surround her forever.

"Did you hear anything I just said?"

He puts his arms around her. She denies him her face, hiding in the paper like a child.

"I'm just saying," he remedies, "I don't think you should care what other people say about your writing. Has she published any books?"

"Who?"

"The woman who wrote the article."

He's serious now, pointing sternly like God in a painting from the times when artists didn't sign their names. And just like that, she doesn't feel alone anymore. She wishes his reasoning were a place. She would live there.

Julia scans the italicized blurb at the bottom of the review. It makes the usual witty, unoriginal references to a dog, a husband, and show-off hobbies.

"No," she confesses.

"She's probably just bitter." She wishes there were more condemnation in his voice. "Critics usually are."

You would know.

She doesn't say this, because as always he has come, with a relaxed gait, to her defense. But there is no way Derry Newsome, Ph.D., can ever know the little stings. "Derry pioneered studies of genetic mutation—you know, how some people are immune to AIDS and that sort of thing," is the exact phrase she has memorized for the benefit of women at parties. He publishes very long articles in esoteric scholarly journals which unapologetically cater mainly to the people who write them.

That's just like her, to complain, she thinks in her typical third person. In third person, her weaknesses are not ugly, not faults; they are merely quirks, on reserve for her characters.

"Connecticut," he says one day in October, only a brave dilution of his honest reaction. He says this word with the pretend grimness of someone feigning bad news because they're about to spring a surprise on another someone. That is how Julia interprets it—a wonderful surprise. An excuse to lay down the arms so sore from adventure, to retreat into the easy depths of the Home.

It is not pretend. Derry is from one of those sensible austere towns in the Midwest. He does not play tennis. He does not tie argyle sweaters around his shoulders. He does not look down on minorities or poor people, or even women.

Julia is less disciplined than her husband. She allows everything to show on her face. There is guilt, to see the sag, the muscles of his back drooping like an old hammock. And there is triumph, to be granted sugar for her tea, to live the life of little wooden plaques proudly reading *1763 or 1881* without having to claim responsibility.

"I'm sorry, baby," she tells him that night. His beard is scratching one nipple to fever pitch, but she doesn't dare push him away now. "I know it isn't where you would have wanted to go. But you know." She thinks quickly. "You know. I'm from there. It's not all like they make it up to be in movies and things.

"And we don't have to go," she adds, after a minute. "It's your work. It's your choice."

What blows from his nostrils is hot, tickling—the snort of a horse eating from your palm, more exhaust than breath. Condensation forms between her breasts.

"I've moved around before. It'll be fine," he says anticlimactically. "And you'll be happier there."

Careful, now. So easy to lapse, to become Derry's little daughter. When that happens she gets alone.

"Don't feel guilty. I figure we've lived in my neck of the woods for a while now anyway. You got through it. I'll do the same thing."

And it will be easier for Derry. Derry occupies one shelf behind the bathroom mirror. Julia takes up three.

He found her in the shower. Not on the first day, not even during the first week. There was simply too much to be done, even without the children they happily pledged never to have. There were mislabeled boxes to be hunted down, calls to be made to the parents, the siblings; paintings to be hung, wherever there was room on the pink papered walls. It was the one-month anniversary of the move to the apartment in Minnetonka.

It was also like her to plan out her drama, she thinks (creating character), stroking the secret softness in the crease of his elbow. She was folded in half to fit into the square bottom of the stall. Two blue lips. One red wrist.

"I wasn't really going to," she mumbled, flesh around the mouth puffy with motionlessness, with hours of cold pelting water. "They're not deep. One wrist wouldn't do it."

He washed her with hot water, pressed paper towels, slathered her with that antibacterial goop mothers of young children are always such strong proponents of. The telephone, wedged between his ear and his shoulder all the while, calm clear words coming out.

"You won't put me in a..." she tried to ask the doctor, who stood with a clipboard while Derry sat on the edge of Julia's bed, holding her hands in his.

"No, no," Derry said to her, a rustle, while Julia cried, and the doctor said over both of them that he was referring her to a psychologist and a psychiatrist. He asked if she had any allergies to medicines. She didn't know, but Derry did.

"I love you, Derry, I love you," she sobbed on the ride back. They pulled over and made this love.

It was a pleasant memory. She knew she wouldn't die. She knew she would be caressed, pampered. Addressed.

"You could always do something dramatic when we get there," she muses. "We'll be even, then."

He doesn't like it when she jokes about That Sort Of Thing.

He turns away from her to lie on his side. She's pleased. Now he is the son. She plays with his hair, smells it, inhales sugar cane and pineapple and sea brine.

"I'm sorry," she says. "I hope you like Connecticut."

She props him up on the pillows and takes him into her mouth by way of apology. The scars on her wrist leave grooves in his thigh.

He imagines the lawn, the pond, the mahogany they will come to own. He catches sight of the review of her book, thrown to the carpeting, dormant but patient, like cancer. He closes his eyes.

And the Minnetonka apartment is replaced by the Darien house. Here is real tile. Here is fresh paint. There is no mahogany, to Derry's relief, though vestiges of a tennis court linger in the backyard. Julia is buoyant. He knows he can't hold it against her.

He counts the vials and bottles which, for now, in the chaos of the move, scatter the bathroom counter. He opens the door on their room and sits alone on the edge of their new bed, looking through foreign windows.

His wife lies spread-eagled by the garden, oblivious to the mosquitoes, even the wasps. Lots of wasps around here, he thinks; even if wasps do not spread their legs in bare dirty grass. She waves up at him. He observes her through the glass.

The second novel fares better, and so does its author. This one features a character named Anne. She is a critic who endures, resentfully, chapter upon chapter of ill luck until finally committing suicide on page 237. No reviews of the new novel are included in the *Mahaiwe Review*.

In other magazines, and plenty of them, Julia Newsome is glorified, hailed, praised, lauded. Derry slings on a utility belt and begins to build a deck on the south side of the house. It's a knotted, crude little thing, and his hands turn pink and fill with splinters, but the work makes him happy. Together, they throw neighborhood parties and lay the groundwork for new alliances—most of the local couples lapse into confusion when confronted by his science or her art, acclimated to the boozy, temperate realm of televised golf and long hours of bird-watching; but some, who exchange looks when the other bluebloods make certain sorts of remarks, show promise.

August comes. The lawn and the garden have been abandoned. Bright flowers with no names, only colors, wilt in the heat as Julia's hunch becomes more and more pronounced, her eyes fluttering toward stigmatisms and cataracts for the hours they spend failing to penetrate the screen propped nightly before her. Her fingertips sweat into the keys, despite their lack of exertion. So often does she sit up with the computer in bed, Derry privately names the color of their glowing bedroom wall *Career Crash Cream*. He lays with his back turned to her, eyes ticking over bumps and bubbles in the paint. October again. Derry goes into the adjoining bathroom, making a show of tugging at the covers, thudding onto the floor. He does not huddle into the shower with a razor. That is simply not something Derry would do. He sits on the edge of the toilet and masturbates. It isn't something he feels comfortable doing; but neither again is laying nights and nights in a cold bed, inner ears muttering, blocking out the sound of a computer engine whining like the smallest dog in the world.

He leaves the bathroom door open while he does it. He swears, he moans. Most of it is fake. He wonders what she is doing, out there, when she will come—when she will throw herself at his feet.

She enters unexpectedly, without knocking. He stays seated, defiant, hairy thighs sloshed flat against the pressure of the toilet seat pushing up on the flesh from beneath. He keeps his hand wrapped around himself.

"Can you be quieter?" she asks. "I'm trying to concentrate."

With that she leaves him to it, pulling the bathroom door until it clicks shut behind her. No more than a worm, he lets go, pulls up his pants. He sleeps on the floor, with the light on, shivering against marble.

"Julia," Derry says one night at dinner.

The scraping of tines on ceramics lifts to a halt.

His fishbowl eyes are filled with water. He reaches for her hand. Jostled by his elbow, the salt falls, heaping fine white crystals onto Julia's plate. The wife looks at the husband's face, ignoring his outstretched hand. So close, so easy to take.

He folds his fingers over his nose and mouth like a mask to hold something in, or keep something out. After a while he leaves the table. She brushes the spilled salt away, keeps on eating her chicken.

Sam Chattin

The Warmth of Another in Winter

The kitchen was a labyrinth of shadows, until the light switch chased away the cliché description. Then his path was straight to the kettle—a pot for boiling, and up in the wood-shrunk cabinets that refused to close were his packets of tea. Gabe had never liked tea before. It had seemed pointless—the dressing up of water. Then again, every drink can be cut down to the bare ingredient of water. As of late, Gabe felt like a bare ingredient. With his retirement he felt little more than a hunk of flesh, bones, and organs—all of which were slowly deteriorating. So, nowadays, he dressed up his water.

His tea bag collection had grown quite large as of late. He had a brand for every day of the week. How sad his Tuesday selection was: Kukicha Tea, known also as twig tea. He had downgraded from his daily dose of leaves to ground up twigs; was he no more than a toothless, old mutt?

The buoy motion of the tea bag reminded him of sex: dull, repetitive, and seemingly without an end. Sex used to be exciting, a relief after a long day of work. Now, it was a chore, without any sense of accomplishment afterward. He couldn't have sex with someone whose very presence annoyed him. Everything bothered him about her, right down to the way she combed her hair in the morning, the flick of the lengthy strands interrupting his flossing. It was odd—things like that used to make him smile. Now, solitary confinement looked like a vacation.

As he waited for his tea to cool, he noticed small flashes of movement outside in the trees. He switched off the kitchen light and pressed his head to the cold, sliding glass door. It was a weird sensation: feeling the hotness of the mug and the coldness of the glass against his skin. It made his hands and head feel disconnected from his whole body; one was in Alaska and the other retired to Florida. He really needed to get retirement off his brain.

After a couple of moments the flashes returned. They looked like tiny comets racing through the snowy wilderness of his backyard. As they moved closer, the lights grew longer, transforming into beams that pierced through the trees like some monstrous cephalopod's tentacles reaching rigid to the sky. There were ten, maybe fifteen of those bobbing flashlights, and they were coming directly for Gabe's cabin.

Gabe left his tea on the counter and went to his closet to fetch his boots and winter coat. His long johns made his legs look like scrawny birch branches when compared with the bulkiness of his coat and boots. He reached up into a shoebox above and pulled out a revolver. He looked out on his backyard—he could now make out the ten or fifteen shadows that held the flashlights. Gabe flicked the revolver open and looked at the six chambers. He sighed and put the gun back in the shoe box.

He tromped across the kitchen floor. The boots made him feel awkward on the tiles—like an ostrich scrambling over asphalt. He switched the outside light on; the blizzard resembled a pillow fight gone messy... or a flock of geese caught in a jet's propeller. Either way, the flakes were thick, fluffy, and moving at lethal speeds.

Gabe slid the door open and the blistering blizzard's wind whirled in and stole away his breath. He recovered from the initial icy shock, threw up his hood and stepped out into Mother Nature's snow globe.

The snow had accumulated quickly over the few hours he had slept. He was forced to lift his boots high in a motion similar to the exaggerated tip-toeing of cartoon villains. Each step brought a fresh crust of snow that clung to his long johns for a few moments before it crumbled into the lining of his boots. He could feel it seep into his clothes—a frigid burn until it melted into numbness.

The flashlight-wielders were huddled in a circle just beyond the arc of the backyard light. Only a few now had their flashlights on. They scrutinized over what appeared to be a map. All were dressed in ridiculous, overly padded winter jump suits—something an explorer might wear in the sub-zero degree North Pole. Maybe, while Gabe was asleep next to his snoring wife, the house had been sucked up by a migratory tornado that carried it to the top of the world. And maybe the Wicked Witch of the East now lay dead underneath his house. He doubted her ruby slippers would do him any good in this weather.

Three of the wintry golems made their way to Gabe. The leader shined his flashlight almost accusingly in Gabe's face. Gabe shielded his eyes, as the leader spoke.

"You live here?"

"Yeah," answered Gabe, though the question was unnecessary and stupid.

The leader flashed a badge that Gabe couldn't for the life of him read in this blinding snow. He assumed it was some sign of authority.

"I apologize for intruding on your property, and at such a late hour. We're looking for a girl. Their daughter," he explained, motioning to the couple next to him.

Gabe could barely see their faces, but he could imagine the worrisome creases formed around their desperate, parental eyes.

The officer continued, asking, "Have you seen a girl of sixteen, with short, dark brown hair, possibly glasses, and wearing a pair of rainbow-colored, overall snow pants?"

Gabe shook his head, answering, "No, sir. I haven't seen anyone. I was asleep for three hours or so, but my wife woke me up and—"

The mother burst forward, shoving a picture into Gabe's face and pleading hysterically, "Please! Just look at her! Have you seen her?! Have you seen my Abby?!"

Gabe stepped back, which proved to be difficult despite his previous footprints, and stared intently at the photograph. It was weathered and wrinkled, like it had been run through the washer, but he could still make out the girl named Abby when the flashlight was raised to illuminate it. The girl's smile looked uncomfortable and forced in the photograph, but she was pretty, in the kind of way that one might trust their children with her.

Gabe looked back at the grief-stricken mother and shook his head solemnly. The mother slid the photo back in her glove, where it was sure to lose more and more detail from her sweaty palms. Maybe she felt some sort of calm, clutching her daughter's image in her hand.

The mother and father turned and trudged away. The officer remained and requested:

"Let us know if you see anything, all right?"

"Yeah. I'll let you know. What'll you do now?"

The officer shrugged hopelessly. "Continue the search."

"You won't find anything out in this mess."

"Well, we can't wait till morning. She's bound to freeze."

Gabe looked down at the officer's winter cocoon and thought, *not if she's dressed like you.*

"Well, I hope you find her before then."

"Me, too."

The officer turned and rejoined the group huddled over the map. Gabe traipsed back to the house, with his thoughts whirling in the excitement of the search party. He wanted to go back and offer his services. He wanted to join their parade of bouncing flashlights. He wanted to put off returning to bed as long as he could, maybe till morning, though he hoped they would find her before then.

He kicked his boots against the siding of the house—the snow dropped off in jagged pancakes. He stepped back into the kitchen and looked at the kettle. Maybe he would invite them in for a quick cup of tea. He stuck his head back out the door, ready to call to them, but the flashlights were already bobbing back into trees, the tentacles retracting and the prospect of adventures disappearing with the beast.

Gabe took a sip of his tea. It had cooled substantially. He let it dribble from his lips, back into the mug, before he tossed it in the sink. He kicked his boots off and carried them to the closet. As he opened the door, a pair of snowshoes fell out, the high-tech kind a granola-gobbling, mountain-climbing couple would wear. He looked back out into the Arctic storm and felt Jack Frost calling him with snow-laced fingertips. He hesitated a moment, and then ran for his snow pants.

***

Gabe followed low, with his flashlight pointed downward. A halo of light surrounded him, like an extraterrestrial tractor beam tracing his movements as he ducked branches and slipped past bushes of shark-toothed thorns. He wanted to remain invisible to the search party. He would follow and see the outcome within the shadows of the forest he had come to know over the years. Though, it did appear quite alien shrouded in snow and night.

The sky had suddenly cleared when he entered the forest, and with the moon emerging the fallen snow seemed to pulsate with an odd, turquoise glow. All was quiet, except the soft whisper of his snowshoes. He walked between the banks of a snow-coated stream, the low elevation helping him hide the glow of his flashlight.

His wife and he used to wash their feet in the stream after an exhausting day of gardening. He recalled fondly of the day he made love to her in a bed of ferns by the brook. It started out romantic, like some grocery store paperback novel about a long-haired, Austrian Princess. Then, the centipede—probably territorial of its home being rolled over by an aging couple copulating— skittered up his wife's thigh to bite his scrotum.

The rash was worse than the bite, but his wife never once showed signs of disgust. She tended to his swollen sack with as much love as a mother would treat her child after their first bee sting. He never felt more close to her. He missed that closeness.

In his reminiscence, Gabe had tripped over something and fell with a condensed thump into the cushiony snow bank. Gabe rolled over, making a cookie-cutter image of his fall. There was something jutting out of the snow.

Gabe tried to heave himself upward, but gravity and his winter wear would not agree. He settled for crawling toward the source of his fall. It was the rubber, rounded tip of a boot.

Gabe hesitated, noticing for the first time the crisp wisps of his breath as it quickened. He then, careful as a paleontologist, began dusting away the snow. Working his way up from the boot, his gloves brushed side-to-side, revealing more and more, seemingly airbrushing the image of her rainbow overalls. He stopped at the neck, and shoveled away the layers of snow from her shoulders to her palm-up hands. The fingers looked brittle, like a ceramic sculpture, in the gloves.

A gust of wind whipped up a white-flaked whirlwind from the buried banks. It seemed to warn him of what lie beyond that neck. He looked out into the forest. The chasing comets of the search group had disappeared, hopefully returned to the night sky and away from this... this *horror*.

Gabe noticed he was shaking. Was it the cold that made his gloved hands skitter up her still chest? Skitter up like a centipede—a wooly one. God, he couldn't do this. But still, his hands went up. He closed his eyes as he parted the snow from either side of her face. Then he paused, hearing only the rattle of his breath and the beating of his heart. When he finally opened his eyes, what he saw made him run.

He had made it only a couple of feet before he fell like a wounded deer running blindly from an unseen enemy. He quickly scrambled up and his snow shoes carried him back along the stream, over the thorny bushes, under the low-lying limbs, and all the way to the kitchen.

Off went the snowshoes, the snow pants, the snow jacket, and with the gloves, off went the snow. Up the stairs he scrambled—they no longer conversed with the walls. Finally, he burst into his bedroom and dove under the covers.

He lay there, staring at the ceiling, staring at the girl's face. What was her name? He couldn't remember. All he remembered was that face: coated in thick, vicious blood that shone black in the moonlight. The top of her head had been split open against a rock. She must have slipped on the ice before the snowfall. What could she have been running away from? Had she been running from anything at all?

Gabe shuddered: to die out in that wilderness, to be lost underneath the snowfall, to disappear from the world entirely alone.

A coldness Gabe had never felt before spread from the pit of his stomach, numbing every vein and every slowly deteriorating organ in his body. He needed to find warmth, so he rolled over, bridging the gap of the once frozen medium. He reached his arm over his still-snoring wife. She stirred, but did not wake. Gradually, the warmth spread from her body into his. Gradually, the cold winter air disappeared. Gradually, the horrors of the night slipped away, and Gabe fell asleep, still holding that lovely beast of a woman.

Michael B. Harris-Peyton

Canned Pineapple

Hank Greenblatt's wife, Sunny, was not capable of having children. When they had met in graduate school, it was one of the first things he learned about her, because it was in one way her most primal anxiety, and in another way, her best pick-up line. He had known about, and been fine with, her inability to have children since day one of the relationship—in fact, he had a harder time with her irrational fears of car accidents and of one day becoming obese.

Until, inexplicably, at twenty-nine, Sunny began having miniature panic attacks about a lack of little feet in their apartment. When one of these little panics would come up, Hank would run down to the store and buy her canned pineapple, and she would sit on the end of their bed sniffling and eating the tropical fruit out of the can with a fork.

What was becoming troublesome was that, for the past two months, Hank had to quietly keep cans upon cans of the yellow fruit in their refrigerator, as the episodes had become more frequent. He found empty cans of pineapple next to the bed when he came home from teaching, sometimes three or more. When he went into the bathroom, the bottles for Sunny's thyroid pills would be turned upside-down, something she did only to remind herself that the bottle was empty. Thirty days of thyroid hormone supplements would disappear in twenty-five, then twenty, and now finally in two weeks.

When the work schedules for the second semester of the year rolled around, Hank made sure to consolidate his history classes into the first four days of the week, so that he could be home on Fridays. He hoped that by spending more time with Sunny, she might slip out of whatever it was that was disturbing her.

"Hey Peanut," she said, on the first of those Fridays off, from the bedroom. "What are we doing for lunch?"

Sunny worked odd hours for one of the city's forensic labs. She described her job as "Running gel electrophoresis experiments all day, and occasionally staring at dead folks."

"We could always go down to campus and eat at that deli," she suggested, sounding too hopeful to be neutral.

She entered the kitchen, watching him obsessively sterilize the counters and the handles of the refrigerator door. The floor of the kitchen was made of hardwood, a fact which perpetually drove Hank insane. He was slightly obsessive-compulsive, and would count the number of planks until something else distracted him. He tried not to look down.

He glanced up and saw her standing in the doorway wearing an old t-shirt.

"Yes, I will change clothes," she said, unprompted.

"You really want capicola, don't you?"

"Yes!" she said, clapping her hands together like a child. "Can we go? Please?"

She extended the "please" over five seconds. Hank counted each second of it.

"Sure."

She kissed him on the cheek cheerfully.

* * *

On the walk towards the university, Hank noticed that she was walking on the outside of the sidewalk, near the street. Usually she put him between her and the moving traffic, as part of her car phobia, but today she was striding confidently next to him, in jeans no less, as if she had never been in a car accident.

While the fact of her sterility had been early on the discussion list when they were dating, the issue of how it was caused occurred well after most other relationship milestones. She'd finally filled him in when it came time to meet her parents—a full month after she had been subjected to the Greenblatt family scrutiny. On the car ride out to New Brunswick, she had turned to him, flicking the fried chicken crumbs off her lap one at a time, and simply started talking.

"I have a twin sister named Meena. She's a chef in a restaurant in Philadelphia. When we were twelve we were riding bikes around our old house in Sayreville when this guy driving a Nissan Hardbody pickup truck came screaming around the corner and hit me, narrowly missing Meena, who was next to me on her bike. I really loved riding my bike. He hit my bike so hard that the bike broke into pieces and sent me flying. I landed on the bike, with my knees hitting the ground first. My body weight threw my face forward onto one of the bike's broken wheels, and four of the spokes went in the front of my neck. If they hadn't gone precisely where they did, they would have punctured my artery and killed me or my larynx and left me mute. Instead, the spokes tore my thyroid up pretty bad."

Hank had been so shocked by this torrent of words that he had taken his eyes off the road and looked at her. She was staring straight forward, not blinking.

"That's why I can't get pregnant. With my thyroid messed up, I can't carry a child to full term."

They sat in silence for a moment, as the turn signal ticked away.

"I figured I might as well tell you—my parents don't shut up about it."

* * *

Sunny was eating her sandwich vociferously, as if she hadn't eaten breakfast and a can of pineapple already that day. He couldn't imagine that capicola ham and dill pickles tasted good together at all, even on a whole wheat baguette, and yet Sunny was certainly swallowing it faster than her teeth could chew. Occasionally the deli napkin would flourish up from her free hand and blot away the yellowish pickle-meat-grease-juice that leaked from the sandwich, and she would smile at him.

"At work we always get this greasy effing Chinese takeout stuff," she explained, gesticulating with her napkin hand as if to sweep away boxes of waxpaper lo mein.

Hank wondered in that moment, as he sometimes did, how it was that she could eat lunch at all in a room lined with filing cabinets filled with dead people. He found he could no longer finish his corned beef sandwich.

"You wouldn't believe how much of that stuff the people at the office eat," she said. "I swear they're nursing some secret addiction to indigestion or something. With all the noodles, I'm beginning to wonder if I haven't gained a few pounds."

"You haven't," Hank said, smiling over his now-inedible sandwich and nipping that topic in the bud. She had gained weight, but it seemed more that she was filling out her frame than anything else. He couldn't think of a way to say that she had but that it had not affected her attractiveness.

"But would you really say so if I did?" She gave him a sly look, setting the sandwich down on the white wrapping paper.

"Not if I were smart."

She grinned. He had worried for a moment that she would press the point.

"I'm so glad I married a not-smart man."

"Too dumb to lie," he joked, sipping his canned coffee.

* * *

The following morning, Hank woke up to the sound of his wife talking on her cell phone in the other room, employing the jargon of the crime-scene nastiness industry. He slipped past her and took a shower, only to find her standing right outside of the bathroom when he got out.

"We have a bus to catch, Peanut."

"Oh?" Hank said, managing only monosyllabic responses that soon after waking up.

"Put some pants on."

He'd also followed his wife, after the bus ride had ended two hours later, in walking across Philadelphia. She seemed to be thinking intensely, and didn't answer any of his questions in a substantive way. Hank was along for one of his wife's stubborn whims, and there was nothing he could do about it. Hank, of course, was smart enough to know he didn't want to do anything about it; when she was like this, he let the whim play out, hoping to understand along the way.

The restaurant that Sunny made him walk to was one of those commercial spaces that could only be used as a bar or a shady Chinese restaurant. The place was made for expensive whiskey and freeform jazz. Sunny had brought him here, and the only thing he could determine was that they didn't belong there. There was no ornamentation besides the juxtaposition of the old wood and the clean, modern lines, and the rows of a hundred and fifteen aristocratic forms of whiskey. There were six awkwardly tall tables near the street-side wall of the restaurant, and twenty-six barstools along the bar.

Sunny sat Hank down at the bar, leaving him unattended for a moment. He ordered a cheap whiskey from the menu and sat quietly.

Hank had no idea what was going on. Any tendency towards problem solving was gone—he was bus-lagged, if such a thing were possible.

Behind him, he heard clipped talking. He could have sworn that both voices were Sunny's. One sounded heavier—like Sunny's when she was tired, only saturated with nicotine smoke.

"Peanut," the Sunny-sounding-est of the two voices said. He turned around, leaving his new whiskey unattended.

There were two Sunnys standing behind him—one was definitely his Sunny, with the four freckle-like scars on her neck and shoulder-length hair. The other one was some alternate version, with slightly heavier features.

"Hank," Sunny said. "This is my twin sister Meena."

"Hey," Meena said, shaking his hand as he stood up off the stool. She turned to her sister again. "Sunny, why are you here?"

The question did not express joy.

"I wanted to see you," Sunny said.

"You could have called ahead," Meena said, flatly. Her voice, Hank noticed, generally sounded more depressed and jaded than Sunny's. "I'm working."

"You're always working."

Meena sighed, sitting down next to Hank and gesturing at the bartender, who began making a drink. Sunny took the stool on the other side of Hank. He had his wife on the right and her twin sister on the left, and he was already confused. He caught himself counting the bottles of whiskey over the bar for the second time.

The bartender put the glass of neat whiskey in front of Meena, who sighed again and began talking.

"Okay, Sunny, why are you really here?"

"I was thinking of you."

"So you brought your husband, too?"

"You haven't even met. I figured you'd want to."

"I didn't come to the wedding. Did you need another clue?"

Thirty-one bottles of whiskey. Thirty-two, three, four, five. End of the shelf.

Sunny sighed, the sigh identical to Meena's sigh thirty seconds before.

"Fine. I'm here to talk to you about something specific."

Meena rolled her eyes, taking another sip.

"And what would that be?"

Forty-one, forty-two, forty-three. Hank had trouble listening to the conversation. He detected some hostility.

"You remember the accident?" Sunny said, sounding suddenly smaller.

"No, Sunny, I *forgot*. I'm not stupid."

"I've been thinking about children."

Fifty-five. Next shelf. Fifty-six, fifty-seven, fifty-eight, fifty-nine. Hank began to feel the tension in his stomach. He rotated the whiskey glass absentmindedly with his left hand. It was beginning to sweat. Both the glass and his hand.

"Okay," Meena said.

"I can't have any."

"And I can't quit smoking. I should be at work."

Seventy.

"Meena, I'm your sister."

Seventy-one.

Meena drained her glass and went to stand up.

Seventy-two. Seventy-three.

"Meena, I want you to have a baby for me!"

Hank lost count.

"Wait, *what*?" he said, turning around in the stool. Sunny had Meena by the arm.

Meena stared at her and eased down into her seat. Meena glanced at Hank, looking him in the eyes for the first time.

Hank and Meena waited for Sunny to continue.

"I've got eggs but I can't carry," Sunny said. "I want you to carry."

Suddenly, Hank was very aware of the smell of cigarettes coming from Meena.

"Wait," Meena started, eyes out of focus.

"They can transplant these sorts of things."

"Uh, Sundari..." Meena said, raising a finger.

Sunny looked hopefully at Meena.

"Your thyroid—you don't even menstruate regularly, it's..."

"Or you could—"

"Wait," Hank said, quietly. He was drowned out by Meena groaning.

"Honey, you've been spending too much time around dead people," Meena said.

"No! I talked to the doctor—"

"When did this happen?" Hank said, finally gaining his voice. He noticed a second whiskey had appeared next to him, and saw the bartender out of the corner of his eye, giving him a sympathetic look.

And Hank realized that everyone in the restaurant was listening to them. There were only a few customers this early in the day, and Sunny talking about a baby had apparently gained their attention.

"You talked to a doctor, huh?" Meena said. "Never occurred to you that I'm not a rent-a-womb?"

"You're not even married!"

"You're not even thinking, are you?"

Hank gave up, and ducked so that they could argue around him more easily.

While sipping the second whiskey, Hank carefully considered his position. He was pretty sure that, should he side with his beloved Sunny and try and sell Meena on being a surrogate, Meena would run them both out of the restaurant, possibly employing the door-sized bouncer. As a secondary effect, Sunny would surely blame him for losing the argument and not speak to him for a week or so. Inversely, should he express his opinion that asking Meena to do such a thing was a bad idea, Sunny would almost surely murder him where he sat. Additionally, once he expressed this opinion, he would surely be asked to explain; he would have to mention that he didn't want a woman who apparently smoked constantly—who he'd just met—carrying his baby. Then, he would be run out of the restaurant.

Having gained the attention of the restaurant, his wife and her twin sister had resorted to tense, low whispering in the language of their parents, and he had lost the opportunity to interject for the time being. They would exhaust their vocabulary eventually. He could already detect medical terminology flying around in English.

Hank was developing a headache. The whiskey wasn't helping, but he didn't stop drinking it.

"Why don't you just adopt, like a normal sterile person?" Meena said, abruptly returning to English and throwing her hands up in the air.

"I want *my* baby!"

"Our baby," Hank mumbled at the bar. He remained unheard, an inconvenient barrier between his wife and her sister.

"How selfish are you, anyway?" Meena said, beginning to stand up again. "You want to force me to take leave and carry a baby because you don't want to raise one that isn't *yours*. Let's just think about that for a moment."

It was very selfish, Hank thought, but it did seem to be something altogether different, having one's own child versus adopting one. He couldn't say, though, that he had a particular opinion one way or another.

"Ugh! You always were so grouchy!" Sunny said, disgusted.

"You're asking me to have your baby! How am I supposed to react? 'Oh, sure thing, sis, I'll just go ahead and bang your husband for the team,' right? No. *No.*"

"You do realize that they can just—"

"Please, please don't explain!" Meena said, covering her ears.

"What are you, eight?"

Hank sighed quietly. The bartender took the empty glass away, saying nothing.

"I want to have a baby! And I want it to be Hank's baby, too!" Sunny said. The reference to Hank seemed to remind the both of them that he was there, and they both looked at him.

He finally sat up, looking first at Meena, then Sunny.

"Why don't we ask him what he thinks?" Meena said.

Sunny nodded.

"Hank, you want our child to be ours, don't you?"

Hank opened his mouth.

"Or you could adopt a child who needs you, and spare your sister-in-law her sister's bizarre schemes," Meena said.

"Quit trying to persuade him!"

"What about you? You're sleeping with him—I'm just trying to even out the manipulation by showing him some reason!"

"Ah! You are such a—"

Hank's brain was consumed with a sort of gray haze. He began speaking.

"I think that—"

A cell phone had started ringing, loudly. Hank paused and looked at Sunny's bag, where he could see the screen blinking.

Sunny snatched up the phone, and answered it with an annoyed tone. The volume was turned all the way up, and by chance, both Hank and Meena could also hear the voice on the other end. The bartender, who was approaching with another whiskey for Hank, paused, listening from a meter or so away. A safe distance.

"Mrs. Greenblatt?"

"Yes?" Sunny said, putting on a more pleasant voice. She looked at the both of them, gradually becoming aware that the volume on the phone was very high.

"This is Sharon, calling from Dr. Taylor's office. I'm sorry to disturb you on the weekend, but the tests you requested last month on your thyroid function are back."

"Uh huh?"

"Mrs. Greenblatt, do you know that you're pregnant?"

"Sorry, what?" she said quickly. Meena lost her balance on the stool, and one of her feet struck the floor loudly.

"You're pregnant, Mrs. Greenblatt. About nine weeks."

Meena looked back and forth from Sunny to Hank. The bartender remained where he was, holding the glass of whiskey.

"Thank you," Sunny said, closing the phone. She wasn't blinking.

Meena stood up abruptly, knocking her stool into the counter.

The bartender put the heavy glass of whiskey down in front of Hank. It hit the mahogany bar with a dull thump.

Ali Rahman

Threat Level Orange

"Okay *Mamoo*, thanks for the ride," my brother said as he heaved his suitcase onto the curb.

"Take care, fly safe, *salaam*," my uncle replied in Urdu with his arm hanging from the driver side window of his car. We replied with our own *salaams* and headed into the American Airlines terminal. I dragged my luggage across the floor, following my brother into the maze that was the line to check in. After ten minutes or so we reached the counter and plopped our bags onto the weighing station.

"May I have your tickets please?" asked the robotically polite woman representing the airline. As soon as my brother handed her the papers along with our IDs, I saw her eyes widen.

"Excuse me one moment please." She picked up a phone a few feet away from her and dialed an extension. Damn, I thought this might happen. I looked up at my brother's face. We exchanged looks, mine saying "Why couldn't you have shaved your beard or at least trimmed it to a non-threatening length?" and his saying "Don't say anything that's going on in your mind aloud, stupid." I watched the woman's lips as she whispered into the mouthpiece of the phone. I could make out her repeating our names as she read off our IDs. "Muhammad Umar Rahman" and "Ali Muhammad Rahman," as our parents so originally named us. There must be thousands of people with those names. Well, not here in America necessarily, but back in the motherland. I was struck by the thought that perhaps someone on the airport's watch list had the same name. Damn. We'll be here forever if that is the case.

Sure enough, we spent the next hour and a half standing, observing countless airline employees popping up next to our original check-in lady to investigate. Once it seemed as though a thorough background check had been conducted, they allowed us to proceed. Next up: airport security. I grabbed a rectangular rubber container and discarded the contents of my pockets into it. I pushed the tub of electronics and metal onto the conveyor belt and it sped through the x-ray machine with my backpack in pursuit.

"Shoes."

"Excuse me?" I responded, puzzled.

The security lady looked at me sternly, "You have to take off your shoes and put them through the machine." My shoes? Take off my shoes and expose my unwashed, sweat-soaked socks with holes, exposing my toes to the world?

"Just do it, Ali," my brother said, anticipating my objection. He looked down at his watch. "We're going to miss the plane, so hurry it up." The entire security staff listened to this closely. I did as told and walked through the metal detector sans footwear.

"Sir, is this your bag?" inquired the shoe inspector, lifting my bag from the other end of the x-ray machine. I told her it was and she asked if I could step aside for a moment. If all eyes hadn't already been on me, they were now. A hush of whispers from the people behind me announced the birth of theories regarding my "random" bag check. A new woman was now opening my bag and searching through my socks and Simpsons-covered boxers, looking for whatever pocket-size weapon of mass destruction I might have managed to smuggle in my carry-on. She stopped sifting and I thought the search was complete but then she pulled out a square of what looked like a fabric softener sheet and rubbed it through my belongings. Could my unmentionables really smell that bad? She put the square into a machine slot along the wall and turned back to me. Pushing my curiosity about what exactly just happened aside, I turned to the woman.

"Listen," I paused to find her nametag, "Rhonda... isn't there any way this could go faster. I'm getting late for my flight."

She looked at me for what felt like a good minute. "So is everyone else."

"Do I really look that threatening? I mean, look at him," I jerked my head towards the tall, dark, and hook nosed specimen that was my brother, "I would understand if he got taken to the side." Rhonda took a good look at him just as my brother spotted me. She walked over and told him to come join me. Damn it. My brother looked at me, mouthing the words, "You fucking idiot."

Thirty-some odd minutes later, my brother and I finally stepped onto the plane. From the ramp we could hear a noisy airplane cabin but as soon as we poked our heads through the doorway, silence spread over the passengers. A man froze trying to stuff his luggage into the overhead compartment, eyes on the two people who had just arrived. For a few seconds, we stood as dumbfounded as our fellow travelers. It was an awkward standoff to say the least. I can only imagine what we looked like to the sea of white faces, speckled sparsely with some black, brown, and yellow. My brother was the tall, bearded,

Middle-Eastern looking figure who was obviously the mentor and mastermind of the terrible twosome. Then there was me, a younger version of the other. Clean-shaven face but because of my people's hairy ancestral background, already sporting a five o'clock shadow even though I just shaved that morning. Perhaps even more suspicious-looking, as if I had shaved hoping to go under the radar. When we regained movement in our legs, we made our way down the aisle. I looked at my ticket.

"29C," I read aloud.

"I'm 27B," said my brother, "I thought we bought two seats next to each other."

I guess the airline wanted to separate us so we couldn't easily communicate and thereby execute our devious plan of attack. I took my seat next to a middle-aged white man who was clearly less than thrilled at the prospect of having me sit next to him. Two rows ahead my brother excused himself as he squeezed by a scared-looking, blonde-haired, blue-eyed twenty-something-year-old. As I tried to make myself comfortable, my brother's deep, annunciating voice drew my—along with everyone else's in a two-row radius—attention.

"*Asalaam alaikum Mamoo... Jhee hum bathai... Jhee* I'll call you... Okay everything is ready? Good... *Inshallah* we will... *Allah hafiz.*" My brother hung up the phone with a loud clap as he flipped it shut. I lifted my butt from my seat and looked at the kid next to my brother. He looked as though he was about to wet himself. Damn it, why couldn't he have just spoken all English or all Urdu? The mix of both languages always seems to frighten to the fullest extent. Would it have been that hard to instead say, "Hello uncle...Yes we're sitting down...Yes I'll call you...Okay everything is ready? Good (referring to the surprise visit we were paying my aunt)... God willing we will (okay maybe there's no way to make that sound less terrifying)...Goodbye."

As we took to the air, a stomach fart erupted from my midsection. Shit. I hate using public restrooms for pooping. I slipped by the man next to me who appeared to have fallen asleep as soon as he put his headphones on. I opened the closet-like door and shut it behind me. OCCUPIED. These damn airplane toilets are so awkward. The shiny metallic seat that would assuredly freeze my buttocks upon impact. The toilet seemed to be built into the wall. The claustrophobic atmosphere of it all was very troubling. And the worst part, the toilet flushed with such an extraordinary amount of force that it was like launching a torpedo from a submarine. I laid the sanitary seat cover down and sat. A shiver ran up my spine because of the cold. I guess it's better than the seat being warm. After a minute or two I decided to take out my phone and play bowling. Yes, I engage in other activities while I defecate. I'm not ashamed of it. You know you do it too. Anyway... I love that electronic beeping noise it plays after a strike. I'm on pace to break my previous record.

A knock broke me from my game. Uh oh. A slightly muffled voice spoke.

"Sir, what are you doing in there?" What am I doing? What the hell does one do in the bathroom?

"Sir I can hear strange noises. I'm going to have to ask you to come out immediately." The door handle started to shake. This lady was trying to get in. Oh God help me.

"No, don't come in!" I said in a clearly panicked voice. "I'll just be a few more minutes."

"Sir, please come out now or else I am going to have to enlist the help of an air marshal." You have got to be kidding me. This is not happening.

"You can't come in! This won't take long, I promise," I said through a struggle as I tried to finish my business as quickly as I could.

"I'm coming in." Words have never inspired such fear in my heart. For a moment there was a silence. An eerily foreboding silence. And then, the rattling started once again.

I broke from my encapsulating fear. I grabbed as much toilet paper as I could amass. I wiped like I've never wiped before, the rattling of the door knob getting louder.

And like a horror movie, I watched in what seemed like slow motion as the handle turned. A clicking sound announced doom. Indecent exposure approaching as the red OCCUPIED slowly turned into a green VACANT. God save me.

In one quick and graceful movement I jumped up with a 180 degree turn simultaneously pulling my pants up and pressed down the handle of the toilet with authority. The powerful, torpedo-like flush erupted but instead of a missile of some kind, sent a turd sailing through the air and undoubtedly striking some poor unsuspecting sea creature, effectively ruining its day. At least in my mind that's what happened. The door swung open and a flight attendant looked at me, looked at the toilet, and looked at me again.

"Sir, what did you just flush?" she asked.

"Um... you know... excrement."

"Sir, several passengers said they heard noises as if some kind of electronic device was being used."

"Yeah, that was my phone."

"Oh." The flight attendant's face grew redder as she spoke. "Sorry for the disturbance."

"Okay... I'm just going to wash my hands."

"Yes, of course," she mumbled at her feet.

After cleaning my hands I stepped out of the lavatory and headed back to my seat. Fifty heads turned to look at me. Thank God I'm not white or else I'd be blushing more than the attendant. Wait, that's not racist, is it? Can you be racist towards white people? Forget it—now is not the time.

I sat down next to my amazingly undisturbed sleeping neighbor. My brother's smiling face appeared from over his headrest. Like the guy sitting next to him earlier, he too looked as though he would wet himself, although for a different reason. I shook my head and closed my eyes as I drifted off.

We finally arrived. Getting off the plane felt a lot quicker and easier than the process of getting on, I suppose for obvious reasons. I made my brother race to baggage claim to grab our things before anyone from our plane could get a decent look at me. Our cousin Usman met us at the airport exit. We exchanged hellos, how-are-yas, and hugs. As we started walking toward the parking lot, our cousin started to laugh.

"What's so funny?" my brother asked.

"You two look like a couple of terrorists."

Steve Polsz

Wings of Steel

I was a bike messenger for nearly ten years. For the most part, we moved around packages that couldn't be faxed. Legal documents, architectural drawings and graphic art pieces—those were our mainstay. A bike could get around in Center City easier and faster than cars.

We were the pony express on wings of steel.

Bikes went way back with me. My uncle Charlie taught me to ride when I was five and I got my first real bike when I was twelve—a ten-speed English Racer. Bright orange, it had those swirly ram horn handlebars wound with black friction tape. Two gears in the front, five in the back, and two little levers to shift them. Trim and sleek.

There were two months of slipping chains, free-spinning pedals and loud clicky noises before Sleek learned to shift smoothly. After that, Sleek and I would go off almost every Saturday morning. I'd have breakfast, pack a lunch, throw it into my backpack and we'd be off. There were many trails to follow, countless unknown sidetracks. We would ride on until noon. I'd stop to eat and then attend to Sleek. I rubbed him down, taking off the dirt, dust and mud that the road kicked up, checked his brake cables and greased his chain and gears a bit.

Then we set out for home. We might not know where we were, but we were never lost. Sleek always knew the way back home.

Sleek had been retired for almost three years before I became a bike messenger. I was twenty-three and at the edge of my parent's patience. I had done a year and a half of college and dropped out; I felt lost there. I was working at Gino's, a fast-food burger chain, looking and hoping for better.

I found better one day in our local neighborhood paper, *The Globe Times*. "Now hiring. Center City bike messenger service. Apply American Expediting. 23rd and Arch Sts."

I smiled wide and broke out into laughter. Every day would be Saturday and I would get paid for riding around all day.

Early the next morning, I hopped onto Sport. He was lime green and a bit shorter than Sleek had been. His saddle was wide, padded and spring-loaded; I could ride forever on that seat without getting sore from the ruts and road bumps. There was a milk crate wired to his handlebars—his trunk. We rode the gentle downgrade into the unknown territory of Center City. It took some time, but we finally spotted a great big blue leather awning with 'American Expediting' in white across it.

I was handed some papers to fill out, told to get a messenger bag from Goldberg's, the local Army/Navy store, and come in the next day at eight with ten bucks for a talkie.

I got to know Center City real quick. It's pretty much a regular grid. Streets that run north and south are numbered. Streets that run east and west are named after trees. Except for the two major streets: Broad Street runs north and south; Market runs east and west and the two met in a circle that goes around City Hall. Other than little tucked-in side streets, it is as regular as a checker board.

I got to know the business fast, too. There were about a dozen major accounts, a dozen pick-up points to learn. We rode back and forth and roundabout through the city, a pick up here, a drop off there. We rode around in circles, big west to east sweeps, quick tight squiggles, smooth easy rides, all at the direction of our dispatcher.

Rob had been a biker for six years before he got bumped up and into the office; he didn't just know Center City, he *was* Center City. After a new biker had been on the road for a few weeks, Rob had him pegged. That's why he was the dispatcher; he had some sort of psychic radar. He tracked half a dozen of us; we were his main team. The rest of the messengers filled in the gaps.

There were two kinds of messengers.

The first were bike messengers, like I was. It was the ride, the freedom of the outdoors that attracted us. There was the adventure; every day, every hour was new and fresh. We looked the same as any other person who rode a bike, but more content, happier.

Then there were bike racers. Being a messenger was their high-speed obstacle practice. You've seen them rushing through the streets. They were the ones with the fly-eye amber colored wrap-around sunglasses, streamlined helmets, spandex tights, racing shoes and a four-figures bike.

You might think the racers made out better than the messengers with all their hustle, but they didn't. As we went from pick up to drop off, there was a good chance that a job got called in that was somewhere along our way.

If you went too fast, you missed it. A tortoise and hare kind of thing.

Being a bike messenger was a dangerous job and everybody eventually got their big one. Getting doored was our number one hazard. We rushed along the street as far to the right as we dared. We would get into someone's blind spot as they were coming out of their car and—WHAM!—there was a car door in our face.

If we were fast and sharp enough, we swerved around and missed clipping the door. If not, when we crashed into the door, we hoped to fly over the window; otherwise we would either smash into the window or bounce off the door and snap our heads against the top of the car.

I was real lucky. When I hit the door, Sport bucked up and his milk crate shattered the window. The impact stopped me, leaving me safely between the door and a shocked driver.

All manners of accidents left their marks on other messengers. Marks like pins holding bones together, a great chest scar from getting hung up on a door, a leg fused at the knee, a small plate to cover a hole in the skull.

Two were killed on the road. One was a fellow worker who lost out to a taxi. The other was a messenger from Kangaroo Couriers; a street cleaning truck sucked him under.

My big one came on a quick run from Independence Park to Liberty Place. Sport and I were starting through a small corridor between a UPS truck and a Brinks Armored truck flashing its four ways. It began to park with us in his blind spot.

I squeezed Sport's brakes so hard that the left cable snapped and whizzed past my ear. I threw all my weight to the right; we slammed hard against the UPS truck as I tried to slow us down. My shoulder and Sport's handlebars hit hard against the truck. We bounced off and smashed into Brinks Armored. The impact shoved Sport's handlebars to the right, and as the recoil threw me back to the UPS truck, Sport's front wheel was snatched by the merciless front fender of the Brinks truck. The hole was shrinking fast. Sport butted his ram's horns hard against the front of the UPS truck. With a horrible screechy screaming they etched a desperate spiral dent along its crumpled side. Sport's horns twisted and compressed, the milk crate snapped apart and pieces flew up and at my face. The hole was closed up to nearly nothing when Sport's mangled front wheel bucked up and I was thrown backwards off the saddle. I rolled to my feet and stood behind the trucks, watching Sport disappear into a trash masher.

The trucks separated and Sport's metal corpse clanged to the sidewalk between them. I ran over to Sport, fell down over him and cried. Two men got out of the Brinks trucks; the UPS man came back; the police took their report— all the while I hung over Sport.

For a long time I looked at Sport's mangled and gnarled body; paint slashed off, his front wheel almost doubled over, his horns crushed. A pedal had snapped off; I found it tucked under scraps of his milk crate. Brinks ran over my talkie and left it crushed amidst little scattered bits and pieces of Sport's remains.

I gathered everything up and into my bag. Then I gently picked Sport up and, cradling him in my arms, walked the long way back to the office.

Maia Livengood

The Winter

After multitudes of communication standoffs, getting on the phone with my mother every few weeks still feels oddly frequent. I try to limit both the rate and length of these conversations, knowing that they almost always leave us exasperated and upset, unresolved issues still unresolved. It's not that I don't like hearing from her—email is fine. In fact, I enjoy her random updates about the garden, the house, or her work. But a phone call in our family is synonymous with argument, bad news, or both. So when my phone recently sounded and I glanced down to see "Momma L" on my caller-ID, I waited as usual until I had missed the call, weighed the pros and cons of returning it, and eventually, guilted myself into calling back (meanwhile hoping desperately to be saved by the answering machine).

My mom picked up immediately and began to explain that I needed to choose which of my belongings would be going to her new vacation cabin in Tahoe—rather irrelevant and quickly filtered through my well-developed selective hearing. But mid-babble, I tuned in long enough to hear "...and someone is coming tomorrow to look at the piano."

Caught off-guard, I began to feel the familiar materialization of a throat-lump. *My* piano? Realizing quite quickly that she was not referring to a visit from Ted, our piano tuner extraordinaire, the lump swelled, and tears followed shortly. Mildly shocked and unable to speak, I couldn't get past the flashing mental bulletin: my most loved belonging was about to be sold on Craigslist.

I really shouldn't call it my piano. It was, in fact, my sister's piano, and she was the more talented musician between us. Avery would sit for hours with her ears glued against our cassette-tape player, which she balanced cautiously on a music stand, spending her afternoons transcribing pop music. Whereas I would take months in memorizing a single piece, she would sight-read entire collections each week. And though I battled a somewhat unhealthy amount of sibling-envy in a variety of areas, it was never so with music. Listening to her beautiful renditions of "Canon in D" and the "Moonlight Sonata"—which I would surely never match—by no means diminished my own enjoyment in playing.

I can't pretend I've always felt this way, though. There have been many days that the endless practicing brought me to tears, never able to fully overcome my incompetence. Sessions often ended abruptly with keys banged in discord and the instrument slammed shut. Maybe that's why it was never in tune. I would like to believe, though, that it is my matured sensibility that has allowed me to tie together how we acquired the piano with my affection for such an unremarkable object.

Had my parents purchased the Winter in a music store, I sincerely doubt that I would care about the piano being sold; I've been through numerous trumpets bought in that fashion, and no heartstrings were tugged into distress. I bet, too, that a shrink would label my reaction as "Displaced feelings, trying to salvage something old and meaningful." I have a personal aversion to overanalyzing of this kind, but in this case, reading a little extra into my attachment is not *too* far off. In a time where permanence seems to be a lost value, I've enjoyed trusting that this one thing would be mine forever.

The piano had traveled with us everywhere, from Pennsylvania to California, from tiny apartments to big houses. On several occasions I've crouched down beneath the beast, helping my father unscrew its pedals, legs, and deck lid, carefully rolling each into old bedding. Makeshift ramps helped us to wheel in (or out) the awkwardly bulky hardwood case, containing all those secret components that Ted knows well, mechanisms that generate familiar comforting notes. I took great care in preventing what seemed to me an inevitable harming of the precious parts while jostling around in the back of a moving truck. Its last home, and our last home, was intended to be the house that my dad built himself, with a space that was created particularly with the instrument in mind. The room was designed with oak floors, a large bay-window, and vaulted ceilings, perfectly showcasing our baby grand.

Part of me always knew my parents would separate. So when the time came to move again, a space in my mother's new home was set aside for the piano as well. We knocked down two bedroom walls, converting marketable space to a music room, and bought a beautiful chandelier to hover above the propped-open lid. The effect of the room is quite stunning, and it remains my favorite spot in the house. Now, struggling to think of what the space could be used for aside from our original intended purpose (a bedroom with no walls?), I found it mildly ironic that she had decided, years later and seemingly at random, that this was the time to sell.

My parents bought the piano when I was four, Avery eight. Making the trip from northeast Pennsylvania to New Jersey in our '76 Town and Country, we found ourselves inside a Hoboken row home, with pink lace curtains and a doorbell chime identical to that of my Oma. Always shy and guarded around strangers, I clung to my mother's side as an elderly woman ushered us into her living room. I distinctly remember the look of her fingers as she began to play, long and graceful, entirely unlike my own.

While playing for us, she fumbled frequently over the keys, nervously laughing her way through each piece in an attempt to conceal her embarrassment. I didn't know then that she was making light of an unhappy situation, and I laughed too. But somehow, paralleling my ignorance, was also the acute awareness that she had once been quite proficient. Maybe I was laughing out my own discomfort, too. This didn't last long; soon there was the discussion about the age of the instrument, its cost and pedigree. My mom is a savvy antiques collector, and was anxious to acquire a piece with the duel purposes of plaything and investment. However, with some parental prodding and the full story divulged more recently, I've since learned the darker circumstances under which the piece traded hands.

This woman, whose name I probably never knew and certainly wouldn't remember if I had, was being committed to a home. Her husband had recently passed, and though I can't say with certainty that his photograph rested reverentially on the piano, I retain the impression of the important role he played in her life without ever having known them. The piano, which had been an engagement gift from this man, had to go.

Piece by piece my dad loaded the Winter on to the trailer we hitched to our wagon. At last, time came to bid goodbye and thank you, and the woman could clearly no longer stifle her pain. Her taut lips began to quiver, and as she pressed her fingers tightly against them, tears began streaming down her face. Her expression, her posture, and her faltering voice screamed sheer anguish. I was overcome by an instant rush of sadness, unfamiliar to me at such a young age: my first encounter with the mark of contemporary life's minute tragedies.

The separation was my second experience of this sort. Divorce happens, and it's rarely shocking. There was bickering, common to many relationships, and disrespectful fights, too. On one particular evening, a fight escalated to guttural screaming—of the kind that my running shower and blaring radio couldn't drown out. Hours later, deciding it was finally safe to emerge from the bathroom, I discovered the aftermath: a massive hole in our living room wall. By the next morning, plaster covered most of the evidence. Though, I'm sure the emotional damage couldn't be patched as easily.

But like most couples who loved enough to tie the knot, there were good times, too. A Mother's Day has yet to pass for which my father has not sent long-stemmed roses. It's clear to me that there were (and are) feelings here, despite the flaws.

I've given significant thought to what constitutes the final breaking point in a relationship. When do the problems become too much of a burden? We love our puppies in spite of their accidents, our favorite jeans in spite of the holes, and our siblings who "borrow" much too often. In fact, the things we value most in life are often flawed. How and when did they decide what *wasn't* worth keeping?

Over the years the Winter has been subject to some wear and tear. The ivory keys are chipped and difficult to press evenly. Our cats have left a series of claw marks along its top and sides—certainly not beautiful by any traditional aesthetic standards. But as people's quirks build character, the Winter's shortcomings give way to a rustic voice, mighty in power and pleasing in tone. Had my music acumen been greatly developed, I could better relate the specific sound characteristics in terms of quality, objectively. Or perhaps my tastes would be too refined to enjoy the piano in its deteriorated condition. Better yet, it may be that in the realm of description, sounds are similar to emotions: evanescent and often impossible to express given the limitations of language. In my case, emotions bound by sounds.

Anjana Santhanam

Turtles at Tinicum

Today, I am watching the turtles at John Heinz Wildlife Refuge at Tinicum. The ecologist hidden behind my molecular biologist façade bursts out with excitement at the chance to see the reptiles again. I had gone to see the turtles with my ecology course before, and while we talked at length about the native plant species and the birds that used the Refuge as a landmark on the Atlantic flyway during their yearly migrations, what really caught my attention were the reptiles, which have roamed the earth since the Triassic Period.

The sky is the dull gray color that comes after morning drizzle, and the humidity and cool breeze cause my hair to frizzle out and obscure my vision from time to time, but the air is chill and comfortable, and I can hear a robin chirping in the background.

The John Heinz Wildlife Refuge is the largest freshwater marshland in Pennsylvania. Unlike swamps, which also contain nutrient- and oxygen-rich water that comes from streams or rivers, marshes do not support woody trees. Instead, myriad other plants can live within or along the edges of a marsh such as this one. I pass yards of phragmites alongside the marsh on the west end, their flexible bodies swaying in the wind. My favorite sight, however, is the clump of yellow lilies about two yards from the shoreline that provide a spark of intense color against the dull background of gray sky and water.

As I sit on the edge of the dock, I can see silvery fish under the water. After about twenty minutes, a fish disappears out of view as a turtle sneaks up from the muddy marsh bottom and snags the fish in its mouth.

There are many species of aquatic turtles at the Refuge. Painted turtles, *Chrysemys picta*, are native to the region, and can be identified by the beautiful striped yellow pattern on their side scutes. The subspecies found at the refuge, the Eastern Painted turtle, has a deep yellow plasteron with one or two dark areas. The one I watch climbing out of the water and onto an exposed rock surface seems to be about the size of my hand, not a fully grown adult, which are about the size of a composition notebook. This behavior is called basking—turtles, like most other reptiles, are ectothermic, which means they are unable to use their metabolism to generate body heat. Instead, ectotherms such as this Eastern Painted turtle rely on sunlight to maintain their internal temperature. While basking, the turtle tucks his head into his shell, and I can see automatically that this turtle is a pleurodire. Turtles can be classified into two categories based on how they move their heads into their shells. Pleurodires, such as the Eastern Painted turtle, tuck their heads into their shells horizontally, while cryptodires tuck their heads into their shells vertically, moving their necks under their spines.

With its head tucked into its shell, the painted turtle looks like a smaller rock, with its muddy green carapace shining in the sun.

Another aquatic turtle I see is the Red-Eared Slider turtle. Unlike the Eastern Painted turtle, the *Trachemys scripta elegans* is an invasive species outside its home range. While originally native to the southeastern parts of the United States, the species makes for a popular pet, and in our disposable culture, people let the turtles go as soon as they outgrow their tanks. While people may think that they are doing the turtles a favor by letting them back in the wild, they compete with native species for space and food, threatening other turtle species in the area such as the Red-Bellied turtles.

It's hard to believe such a cute-looking little creature could send one of his cousins into near extinction. The Red-Eared Slider I am watching is about six inches long and has a high, domed carapace, quite different from the flat shell of the Eastern Painted turtle, with an intricate swirling pattern in various green tones that resemble a child's Spin Art. The Red-Eared Slider also has yellowish stripes on its head like the Eastern Painted turtle, but when it turns its face towards me, I can see the thick vermillion stripe above its eye that gives it a Groucho Marx-style eyebrow. Though it is small, it has sharp, fierce-looking claws that would make a predator think twice about getting into a fight with it.

Sadly, however, the worst predator of all the different species of aquatic turtles at Tinicum isn't among the numerous species of birds that use the area as a flyway. Rather, the greatest harm comes in the form of *Homo sapiens*, such as myself. On a previous visit, the park ranger told my ecology class that a patch of land opposite the dock felt the effects of the Athos I oil spill five years ago, which dumped about 300,000 gallons of crude oil in the Delaware River. One of the turtles that the ranger showed us was missing an eye, but there was no scar tissue or any other signs of a fight present on the Red-Eared Slider's face. I asked the ranger what had happened to her to cause her to lose her eye.

"She was born that way. In fact, many of the younger turtles in the area have birth defects because the hydrocarbons affected their development while they were still inside their shells," he replied. "We're still cleaning up the mess here, five years later."

It's hard to believe that something that happened when I was still in high school, which seems like it was an eternity away from my life now, could still be affecting the plants and animals that call the area home today. But the proof was in front of my face then, as it is now. Many of the smaller turtles in the area such as the Stinkpot turtle, *Sternotherus odoratus*, so named for their foul-smelling musk found in glands by their tails released to deter predators, had to be moved from one region of the marsh to another. I see several Stinkpots being fed and studied in the Cusano Environmental Education Center, a few with defects of their own. One has a deformed right limb, making it unable to swim as fast, making the tiny turtle vulnerable to predators.

Another turtle I see only in the Cusano Environmental Education Center is the Eastern Red-Bellied turtle, *Pseudemys rubriventris*. The Red-Bellied turtle is a state-endangered species, and the park ranger tells me that there might be only about thirty individuals living in a colony at Tinicum. The Red-Bellied turtle, with its yellow-striped face and raised-dome carapace, only superficially resembles the Red-Eared Slider, for when you turn the Red-Bellied turtle over, you can see the bright red coloring of his plasteron. The rarity of seeing one in the wild disappoints me, though I am grateful that I get the opportunity to see the one at the Center defecate on the park ranger's hand. The Red-Bellied turtle, a species native to the area, again encounters problems due to *H. sapiens*. If habitat destruction and encroachment of nesting sites by *H. sapiens* wasn't enough, the Red-Bellied turtles must compete for any remaining nesting and basking sites with the Red-Eared Sliders introduced into the area by the *H. sapiens*.

It's enough to make a *human* want to cover her own ears and slide her own head into the safety of her carapace, to think nothing of the animals that have existed since the Triassic Period, when dinosaurs still roamed the earth. Unfortunately, the turtles cannot control the conditions essential to their own survival—only we, the *Homo sapiens*, can make those choices, if only we are willing to try.

Justin Gero

Glenn Beck Blames Speeding Ticket on Obama

Brandishing a speeding ticket last night, *FOX News* host Glenn Beck dedicated his entire hour-long show to decrying President Obama's communist roads. "This is just the beginning. First they tell you how fast you can drive, then they tell you that you can't drink and drive. What's next America? Next time they might tell you to drive straight to the gulag!"

In response to his ticket for a minor traffic violation, Beck called for his viewers to stand up to "government tyranny of American roadways." Beck added, "You know what other country had speed limits? Nazi Germany."

On his show Beck was clearly irate about the incident, illustrating a larger conspiracy on his chalkboard. "I was issued a ticket America, that's T-I-K-E-T. The T is for tyranny, as in this government. The I is for illegal aliens driving on the roads that American citizens pay for. The K is for King Obama! The E is for embezzling money in Chicago—Obama is from Chicago, Obama is embezzling money! And the last T? The T stands for the great people who will answer the call of liberty, the Tea Party!"

Beck even suggested that he was a target of the Obama administration, which was trying to silence one of the most listened-to right-wing TV and radio hosts. "They are afraid because I'm speaking the truth, the truth about America's fascist roads. Who is in charge of the so-called 'Department of Transportation' anyway? Did you vote for him? I didn't!"

"This president I think has exposed himself over and over again as a guy who has a deep-seated hatred for drivers and driving-culture." Beck then showed his viewers a map of President Obama's high-speed rail plan. "See? You see it America? He's not building more roads. He's building trains. Excuse me mister President, but I worked hard my whole life so I could afford the car I want, and you can't tell me I have to ride this socialist transportation!"

Beck also called for President Obama to release copies of his driver's license. "How do we even know he's qualified to tell me how to drive? Have you seen his driver's license? I haven't. What is this President trying to hide?"

At the end of his show Beck burst into tears. "Excuse me, America," a teary-eyed Beck sobbed, "I just love driving so much, and this President is taking that freedom away. The freedom to drive as fast as we want, where we want, with absolutely no regard for the well-being of our fellow citizens."

New York City police officer Antony Jones clocked Beck driving 40 in a 25 zone. When reached for comment Officer Jones said, "I would have let him go with a warning, but he wouldn't shut his big mouth. I can take a lot of abuse, but once this prick called me a fascist and said he'd picket my house, I told him to kiss my fat Brooklyn behind and slapped him with the maximum fine. I gave him several chances to say his piece, but it's almost like that jerk wanted the ticket."

After appealing the traffic violation today Beck was ordered to pay the $25 fine. He vowed to continue to fight Obama's "evil highway dictatorship" and was later issued an additional fine of $250,000 for contempt of court after the judge's orders failed to stop his 45-minute freedom-rant about a lot more important things people cared about.

Anjana Santhanam

Local Upswing in Popped Collar Cases
Attributed to Rise in Teen Vampire Novel Popularity

Trenton, NJ—Local medical authorities warn that the Popped Collar Epidemic of 2005 has returned and that the cause may be the popularity of teen vampire romance novels.

The World Health Organization (WHO) classified Popped Collar, a disease caused by the bacteria *Totalus idiotii* in which the victims pop the collars of their polo shirts, as an epidemic between the years 2004-2005, when an estimated 60% of all teenagers contracted the illness. The only cures appeared to be a steady infusion of a 70-20-10% French *Vogue, Gossip Girl*, and *The Devil Wears Prada* medical cocktail, or a generic version of the drug, called "A Mirror."

Dr. Mark Stevens, chairman of the Popped Collar Task Force (colloquially known as the Fashion Police), created by the WHO to combat the epidemic in 2004, states that these potent treatments drastically reduced the number of cases reported in the following years. "The treatments appeared to cure the cases in nearly all target groups. Since early 2006, only the high-risk population of *guidos* continued to have high infection rates and low treatment rates. Until now, that is," Dr. Stevens said in a press conference last Tuesday.

A press release on the Popped Collar Task Force website states that in the current epidemic, nearly 85% of teenagers and 45% of adults have been infected. Local hospitals have been inundated with cases, but initially it was unclear what had triggered the latest bout of cases. "We had originally thought that the *guido* population had been spreading messages of their practice of unsafe style through the show *Jersey Shore*. Upon closer inspection, however, we noticed that new cases had unusual characteristics," Dr. Stevens said in a private interview.

Dr. Cecilia Miller, an oral surgeon specializing in pediatric cases, noticed the unusual nature of the current infections. "In the last epidemic, both sexes had approximately equal infection rates, and heterosexual males between the ages of 15 and 35 were actually slightly more likely to contract the infection. In the recent cases, though, females between the ages of 13 and 19 are being infected 340% more than males in the same age group. The next highest infection rates came from middle-aged soccer moms with nearly zero love-lives," Dr. Miller said.

Dr. Miller said that she did not think to study the cases until she noticed that an unusually high number of teenagers were coming in for extra-long canine veneers and requesting that she sharpen them.

"I was shocked to remove the bibs from many of my female patients, only to see Popped Collar. Many of the males requesting the procedure did not necessarily test positive for *T. idiotii*, but they did tend to have some remarkable similarities. Most of them came in with dollar store body glitter covering their faces and bodies, and while I initially mistook them for gay ravers, they all seemed to have girlfriends infected with Popped Collar," Dr. Miller said.

Dr. Miller's proposed mechanism of action involves the popping of the collar as being symptoms of the patients' desires to become one of the supernatural beings. The popped collar is analogous to the stiff collars on the capes of royal vampires such as Count Dracula, Count Chocula, and Count the Count on Sesame Street. Additionally, popped collars are supposed to mask self- or boyfriend-inflicted bite marks on the necks of the female patients, replacing yesteryear's hickey-hiders: turtlenecks, scarves, and concealer.

Dr. Miller joined the Task Force, which quickly accepted her theory. Her theory links the upsurge in Popped Collar to the rise in the popularity of vampire romance novels aimed at teenage girls.

These stories are sold in the Waste of Time section at Borders, Merchandising Cash Cow section of Barnes & Nobles, and the Clichéd Plot and Mary Sue Characters category of Amazon.com.

Local book vendors, however, are denying the accusations, saying that there is not enough proof to implicate teen vampire romances in the rise of Popped Collar.

"To implicate the entire teen vampire romance genre in this dreadful disease is absurd. People have been reading vampire novels since Bram Stoker wrote *Dracula*," said Kate Reilly, owner of the Trenton area bookstore Dog Eared. "Besides, anything that gets kids reading these days can be considered a blessing."

Dr. Richard Terry, a statistician at Drexel University, criticizes the claims that Reilly and other book vendors are making. Dr. Terry said, "While many bookstore owners are saying that teen girls are reading more than ever after they pick up these vampire romances, the data show that there is no significant increase in the number of girls going on to read *Dracula* or other pieces of literature. In fact, the data show that most of them re-read the same vampire series over and over."

Annette Ortiz, a florist in Plainfield, New Jersey, and mother of two daughters, Amanda, age 14, and Carly, age 16, infected with Popped Collar, agrees with Dr. Terry. "I was devastated to see that after I bought my girls those dreadful books, they got Popped Collar. I brought them to my Book Club meeting one Thursday night, hoping they would pick up something else, anything else—an Oprah's Book Club selection, a dictionary, even a Harlequin romance! Not only did they refuse all of my suggestions, but they got the Book Club reading their vampire novels, and there are two moms now infected, too. I've started hiding the apples and Ivory Pancake makeup just to be on the safe side."

The apple- and pale makeup-hiding precautions are some of the many found on the Popped Collar Task Force website to prevent *T. idiotii* infection. Others include properly using the word "chagrin" in sentences, engaging in healthy and non-dependent relationships with people of approximately the same age, and reading vast amounts of fan fiction.

When asked about the last precaution, Dr. Stevens said, "Fan fiction serves as a way to build up immunity, sort of like a vaccine or being exposed to numerous types of germs at a young age helps ward off other types of infections. You eventually get used to the Mary Sue characters, the predictable plots, and the emotionally abusive and controlling relationships being portrayed as healthy and admirable, and you realize these vampire novels are not unique or interesting after all."

Ari Melman

Religious vs. Secular Backgrounds

People don't get along. We all have different ideas on how to best live life, and we've been forced to separate into two sides just to speak our mind. A small-town Kansas boy doesn't want a bunch of gay New Yorkers moving in and turning his peaceful life into constant Woodstock just as much as a bunch of gay New Yorkers don't want the boy telling them they can't live in Kansas. That Kansas boy could care less about socialized medicine or abstract terrorism, but he'll vote Republican to keep his way of life. He will listen to people telling him, "I'm on your side" or "I stand shoulder to shoulder with the hard-working American farm families,"[i] and will learn over time to accept the other party positions. Politics succeed by dividing people and preying on emotions, yet what Americans overwhelmingly want is bipartisanship. The number of self-proclaimed moderates has risen from 36% in 1980 to over 50% in 2000, even as the two parties become more polarizing and negative.[ii] Let's try to understand where the other side comes from before we get so quick to anger.

The Religious Right has taken hold of the Republican Party in the last decade. As Republican U.S. representative Shays noted, "This Republican Party of Lincoln has become a party of theocracy."[iii] Because of this, politics and religion are once again becoming tightly intertwined. Preachers used to talk about improving quality of life by following the ways of the Bible. Now, they are increasingly focusing on values that separate us rather than unite us. The Mega-churches, as seen on TV, have risen alongside the Christian Coalition of America and the Moral Majority Coalition, amassing millions of supporters and billions of dollars.[iv] They openly fuse biblical passages with political hellfire, condemning gays, abortionists, Muslims, and immigrants.[v] Many local pastors in turn are taught and inspired by these powerful preachers.[vi] Caring members who come to church for community and to feel closer to God in turn absorb new political beliefs. In the words of George Orwell, author of 1984, "If the speech he is making is one that he is accustomed to make over and over again, he may be almost unconscious of what he is saying, as one is when one utters the responses in church. And this reduced state of consciousness, if not indispensable, is at any rate favorable to political conformity."[vii]

The left is becoming equally divisive. Despite having the idealistic dream to erase cultural prejudices in society and live together in a utopia free of racial, religious or sexual hatred, they choose to go about it by hating on the very people they are trying to convince. Three of the most popular leftist blogs—*Politico*, *Huffington Post*, and the *Daily Kos*—constantly spew headlines meant to incite anger. For examples: "Lieberman: Uninsured can wait until Recession is over" [viii] or "Neocons root for Ahmadinejad." [ix] Liberals aren't any more hate-free than religious people, yet they justify their hate with the same line their opponents use: *that* group threatens *my* way of life.

One of the issues that most divides the two American cultures (we've left the heat on the melting pot so long, we're only able to separate left from right nowadays!) is same-sex marriage. The same arguments used to keep gay rights suppressed today were used in the 1850s to justify slavery. In the Supreme Court's now infamous Dred Scott decision, slaves were thought of as inherently inferior. It would be against the spirit of the Constitution and southern Christian morality to treat them as human beings (as was quickly becoming the sentiment of the time). In 2003's *Lawrence v. Texas*, three of our Supreme Court justices attempted to uphold the laws against consensual gay sex with the same judicial restraint position: that it would go against the values of our country's founders. Among them was Antonin Scalia, a man who previously bemoaned "the tendency of democracy to obscure the divine authority behind government." In his dissenting opinion, he said legalizing consensual sodomy (defined as any non-vaginal sex, usually oral or anal) would undermine moral law. "State laws against bigamy, same-sex marriage, adult incest, prostitution, masturbation, adultery, fornication, bestiality, and obscenity are sustainable only in light of Bowers' validation of laws based on moral choices. Every single one of these laws is called into question by today's decision." [x] To Scalia, and those fighting to keep restrictive morality on the books, because masturbation and fornication (unmarried sex) were considered taboo 200 years ago, they must continue to remain illegal today!

Today, few would agree that slavery should be condoned. Yet we continue to use the same arguments to keep down minorities. With ongoing legislation against minority rights, is it fair to condemn someone merely due to different, though harmless, values? It seems that the more things change, the more they stay the same and yes, history has a way of repeating itself. But there's no need for it to take homosexuals another 50 years before they are granted legislated freedom, and another 100 before they are allowed social freedom, as has happened to African Americans. We need to take a step back and stop hating those around us, both secular and religious. We need to understand that time and values do change, and when people embrace those changes, society evolves as a whole. It would be a whole lot nicer for everyone if we could grow without going through the pain that every generation has gone through before us.

Notes

[i] Lincoln, Blanche. "Arkansans and other stakeholders weigh in on Senator Blanche L. Lincoln's new role as Chairman of the Senate Committee on Agriculture,Nutrition, and Forestry." *Blanche Lincoln's Senatorial Page. N.p.,* 9 Sept. 2009. Web. 2 Apr. 2010. <http://lincoln.senate.gov/newsroom/ 2009-09-09-2.cfm>. "I Stand Shoulder to Shoulder with the hard working American farm families" - Cliche political speak.

[ii] Independent Nation. "Rise of Independents." *Independent Nation.* N.p., n.d. Web. 2 Apr. 2010. <http://www.independentnation.org/ rise_of_independents.htm>. Growth of Independents in America

[iii] Shays, Christopher. *Theocracy Watch.* Web. 2 Apr. 2010. <http://www.theocracywatch.org/>.

[iv] "Christian Coalition of America." *Wikipedia.* N.p., n.d. Web. 2 Apr. 2010. <http://en.wikipedia.org/wiki/Christian_Coalition_of_America>

[v] Esquivel, Laura. "Religious Right Groups Join Immigration Debate." *Right Wing Watch.* N.p., 9 Jan. 2007. Web. 2 Apr. 2010. <http://www.rightwingwatch.org/content/ religious-right-groups-join-immigration-debate>. Anti-Immigrant,

Birkey, Andy. "Health care reform is against God's design." *The Minnesota Independent.* N.p., 7 Aug. 2009. Web. 2 Apr. 2010. <http://minnesotaindependent.com/41364/ religious-right-watch-obamacare-is-against-gods-design>. Anti-Science

Harrison, David. "Christian preachers face arrest in Birmingham." *Telegraph.co.uk.* Telegraph Media Group Limitied, 31 May 2008. Web. 2 Apr. 2010. <http://www.telegraph.co.uk/news/uknews/2058935/ Police-advise-Christian-preachers-to-leave-Muslim-area-of-Birmingham.html>. Anti-Muslim

[vi] James, Russell, III. "Where do Megachurch Preachers Come From?" *Christian Standard* 6 June 2004: 361-362. Web. 2 Apr. 2010. <www.christianstandard.com/pdfs/638.pdf >.

[vii] Orwell, George. *Politics and the English Language.* N.p., 1946. Web. 2 Apr. 2010. <http://www.mtholyoke.edu/acad/intrel/orwell46.htm>.

[viii] Huffwatcher. "Grossly misleading headline about Sen. Lieberman, incites user hate comments (HuffPost: 'Approved!!!')." *Huff Watch.* N.p., 25 Aug. 2009. Web. 2 Apr. 2010. <http://huff-watch.blogspot.com/2009/08/ 82309-grossly-misleading-headline-about.html>.

[ix] HuffWatcher. "'Neocons Root For Ahmadinejad' --- NOT; users espouse hate based on lie (HuffPost: 'Approved!!!')." *Huff Watch.* N.p., 14 June 2009. Web. 2 Apr. 2010. <http://huff-watch.blogspot.com/2009/06/ 61209-neocons-root-for-ahmadinejad-not.html>.

[x] Dershowitz, Alan. *America on Trial: Inside the Legal Battles That Transformed Our Nation.* NYC: 2004. Print.

Vennila Padmanaban

The United Nations Must Remedy Humanitarian Aid Efforts

Vast expanses of tectonic plates are molded by powerful, mingling ocean currents which extend and interact to form the geographic framework of the earth. Just as the world is connected by soil and water, its inhabitants are linked by the ever-increasing trend of global interdependence. One of the greatest embodiments of the global nature of human relationships is the United Nations, an international organization comprised of nearly every sovereign state in the world.

The United Nations is a renowned organization founded after the Second World War for the preservation of peace, security, and human welfare internationally. One of the primary functions of this unified body is to provide immediate assistance and relief upon the occurrence of a massive crisis or natural disaster. Despite their efforts, the UN fails in many critical areas of relief, resulting in the loss of countless human lives. The loss of these lives and the failure of the unified world to provide critical aid to humans in need weigh heavily against the astonishing pace of human development. In an era where humans have produced crafts that travel faster than the speed of sound, the loss of lives from tardy and inadequate humanitarian aid demonstrates major failures of the United Nations. These issues must be addressed and remedied immediately.

A shifting of tectonic plates may cause the disturbance of oceans, resulting in large storms and deadly tsunamis. The Indian Ocean tsunami of 2004 left immense destruction in its wake, with approximately 240,000 deaths across twelve countries and more than one million victims displaced from their homes. In response to appeals for assistance from the affected countries, UN agencies mobilized to provide emergency resources and services to the tsunami-stricken areas. However, the response was largely insufficient in providing adequate water, shelter, and measures for sanitation (Couldrey 6-9).

Despite the widespread flooding of water inland as a result of the tsunami, its victims were left with an ironic lack of safe and clean water, a human necessity. Safe, clean water is important for drinking, food preparation, washing, toilets, and so forth. However, in many of the regions affected by the tsunami, the water supply was broken or disrupted, breaking access and causing a severe deficit. The massive breaks in water supply perpetuated problems of dehydration, lack of hygiene, and Gastroentiritis diseases, many of which can be fatal (Youngmeyer).

Temporary relief shelters were far below UN minimum standards: camps had a lack of toilets and running water, perpetuating health problems. There is a distinct link between shelter and the health of victims; the close confines of inadequate, unsanitary shelters promote the spread of disease. The issues of poor waste management and water-borne diseases aggravate the issue of healthcare. Although healthcare was supposed to be free for the first two months after the tsunami, administrative procedures became prohibitively expensive ("Tsunami Response: A Human Rights Assessment" 3-64). Additionally, politics plays a significant role in hindering the effectiveness of humanitarian aid, and media coverage often places the world's focus on a particular crisis area (Fleshman 5).

The impact of media coverage on global crises is evident in the genocide occurring in Sudan's western region of Darfur. In the Darfur region, ethnic violence has caused 70,000 civilian deaths and left more than 2.5 million refugees since 2003. However, the discussion over the Darfur region is not centered around how to stop the bloodshed and bring aid to its victims, but on whether the word "genocide" can be applied to the crisis (Straus 123).

Through the ongoing conflict between government forces, militias, and rebels in large areas of Darfur, the delivery of food and aid operations faltered and gave rise to a food deficit. In April 2006, the United Nations had to cut its daily rations in half as a result of a funding shortfall. The decision impacted nearly three million refugees depending on food aid, and is a direct result of the World Food Program's lack of success in soliciting the necessary funds from its donors ("Darfur Food Rations Cut in Half" 1).

The war ended with a grave reality—that the UN's World Food Program was unable to meet this need despite its vast funding, resources, and workers ("South Sudan hungry 'quadrupled' in a year'"). Despite the severity and magnitude of the crisis, the unified countries under the UN have been unable to fulfill its aid mandates, primarily because of a lack of funding. Countless lives have been lost as a result of this inadequacy ("Aid Agencies in Darfur" 1).

Currently, the aftermath of a crisis is unfolding in Haiti. A massive earthquake struck Haiti in January 2010, leaving the country with an unimaginably heavy toll of lives lost, buildings destroyed, chaos, and devastation. The country, already impoverished, is in desperate need of aid (Romero 1). The most urgent needs in the region are field hospitals, emergency health, water purification, emergency shelter, logistics, and telecommunications ("Aid Groups Rush to Haiti" 1).

As the UN relief efforts proceed, survivors have become increasingly desperate as they are suffering. Although the United Nations claims to be engaging in a massive relief effort, the body has been largely unsuccessful in finding solutions to logistical and organizational barriers to aid relief. Approximately 300,000 Haitians are homeless, with a death toll as high as 100,000. As aid groups attempt to rescue survivors, the necessity of efficient relief is evident ("UN Launches Haiti Earthquake Relief" 1).

As the aftermath of the Haitian earthquake continues to unfold, the United Nations must overcome its past failures and current obstacles to provide necessary relief and save the lives of untold numbers of Haitians. In a world of international connectivity where a unified body of many great countries is possible, the people of a nation should not suffer alone in a crisis. It is deplorable that days often pass before victims of a crisis receive essentials like food, water, shelter, and healthcare. These issues reveal major faults of the United Nations organization that must be remedied now. The victims of these crises are dying to this day.

Works Cited

"Aid Agencies in Darfur Deplore Donors' Failure to Fund the African Union and Jeopardizing Lives as a Result." *Oxfam International.* 18 July 2006. Web. 5 March 2010.

"Aid Groups Rush to Haiti." *CNN.* 13 Jan. 2010. Web. 5 March 2010.

Couldrey, Marion and Morris, Tim. "UN Assesses Tsunami Response." *Forced Migration Review,* (2005): 6-9. Web. 4 March 2010.

"Darfur food rations cut in half." *BBC News.* 28 April 2006. Web. 4 March 2010.

Fleshman, Michael. "Fixing the Humanitarian Aid System: UN, relief groups seek to bolster and speed up food delivery." *Africa Renewal,* 19 (2006): 5. Web. 4 March 2010.

Gettleman, Jeffrey. "Darfur Withers as Sudan Sells Food." *The New York Times.* 9 Aug. 2008. Web. 4 March 2010.

McGreal, Chris and Addley, Esther. "Haiti Aid Agencies Warn: chaotic and confusing relief effort is costing lives." *The Guardian.* 18 Jan. 2010. Web. 5 March 2010.

"Millions without safe water following tsunami." *US Water News*. Jan 2005.
Web. 5 March 2010.

Romero, Simon and Lacey, Mark. "Fierce Quake Devastates Haitian Capital." *The New York Times*. 12 Jan. 2010. Web. 5 March 2010.

"Secretary-General lays out challenging UN agenda for 2008." *UN News Centre*.
4 Jan. 2008. Web. 4 March 2010.

"South Sudan hungry 'quadrupled in a year.'" *BBC News*. 2 Feb. 2010. Web. 4 March 2010.

Straus, Scott. "Darfur and the Genocide Debate." *Foreign Affairs*, 84 (2005): 123-133.

Tsunami Response: A Human Rights Assessment.*Actionaid*, (2006): 03-64.
Web.c4 March 2010.

"UN launches Haiti earthquake relief appeal." *BBC News*. 16 Jan. 2010. Web. 4 March 2010.

Youngmeyer, David. "Safe water vital for life in tsunami-hit Samoa." *Unicef New Zealand*, (2000): 1. Web. 4 March 2010.

Anjana Santhanam

Obligation to the Earth: Canadian Geese

If you never thought your decisions could impact another creature's life, I dare you to drive along U.S. Route 1. Aside from the occasional blown-out tire, you will see the sight that I am greeted with every day of my commute.

I am talking about a litter of Canadian goose corpses lining the sides of the highway from North Jersey to the Philadelphia border, like fluffy decorative pillows lining a couch. I never used to care for these animals; they pooped on the pathway I used to get to my elementary school, making it difficult to keep my white Mary Janes clean on rainy days, and would honk at daybreak while I slept.

But the sight of a single goose nesting on a small strip of land surrounded by a jug-handle and four-lane highway is a haunting one.

Canadian geese, *Branta canadensis*, tend to nest close to water sources. The only water source within a half-mile of the nesting site was a sink that on rainy days would fill up with water. The water is stagnant and attracts a swarm of mosquitoes during early summer and by mid-July dries up to a chalky, red-brown clay. A tributary of the Delaware River is nearly a mile away and on the opposite side. Any animal trying to find suitable water would have to cross a four-lane highway. Adult men and women often have difficulty crossing a normal street; add to that the challenges of being two feet tall and forced to walk instead of fly because you are hampered with goslings and you have a recipe for disaster.

With their grayish-brown body plumage and long, black necks, Canadian geese are a regal sight on a bleak early spring morning. Over the course of the last few months, one may notice that something is missing from their usual lifecycle. Ten years ago one could hear the honking call of the Canadian geese around early March and know to look up and see the v-formation of geese, a triumphant return from migration. These days that sound is missing.

The climate has changed, and whether humans are or are not to blame in that fact is no longer an issue. What is the issue is how we as a species are going to use our place as the most powerful animals on this planet to save our fellow creature. Many Canadian geese populations in North America have not been migrating, choosing instead to stay in the newly mild climes in which they grew from gosling to adult (Hupp et al. 2010). Contrary to what one might think after seeing goose corpses on the highway, the population of Canadian geese in North America is increasing to the point that they are considered pests in certain areas (dncr.state.pa.us, retrieved April 10, 2010).

If the Canadian goose population is going up, is it still worth saving these creatures? Do we have an obligation to the earth? The short answer: yes.

Canadian geese, like many other animals, show how humans are affecting the landscape in ways that affect entire ecosystems. Climate change and habitat fragmentation are two factors that often act synergistically: with increased deforestation comes the rise in temperatures of formerly "temperate" regions of the earth, and with the increased temperatures comes a change in the local environment that affects the lifecycles of both flora and fauna in the region.

Most people think they cannot have an impact on the ways these animals live. *Let the government take care of it! Let the ecologists and environmentalists figure out what to do!* We are quick to pass the buck.

However, the simple steps taken by individuals, just like you and me, can make a huge difference. The government does not take any actions unless the constituency makes the issue a priority on politicians' platforms. Oppose the expansion of highways beside natural woodlands and wetland ecosystems in the area. Promote instead the improvement of current roads and construction of overpasses which would increase traffic flow without destroying horizontal land space.

These are only the ideas of a single student. With an entire community's worth of ideas, motivations, and efforts, we can solve not just the issue of habitat destruction and climate change, but any problem.

Sometimes the only thing preventing us humans from changing are our own fragile egos. When faced with that reality, I remember these lines from Coleridge's "The Rime of the Ancient Mariner":

> He prayeth best, who loveth best
> All things both great and small;
> For the dear God who loveth us,
> He made and loveth all.

These lines show that while humans think that they as individuals are so insignificant, we have the extraordinary ability to love the creatures all around us. That love can make the world a better place.

Works Cited

Hupp, Jerry M., John I. Hodges, Jr., Bruce P. Conant, Brandt W. Meiexll, and Debbie
    J. Groves. "Winter Distribution, Movements, and Annual Survival of Radiomarked
    Vancouver Canada Geese in Southeast Alaska." *Journal of Wildlife Management*
    74.2 (2010): 274-84. Web. 12 Apr. 2010.

Pennsylvania Department of Conservation and Natural Resources. *State Parks to Open*
    for Early Goose Hunting. Resource. Pennsylvania Department of Conservation and
    Natural Resources, 12 Sept. 2007. Web. 10 Apr. 2010. <http://www.dcnr.state.pa.
    usnews/resource/res2007/07-0912-earlygoosehunting.aspx>.

Faculty
Writing

Introduction

Writers render their perceptions from far off places and times; rarely do they live close to us, and rarer still do we know them or have the opportunity to know them, if only because they have died. They're almost always strangers with disembodied voices to whom we have no easy access. This can be a source of frustration to anyone who has wanted to ask a writer to elaborate on a particular point or share their experiences with the nuts and bolts, from conception to execution, of a written subject.

In the following section, examples of the work by Drexel faculty have been included in *The 33rd* as representations of fine writing. The authors are alive and kicking and on campus; some may be your teachers now or in the future. You can see from the pieces that the approaches and subjects range from original works of poetry, fiction, satire, and personal essay to essays and articles on the teaching of literature, hunting wild boars, financing public schools, and building homes in areas prone to wildfires and flooding. You can assume that each subject presented particular challenges that the authors had to grapple with in the same way that all writers must, including, of course, those in a composition class.

Stacey Ake

An Introduction to Modeling for the Non-Scientist

The problem at hand may be articulated simply and directly as "What do computer models and simulations mean by their results?" This is not as straightforward a question as it may appear because all models are created within very particular contexts, and the interpretation of modular results outside of a model's particular context renders those results at best unintelligible and at worst illegitimate. A model, particularly a simulation, is a rare bird. It is a hybrid between theory and experiment. It is both hypothesis and corroboration. This hybrid nature of computer modeling becomes increasingly evident as more and more advanced statistical methods are applied to the model.

For the purposes of my discussion, I would like to distinguish between two kinds of models. The first kind of model is one I deem *heuristic*. Generally, such models are simple, pedagogically effective, and misleading about other related, but more complex, phenomena. Traditionally, such models contain, at most, three parameters. One of these parameters may remain undefined (i.e., it becomes a *variable*) and can thus be solved for, if the other two parameters are known. Winsome examples of this kind of model are $f = ma$, $v_t = v_o + 2as$ (this may appear to contain four variables, but in fact v_t and v_o are simply different measurements in time of the same variable—velocity; thus this equation only contains three variables: velocity, acceleration, and displacement), and $p + q = 1$.

The other type of model is one I call *predictive*. These models are attempts to simulate current phenomena in the hopes of understanding present relationships and calculating future outcomes. Such models are designed using an almost exhaustive quantity of past data observation and their "future" predictability is actually based on past "probability." Weather forecasting exemplifies this type of modeling. When tomorrow's forecast is announced as an 80% chance of rain, 20% chance of snow, it simply means that in the past number of years x on occasions when all the parameters were y (such as they are at this time z), 8 out of 10 times it rained. Note that this is *not* a determinative model. It cannot tell anyone what *will* happen.

A second example of a predictive model would be a simulation of ecosystem dynamics within a closed system such as a lake. If enough records are fastidiously kept (ion input, ion output, temperature fluctuation, organic matter build up, phosphate accumulation, oxygen-carbon dioxide measures, tannin uptake, etc.), the effects on the lake's chemistry of changes in these indicators (parameters) may be predicted. Also, the interactions of other chemicals (e.g., H_2SO_4 from acid mine drainage) may be predicted. However, the effect of sulfuric acid and other chemicals on the lake is readily predictable only because laboratory experiments have set well-known precedents as to the effect of H_2SO_4 on $CaCO_2$ (i.e., there will be calcium leaching). The only predictions this kind of model/simulation can make are based in prior knowledge. The parameters used to create the model are themselves monotonic; they cannot account for any synergistic interactions among themselves *per se* unless the mechanism is previously known through experiment. Since there is no way to record exhaustively every possible parameter within the lake, much less understand every possible synergistic interaction, this type of predictive model cannot be considered positivistically determinative in its predictions either.

No one considers a heuristic model to be positivistically determinative in the "real" world. When, after an experiment, *f* does not equal *ma*, friction, an updraft or downdraft, or the fact that the experiment was not conducted in a vacuum are put forth as reasonable explanations for the differences between prediction and result. A similar method, albeit with a subtle twist, is also employed to explain discrepancies between prediction and outcome for a predictive model. The meteorologist nods gravely when told about the "El Niño Effect" and, adding this datum to his calculations, believes he has solved the problem until the eruption of Mt. Pinatubo in the Philippines whereupon he nods gravely...

In a similar fashion the hydrologist is perplexed by the absence of calcium leaching in the lake after the influx of sulfuric acid. The geologist informs him that erosion has unearthed a stratum of limestone, thus providing the lake with calcium. However, neither of these facts can explain the fish die-off that the ichthyologist has just discovered. . .

In both of these cases, the scientists involved have attempted closer approximation to "reality" as expressed/predicted by their models by the addition of heretofore unknown data. They have added new (more) parameters. However, what they have actually done is to have understood a *past* event in its entirety. They have in no way increased the predictive value of their simulations because their underlying assumption is that time is monotonic and that tomorrow will be like today. This, despite the fact that today was obviously *not* like yesterday. Thus, not only are the discrepancies between actual events and a simulation's predictions rationalized away as the fault of a missing parameter, said parameter is then added to the model in hopes of improving its predictive ability. One could then view the predictive model as not predictive at all; rather it is an *historical* heuristic device.

This is a very important point. A predictive model does not tell one what will be; it does not even tell one what *is*—it simply explains what has been, specifically what has been *understood*. And the future has not been understood, nor has the truly random. (I distinguish *random* from *stochastic*, which is the statistically random or, rather, the probability that an event x will occur that is not predicted by a particular theory or model. Thus, stochastic events occur with a particular probability.) If there were not truly random events—events that occur outside theory—theory would never change.

Nonetheless, a more sophisticated theory can convert a truly random event into a stochastic one by inclusion within it. The "revolutions" of physics are exemplary instances of such conversions. And it is at this juncture where the individual must decide whether he is a reductionist (eventually—given enough time—all theory will encompass all of nature) or not. Does one believe that the unknown quantities in the universe are diminishing and our knowledge increasing such that someday they both shall meet? Or, is there an asymptote such that all theory may approximate it but never subsume it? Simply put, it is a matter of the one and the many.

Genevieve Betts

Nepantla

He said
    I wish
I had my gun.

We were in the Huachuca Mountains,
a crossing-ground
near the Mexican border,
Coronado National forest.

I told my father
    It's more likely
we'll meet a bear in camp
than an immigrant.

*

As I look up at Miller Peak,
I see Argus, a pink blimp
    floating, poly-
        eyed balloon
with one lid down.
He does not see
humans, but cows
    (a million Io's)
escaping pens of country—

there is no father of convoy.

*

The trail is lined with relics:

    Bimbo tortilla wrappers,
    diapers,
    one cowboy boot.

But what of the foot,
the ghost of it a history—

the man falling off the edge,
         his shoe snagging on pine.
A man fleeing immigration police,
         they do not return it after he is seized.
The man hallucinating with thirst,
         dragging his body through dirt
         to a spring dry since May, he sees
         its bed; branch thistles are the tentacles
         that drag him underneath.

*

Camp-

         near the tip
and right off the trail.
I settle between a tree
and my parent's shelter.

Past midnight, the thumping
becomes apparent—
         and like words,
         expectant—

a black bear
brushes its breadth
against the wall
of my tent.

Circus-like, he paws
at my mother's objects
on a rock—

First choosing sunglasses
he chews the soft plastic,
swats a black umbrella
till it rolls down the slope.

I could not help but envision
Magritte's newest subject—

         the surrealist image of the bear,
         glasses on, umbrella open

and revel in the I Told You So of tomorrow.

*

In daylight, Hermes
does not hear
    tumbleweed
    beneath stumbling feet.

Russian thistle,
devil weed.

    Does not see the people
    lined up behind coyotes,

paid guides of the underground
above land,

    my father handing food out,
    passing his canteen around.

Ron Bishop

The Organist Needs a Cheeseburger

Having a father who fixed pipe organs for a living made show and tell in elementary school an adventure. The artisanship, the skill, the fact that so few people practice the craft—all of this was lost on a seven-year-old trying to compete with classmates whose parents were doctors, lawyers, or ran successful businesses in my hometown, a verdant bedroom community located about 12 miles west of midtown Manhattan.

My father had been in business for himself since he was 14 and found himself fascinated by the inner workings of the pipe organ at the Presbyterian church he attended in the 1940s and 1950s with my grandmother. It was the sexton, Howard, angular and always well-dressed, who first let Dad in to tinker with the aging instrument. Armed with perfect pitch and skilled if impatient hands, Dad discovered what he wanted to do the rest of his life. I envied him for having so quickly found his calling, and that he was making a living by doing something with his hands, creating, fixing—leaving evidence of his skill for thousands to hear all over the northeastern United States. Even though my frustration at how easy it was to poke fun at the profession never subsided, I became proud that he could walk into a church, assess the environmental conditions, turn on the instrument, and within minutes discern what was wrong with it.

Mom and Dad rarely threw away anything connected to Dad's business. We arranged the organ parts into navigable sections in our basement, like crop circles made out of wood, leather, and lead. The paths enabled my mother to find her way to our aging washing machine and dryer, and me to my Royce drum set, bought for me from Sears by my parents after nearly a decade of my pleading and playing along to Rush and Kansas and—full disclosure—Carpenters and Partridge Family on the top of a folded cot and, later, after a partial concession, on a metal snare drum and single shrill cymbal.

Every couple of years, my mom would get fed up with what for most other houses would be grounds for condemnation, and hire a dumpster so that she could rid the house of junk. She approached the periodic purges with a troubling matter-of-factness, as if everyone on the block every so often had to discard one or two metric tons of detritus.

A purge made for quite a spectacle in our outwardly friendly but ultimately tight-assed neighborhood. One came days after the woman who lived two doors down, on the other side of the home owned by my dad's 95-year old insurance agent, complained to township officials about the peeling yellow paint on our house and the spillover of organ parts in our garage. So we did what all good Presbyterians turned Christian Scientists do when confronted with shortcomings: we cursed her from a distance. Pristine white aluminum siding soon shielded our neglected exterior walls, but Dad hung on to the organ parts, sure that he would be able to use them in a future renovation. Thanks to his tendency to under-plan and over-commit, these projects often should not have been launched. One, a ramshackle organ tucked near the front entrance of a small Catholic church in Brooklyn near the Bid-a-Wee Home made famous in local New York television commercials, took nearly five years and six different combinations of my father's seven employees to complete. My involvement in the project culminated in a trip on the "E" train and Erie Lackawanna back to New Jersey on a frigid snowy January night with seven eight-foot long Bourdon pipes crated poorly and tied in cardboard in tow— material for the next purge.

And if the profession wasn't hard enough for me to explain to my friends, Dad's self-run business came with a few bizarre extras. He fancies himself an impresario and is blessed with an unerring ability to spot organ-playing talent. So while other kids were going to camp, getting caught smoking, or playing little league, my brother and I were hired during our down time to entertain a roster of organists who would periodically stay at our house. Their visits to Maplewood were a part of their preparation for concerts arranged by Dad to dedicate the organs he sold.

When the organists visited, our three-bedroom Colonial had to be "just so," even though it was rarely "just so" for us. My parents were poor animal disciplinarians; our dog and three cats regularly urinated all over the house. Folded paper towels, like square islands on a map of apple-red carpet, dotted our first floor. When the opportunity arose to suck up to an organist who was going to help Dad build his business, we scrubbed the cat urine and quickly created new crop circles out of the stuff still in the basement.

Next, we had to get our stories in order. We knew them so well that we didn't rehearse; we jumped in on cue. The performances had an eerie Von Trapp feel. Sometimes the stories were our only lengthy interactions during these periods. The older I got, the more they insinuated themselves into my relationships with friends, especially in college, where being sports editor of my high school's newspaper wasn't enough to register on the "I know I'm a freshman, but please look kindly on me for some reason" scale.

Let me share an example:

Yes, yes, Dad, if it weren't for the Music Hall, I wouldn't be here. Yes, you met Mom when she was a Rockette, and you were a lonely pipe organ tuner

working for one of the country's most prestigious pipe organ builders. Yes,
I remember: she was posing as one of the organists as part of a cost-cutting
move by the Music Hall suits. She insisted that the right music be placed on the
console, and, when it wasn't on that glorious day, you brought it to her. Wasn't
it Tea for Two, *Dad?*

My wonderful wife, Sheila, was subjected, as were many of my friends,
to Dad's "tour" of midtown Manhattan, whose highlight was the apartment
building where my Mom lived while she was carving out a Rockette career. .
A few friends endured the tour as a condition of eventual employment with
Dad's company. Not that the stories aren't interesting: I will gladly recount
how George Chakiris, the actor who played Bernardo in the movie version of
West Side Story, lived in my mom's apartment building, and how the two of
them eventually became friends.

But such is life when you are the self-appointed guardian of the "Mighty
Wurlitzer" pipe organ at Radio City Music Hall, the role Dad again assumed
after leaving the Hall years earlier to devote more time to his business. Music
Hall executives came to their senses in 1978 and asked him back. They would
exploit his love for the building, and his inability to resist pouring too much of
his own money into the project, the last of which he only recently got back. But
the organ would be saved for future generations of fans who would someday
pay more than $100 for a ticket for a Christmas Show recycled more often than
a philandering politician, and for theatre organ aficionados who wrote nasty
letters to theater organ magazines when Dad replaced so much as an original
piece of rotting leather.

***

About two months before Christmas in 2007, I learned that John Markham,
one of the organists befriended and later hired by my dad, had died. His mom
found him in his apartment, a rumpled heap on the floor, dead from a sudden
heart attack. He was 43. I was 45.

I Googled John a few days after he died because I wanted to sketch an
accurate picture of his life for the mental archives, a picture with a hell of a lot
more depth than the version colored by Dad's Svengali complex. What do you
know? He *was* a prodigy, a world-class organist by the time he was in college.
Chief organist at Princeton University, and loved by the folks who attended his
temple. On a struggling-to-be-hip New Jersey news/gossip website, couples
wrote lovingly about his fantastic playing at their weddings. And then I found
a picture of John on one of the tribute websites launched by friends and
colleagues. There he was: 5'8", neat, compact, trimmed mustache. The picture

jarred me, as did remembering his diabolical laugh—think Elmer Fudd an octave lower than the voice created by Mel Blanc.

But when I was 21, he was just one of my father's stable of young organists. What a shame—for him and for me. I was just biding my time (don't frustrated heir stories always go like this?) until the day I would finally get up the guts to tell my parents I wanted no part of the organ business. My desire to move on was, to be fair, tempered by colorful adventures: the mouse in the clam chowder at a Friendly's restaurant in Massachusetts; taking the helm of a 1975 Buick LeSabre during a blinding snowstorm with no snowstorm-driving experience because Carl, Dad's foreman, wanted to review an opera libretto; the 15-foot-long plank of wood that fell from an organ chamber and smashed the bridge of my nose, leaving a dent that I still have (I continued to work, at my Dad's urging); dismantling the portico at a Presbyterian church in Connecticut with a well-placed 19-foot U-Haul (my brother at the wheel—me waving frantically in the driveway); and, yes, meeting the members of the rock groups Chicago and the Go-Go's at the Music Hall—the latter encounter coming when I was so tired that I forgot I was scared to approach them. I had my picture taken with Teri Garr (her mom was a Rockette), got knocked to the ground by hockey great Phil Esposito while trying to find a church, and toured the Mighty Wurlitzer given to the great jazz drummer Louie Bellson.

In the summer of 1984, my brother and I claimed the apartment once used by Music Hall visionary Leon Leonidoff as our office. The opulent Art Deco décor was lost on a journalist-wannabe unable to grow a decent beard and unsure about whether his tentative choice of career would save him from having to move to the ass-end of New York State.

John was kind and patient. He would try to explain his love of playing the organ to me. I love playing the drums—even though I'm still a true amateur—so we would cross emotional paths now and then, but I was so anxious for the days to end that his passion barely resonated with me. I was impressed by his ability, but my admiration lasted only until I became angry that I wasn't being afforded any time to play the drums, stuck as I was much of the time on the road fixing pipe organs. Not that I would have practiced, of course, but I liked to tell myself that I could actually become one of the musicians whose names my father dropped. That's the least the gods could do for me after my dad made me listen to that damn *Shirley MacLaine Live at the Palace* record eight million times.

"*Yes, dad, Tom Duckworth is a great drummer. Maybe I can be just like him.*"

At 14, you're not able to see that maybe Dad just liked Shirley MacLaine and was offering encouragement. You leap in your mind right to "What can I do to please you?" and then on to "What? Screw that."

So to call what I had with John a friendship would be stretching it. We were cordial to each other, but there was no depth—not typical conditions for a defining moment. But yet, on an oppressive August night, one came. John had just finished rehearsing at the Mighty Wurlitzer for one of the Music Hall's forgettable series of summer "spectaculars" or *"speck-ta-kells,"* as the Music Hall's house doctor would say in what he felt was a perfect Leonidoff accent. His high-pitched voice brought the impression closer to Mr. Chekhov from *Star Trek.* My parents were there; my mom had just come from a Rockette alumnae meeting held in the seventh-floor rehearsal hall. Discussions were ongoing about the group's annual charity ball. I often schlepped food and drink to the meetings. Dad motioned to John, and they began to walk across the Great Stage, chatting no doubt about the great future Dad was planning for him. Funny, he never put his hand on my shoulder like that.

I was sitting sullenly in the audience, reading—my escape from the job and my unwillingness to find one I actually enjoyed. I had hacked my way through *Crime and Punishment* earlier that summer, and was on to *The Trial.* I spotted my mom, who had almost caught up with my father and John. As fast as musty velvet theater seats would allow, I suddenly ran toward them, like a child, reflexively seeking love, wanting to connect. They were on their way home from work, and I was hoping for a hug.

"Ronnie, get John a cheeseburger, will you?" my dad asked curtly.

The back of a seat caught me in mid-thigh. We were all just goddamn servants to these people. He pointed a hairy finger in the general direction of the Rockefeller Center coffee shop. We ate there frequently. I marveled at how they kept pre-made hamburgers (for the lunch crowd) stacked so neatly by the grill, for easy access by the cooks and opportunistic germs. I'd dream there about finding a publisher for my unwritten novel in the adjacent Simon and Schuster Building, where Dad's friends, the Music Hall executives, spent a fleeting moment or two once a month thinking about the Mighty Wurlitzer. I would unsuccessfully ask out the youngest waitress at the shop, a short, cute Greek girl with wafting brown hair and a killer smile, after months of sharing my dating plans with Richard over lunches where my secondary goal was to convince him to actually work.

I was pissed. I glared at my father. I felt anger, rage—boiling, roiling ire. I looked at John, whose worried smile suggested he thought I might start tearing the seats from the floor. I thought of the French organist, a diminutive brunette named Marie-Claire, who used my bed (not with me in it) during her stay in America; working in smoky, dirty organ chambers since I was nine; leaving pieces of my scalp on screws and shutter frames in churches across the tri-state area because someone 6'5" should not try to arrange himself in a 3'2" space; the missed little league games; the little league game he watched from our car, an 11-strikeout, complete-game performance that culminated in a one-hop smash to the genitals (I threw out the runner at first, then collapsed in a writhing heap near the mound; Dad was one of the first to tend to me); the crop-circled crap in the basement; his "Don't hurt the pipes" warning when I cracked my head on the basement plumbing; rearranging our lives so Dad could feel important in butthole towns in upstate New York and most of New England; tending to his fake heart attacks, orchestrated so we would know how much crap life was throwing at him; the struggling business; the house, which he never lifted a finger to maintain, unless you count painting the front porch by dumping a can of battleship grey Glidden on its creaky boards and spreading it out with a push broom; shielding myself from the toaster thrown at the wall, but meant for my mother, one of the seeds of rage that to this day flower alarmingly in me out of season, frightening Sheila and my son.

I sat emphatically in the last seat in the front row, below one of the consoles. An audible "whoosh" accompanied my impact.

"No."

Not "No, I'm busy right now" or "No, I've got something to finish."

Just an unvarnished, emphatic "No."

John was polite about it. "That's all right—I can grab something later," he said sheepishly. Dad wasn't having it. He seethed right back at me. He wouldn't stand up to the organists who insisted on all-hours emergency tunings and treated him like a fucking waiter, but he'd let me have it. He took a tenuous step toward me and got out the first two syllables of his repeated request.

Another section of backbone sprouted from the cutting I had found.

"I'm tired and I want to go home."

Dad's anger subsided. False alarm. Even in his nonplussed state, he could have said "It's just around the corner" or "It'll only take a few minutes" or even "I'll buy you that new snare drum you've been wanting." No: newly composed, he instead chose to remind me of my place in the great pipe organ business food chain.

"But John's hungry—do this for me."

I don't know where my bravery came from that day—fatigue (for sure), maturity (not buying it), hatred (in part). But it came and I held my ground. I walked away from my dad, past the ancient stage manager's console, a few ambling Rockettes, past the dressing rooms, up the elevator to the stage door, past the coffee shop, through a quick mental recap of my fictional date with the waitress, on to the D train, the PATH train back to New Jersey, the Erie Lackawanna kidney buster, where I'd watch four businessmen play bridge on sections of the *New York Times* arranged to make a table-top, and home to the three-bedroom colonial and the dumpster in the front yard.

I never apologized to John for being so petulant. To this day, I don't know if he finally got something to eat. Dad probably went out and got it for him. But I'm absolutely sure I wouldn't have made it this far if I had gone to get him that cheeseburger. I wouldn't have ventured out of the cocoon that at times still restrains my family. I wouldn't have fallen passionately in love with Sheila, who endures my ranting, my fetishes, and my odd habits. I'm sorry that I didn't better appreciate his skill, didn't learn more from him, that I didn't see that he was more than just an organist whose career my dad took an interest in.

John would likely be happy that my relationship with Dad has, well, evolved. Unburdened of the need to provide guidance, he now talks to me at length; sometimes he even initiates the call. The distance that I wanted so much, then wanted desperately to bridge, now sort of works for me. They're there, I'm here—only now I wish they were here more often. Even some of the stories aren't so hard to take anymore. Dad concluded a recent chat with a speakerphone version of the "tour," direct from the family archives. It ends (as most Mom stories do) this way:

"The only advice I ever gave the two of you was to try and find one..."

Meaning women.

"...just as wonderful as your mother—as if that were possible."

And then it came...

"I love this woman more every day..."

I sarcastically mouthed my dad's words, and then said "I know Dad—every day." I surveyed the portion of my life contained that evening in our kitchen and family room. My son hummed as he gleefully flipped the pages of his favorite book, *Great Cars of the 1970s*, and Sheila, tapped into her iPod, was knitting a Cher-style poncho with attendant fringe, for my nine-year old niece. Deeply in love with both of them, I found myself staring down the still winding path toward accepting my relationship with my parents for what it is. I still try to work the family iconoclast thing to my advantage now and then, but I take solace in the hope that they now treat me as a functioning adult with his own life.

So thanks, John.

Paula Marantz Cohen

Shylock, My Students, and Me

I have been teaching literature for 30 years, and the longer I teach, the more I enjoy teaching Shakespeare. As I grow older and wearier, his plays seem to deliver greater matter and art in a more condensed and lively way than any other text I could choose. To be cliché about it: Shakespeare offers more bang for the buck.

While Shakespeare now draws me more than ever before, one work in particular draws me most. This is *The Merchant of Venice*. For me, this extraordinary play grows increasingly subtle and supple with time. It continues to excite me with its language, its depth of character, and its philosophical, political, spiritual, and pedagogical implications. Looking back over my years of teaching the play, I see that the way it has been received by my students is an index to how our society has changed. I also see how much the play continues to push against established readings and to challenge even the most seemingly enlightened perspectives. *The Merchant of Venice* is both a mirror of our times and a means of transcending the bias of our times. It teaches how to teach.

My response to the play may be connected to the nature of my career in literature. I was exposed to highbrow literary criticism in the 1970s at elite undergraduate and graduate institutions. This was a time when multiculturalism was making inroads in academia but when progressive thinking coexisted with an ingrained snobbism regarding how literature should be taught and who should teach it.

This climate of snobbish virtue that I associate with my education came into direct conflict with the hardscrabble atmosphere of my first and only major teaching job. Drexel University in Philadelphia, where I was fortunate to be hired in a shrinking job market, was primarily a commuter school with a student body of first-generation college students when I began teaching there in 1982. It had, only a few years before, been an institute of technology, and it still focused its resources on its engineering students, mostly Italian, Irish, and Polish Americans from the area's parochial schools. At the time, it was even rumored that the university's president would play golf with the local archbishop whenever he wanted to increase enrollment.

Teaching English at Drexel in the 1980s was a far cry from teaching it as a graduate student at Columbia. But still, there were some strict requirements built into the curriculum—the sort of thing, ironically enough, that had begun to go by the wayside at more elite institutions. One of these was that we teach a Shakespeare play in our freshman writing course each year. Initially, I chose one of the "big" plays: *Hamlet, Othello, Macbeth, or King Lear.* But I soon realized that students had been exposed to these blockbusters, if only in cursory fashion, in high school, and thus brought preconceptions to their reading that were hard to shake. As a result, I started to choose plays that would be new to them: *Henry IV, Part I* and *The Winter's Tale* were especially successful, for reasons that would require another essay to explore. But *The Merchant of Venice* yielded the most interesting results.

Teaching the play during these early years was daunting. I was faced with students who had had years of Catholic school training, for whom Shylock was a familiar stereotype. It did not help that I was almost invariably the only Jewish person in the classroom and, as an inexperienced teacher, uncomfortable with how much or how little I should expose about myself and my background.

But for all its challenges, teaching the play was exciting. My students were responding to it in the way that Shakespeare's audience probably did: Shylock was the villain; Portia and Bassanio the romantic leads; Antonio (the merchant of the title) the noble, long-suffering friend. My students were quick to support the plea by Portia urging Shylock to embrace mercy over justice and give up his legal right to a pound of Antonio's flesh. It made complete sense to them: Shylock's malevolence was un-Christian; his stubborn refusal to be moved by Portia's speech proof that he was incorrigible. In an effort to soften their feelings toward Shylock, I pointed them to the famous lines in Act III: "Hath not a Jew eyes? Hath not a Jew hands, organs, dimensions, senses, affections, passions?" They acknowledged the point: Shylock was, admittedly, a human being. And they were susceptible to the argument that followed:

> . . . if you wrong us [Jews], shall we not revenge? If we are like you in the rest, we will resemble you in that. If a Jew wrong a Christian, what is his humility? Revenge. If a Christian wrong a Jew, what should his sufferance be by Christian example? Why, revenge. The villainy you teach me, I will execute; and it shall go hard but I will better the instruction.

But this passage, which helped them to a better understanding of Shylock's behavior, made me uneasy. It suggested that Jews need to take their cue from "Christian example." My students found that this conformed to the maxim of their religious education: "Whatsoever a man soweth, that shall he also reap" (a principle, some of them explained, that Paul preaches in Galatians), while for me it was an argument that obliquely diminished the autonomous humanity of the Jewish character and thus fed latent anti-Semitism.

In short, for my students at the time, Shylock was unsavory, brutal, and ultimately inhumane. They could comprehend him up to a point, but they continued to insist that he was the villain, and that to say otherwise would be to twist Shakespeare's intention. I knew they were not entirely wrong—but also that their response was, in part, a cover for prejudice. I came away from teaching the play with a sense of incompleteness and unease. In the best instances, my students seemed to feel the same way, which meant that they were potentially open to seeing the world differently, if not then, at some point in the future.

That future came about 15 years later. The change was partially the result of changing demographics in my classroom. Drexel had hired a visionary new president, and the school had expanded its mission, recruiting "better" students—meaning students with higher SAT scores, which translated into students from more affluent socioeconomic backgrounds. As a corollary to this, the university extended its reach. We now began to enroll students from all over the country and even the world, and the result was more diversity: Indians, Chinese, and Russians, as well as people from other ethnicities, including a good share of African Americans and Jews. The university looked different, and the viewpoints in the classroom reflected this.

But if Drexel had changed, so had the society around it. The students who had attended parochial schools were now versed in multiculturalism. They'd celebrated Martin Luther King Day, gone to the Holocaust Museum in Washington, and considered the plight of Native Americans on Columbus Day. The trials and tribulations of otherness had filtered down to them through movies, television, and music. They'd also become sensitized to otherness in themselves, whether in the form of a learning disability, a drug problem, or some more ineffable issue that made them feel different.

In this new, more diverse and introspective atmosphere, the discussion of The Merchant of Venice began to take an entirely different turn. Before, I had had to force myself to teach the play, knowing that it would involve struggling with my students' prejudices. Now, my students began to make my job easy, saving me from apologizing for Shylock by immediately siding with him. They seemed to understand how Shylock felt. The passage that had been so central to my teaching of the play before—"Hath not a Jew eyes?"—hardly needed to be discussed. It seemed a truism.

These students were now put-off rather than convinced by Portia's speech calling for mercy. There was invariably a hoot of disbelief when she ended her plea with the conclusion: "Therefore, Jew, / Though justice be thy plea, consider this, / That, in the course of justice, none of us / Should see salvation." They were outraged by the lack of respect expressed in her generic reference to "Jew" and her assumption that Shylock shared her belief system, her idea of "salvation."

The lines that particularly inspired my students' sympathy for Shylock now were those in Act I, when he is asked to lend money to the merchant Antonio. This is where he spells out his resentment for the treatment he has suffered in the past:

> Signior Antonio, many a time and oft
> In the Rialto you have rated me
> About my moneys and my usances.
> Still have I borne it with a patient shrug;
> For sufferance is the badge of all our tribe.
> You call me misbeliever, cut-throat dog,
> And spit upon my Jewish garberdine,
> And all for use of that which is mine own.
> Well then, it now appears you need my help:
> Go to, then, you come to me, and you say
> "Shylock, we would have moneys." You say so,
> You, that did void your rheum upon my beard,
> And foot me as you spurn a stranger cur
> Over your threshold. Moneys is your suit.
> What should I say to you? Should I not say
> "Hath a dog money? Is it possible
> A cur can lend three thousand ducats"? or
> Shall I bend low, and in a bondman's key,
> With bated breath and whispering humbleness,
> Say this:
> "Fair sir, you spit on me on Wednesday last;
> You spurned me such a day; another time
> You called me dog; and for these courtesies
> I'll lend you thus much moneys"?

It is difficult for me to relay the sort of response this speech now evoked from my students. They heard Shylock's voice in these lines—and it was their own. I was shocked to see the number of students who claimed to have been treated like a "stranger cur"—a dog. The well of resentment here, often going back to grade-school bullying, was deep and abiding for these 18- and 19-year-olds. I was initially mystified by their reaction. Why, as schools had become more adept at teaching cultural sensitivity, did students still manage not only to suffer ostracism but also to feel its effects so palpably? This might lead to the conclusion that teaching sensitivity is not useful, that it may, indeed, be harmful. My eventual view, however, was different. I concluded that in the past the pain of ostracism and alienation went unacknowledged; people pretended they didn't feel hurt because they didn't want to show weakness. Now, they had gained a voice and a vocabulary with which to express their feelings.

What was clear was that these students felt sympathy for Shylock—and more than that, they identified with him to the point that they supported his case. And here is where things began to get complicated. Because now the most powerful speech in the play, according to my students, was Shylock's in Act IV, Scene I, that deals first with the hypocrisy of his antagonists and then with the justice of his claim:

> What judgement shall I dread, doing no wrong?
> You have among you many a purchased slave,
> Which, like your asses and your dogs and mules
> You use in abject and in slavish parts,
> Because you bought them. Shall I say to you,
> Let them be free, marry them to your heirs?
> Why sweat they under burthens? Let their beds
> Be made as soft as yours, and let their palates
> Be seasoned with such viands? You will answer
> "The slaves are ours": so do I answer you:
> The pound of flesh, which I demand of him,
> Is dearly bought. 'Tis mine and I will have it.
> If you deny me, fie upon your law!

The realization by my students that this was a slave-owning society opened the play to another level of dismay. They now began to look upon the so-called heroes—Bassanio, Portia, and Antonio—as world-class hypocrites. How dare these characters accuse Shylock of inhumanity when they owned slaves? Even as they expressed outrage at this, they also embraced the other aspect of Shylock's argument here: his right to his pound of flesh. In short, they argued for his right to kill Antonio as a matter of simple justice.

It became clear to me that my current students were hardening into positions in reverse of what my former students had felt, and that, in some ways, their views were equally limited—and maybe even scarier. For all their sensitivity, these students missed what the earlier students, despite their ingrained prejudices, had grasped: that justice according to the law is a human construction and thus subject to human manipulation. One need not be Christian or even a believer to see this. The play demonstrates that justice is manipulable when Portia uses the very law that Shylock has invoked on his own behalf to strip him of his wealth and his religion. Trusting to legal justice, the play teaches, can only take one so far, and may very well result in flagrant injustice.

Moreover, the tendency of my current students to reverse the judgment of earlier readers and viewers of the play struck me as disturbing. Now, Shylock became the heroic central figure, and the other characters became villains: Bassanio weak and opportunistic; Antonio passive and creepy; Portia mean.

The initial notion that my job had become easy, since I no longer had to defend Shylock, began to change as I realized that the all-encompassing, reflexive sympathy my students felt for him was perhaps even more insidiously wrong than the earlier prejudice toward him. In an odd reversal, I, the Jewish teacher, now became the only person in the classroom to argue that Shylock was still a villain, despite the abuse he had suffered, and that his stubborn call for a pound of flesh was the emblem of his villainy.

Teaching the play in recent years, I also began concentrating discussion on Portia and Antonio. Was Portia's subjection to her dead father's will and her need to dress as a man in order to argue the case connected to her "meanness"—her stripping Shylock of his money and forcing him to convert? As for Antonio, what was to be construed from his confused feelings at the beginning of the play?

> In sooth, I know not why I am so sad:
> It wearies me; you say it wearies you;
> But how I caught it, found it, or came by it,
> What stuff 'tis made of, whereof it is born,
> I am to learn;
> And such a want-wit sadness makes of me,
> That I have much ado to know myself.

My students generally deduced that Antonio was "in love" with Bassanio. But what to make of the fact that he was no more able to acknowledge his homosexuality as a character than Shakespeare could spell out his problem in writing the play? What kind of alienation and loneliness, what kind of morbid depression, might ensue from this sort of profound silencing? Like my earlier students, who drew a line regarding their sympathy for Shylock, my students now did the same with regard to these characters. They could see my argument only up to a point. They refused to equate the difficulties facing people of wealth and position with the hardships facing a social pariah like Shylock. But wasn't the silencing of Portia and Antonio as likely to result in their "acting out" and behaving cruelly to people who existed more explicitly on the margins than themselves? (These characters resembled, it occurred to me, my students from years before, who had shown no sympathy for Shylock in part because they were not prepared—or allowed—to acknowledge their own weakness or alienation.) As I saw it, Portia had diagnosed her own condition in Act I: "It is a good divine that follows his own instructions: I can easier teach twenty what were good to be done, than to be one of the twenty to follow mine own teaching." But my students found this statement lame and disingenuous. They couldn't excuse her intolerance, and believed they would never be so blind—even as their intolerance toward her belied this.

Nonetheless, the question of how those who have been abused can become abusers themselves sparked animated discussion. Students were able to discern the repetition of destructive behavior in families, and some students also proceeded to draw parallels between Shylock and the government of Israel—the children of persecution becoming persecutors in their own right. The latter comparison—that struck me as both upsetting and insightful—never occurred to my students 25 years ago, both because their view of Shylock was too uninflected to permit it and because the political situation in the Middle East had not developed (or been explored) to a point where that reading was possible.

In the end, I found myself urging students to consider the play's concluding structure. Bassanio and Portia are united happily; Shylock has been purged; Antonio, spared death, remains on the margins. Are we to ignore this ending and replace it with our own psychologically enlightened viewpoint? Is it valid to read beyond the text and project, for example, an unhappy marriage for Bassanio and Portia, a suicide for Antonio, and a new plot for revenge from the even more wronged Shylock—a terrorist in the making, if there ever was one?

Some students were adamant in saying that such speculation is encouraged in the text. Others, that the ending simply reflects Shakespeare's need to pander to his audience and their prejudices. My own position is that, if we want a happy ending, at some point we must draw a line and close our eyes to the injustices that it entails. We must accept accommodation to oppression and, in some cases, to evil itself. A happy ending is only an approximate good, pointing beyond itself to a time when happy endings will be happy for all the deserving, and evil will be fully recognized and purged. My students in the old days would have called this The Last Judgment. My students today are likely to call it wishful thinking.

Ingrid G. Daemmrich

From Recorders to Researchers: First-Term University Students' Testing of Journal-Writing as a Medium for Stress Relief

54 students enrolled in three first-term college composition courses in 2000 assumed the double roles of experimental subjects and critical assessors by testing Smyth et al.'s finding that writing about stressful situations has positive emotional and mental effects. Nearly three quarters reported short-term relief, and nearly half, long-term mental or emotional improvement by recording in their personal journal the stresses of being a first-term student. Would the social networking sites on the Internet today provide the same relief as the personal journal? Or does private writing still serve an important function?

From ancient times to the present, writers, scientists, and just ordinary folk have turned to diaries, journals, and notebooks as a useful medium to record and reflect on events, as well as to explore personal and professional insights. The resulting texts range from Anne Frank's intimate diary describing her family's daily life and her nascent emotions while hiding from the Nazis to Thomas Edison's 3,500 notebooks recording in vivid words and drawings his inventive notions, as well as such off-hand scribblings as "My wife Dearly Beloved Cannot invent worth a Damn!!" (McAuliffe 81). In arguing for assigning journal-writing in writing courses, compositional theorists identify the journal as "a place to try out . . . first ideas, to make connections, to construct . . . knowledge" (Gardner and Fulwiler 3) and as a private medium for novice writers to experiment with narrative structures, or "to experience themselves as intellectual beings" (92) and gain "metacognitive awareness" (Feathers and White 264).

Approximately a decade ago, researchers began discussing a new function for journal-keeping: its role as stress-reliever. In a number of studies, Joshua Smyth, James Pennebaker, and others tested the relationship between writing and emotional, mental, and physical health. Specifically, they compared an experimental group of subjects who wrote 15-20 minute essays three times a week for one to four weeks about extremely traumatic events in their lives with a control group who wrote the same number of essays about non-traumatic events. Psychological and physical examinations before and after the experiment, followed by statistical analyses, determined that experimental subjects significantly improved their physical and emotional health when compared with the control group. A number of explanations were offered. Perhaps writing about stressful events had the same therapeutic effect as talking through a trauma with a therapist? Or was it the narratological aspect of the essays that accrued such significant benefits? Could it be that writers improved their mental and physical health because the essay form required them to organize their memories of traumas into "good" stories? When Smyth teamed up with another psychologist and two physicians, one specializing in pulmonary medicine, the other in rheumatoid arthritis, to study the "effects of writing about stressful experiences on symptom reduction in patients with asthma or rheumatoid arthritis," their report of positive findings in the 1999 *Journal of the American Medical Association* attracted widespread interest. Newspapers and magazines around the nation proclaimed that "writing can help with just about anything that causes stress and anxiety—anger, depression, even weight loss" (Kelly 70). For stress relief, proclaimed *JAMA* commentator David Spiegel, write a journal.

But is writing a journal as effective as writing essays? Smyth and Pennebaker doubt it. They argue that the lack of structure of the typical diary or journal entry "may impede the beneficial process" (Smyth et al 84). Their assertion offers the opportunity for a project for first-term composition students: keep a journal in which to write informally about the stresses of being a first-term college student, and then evaluate whether it actually reduces stress. If given total control over the content of their private journals, would they concur or contradict Smyth and Pennebaker? I hypothesized that a significant number of my 54 composition students in the fall of 2000 would—in contradiction to Smyth and Pennebaker—report a positive correlation between journal-keeping and stress reduction.

To test my hypothesis, I designed a study that asked students to assume the twin roles of experimental subjects and critical evaluators of both their journal entries and Smyth and Pennbaker's negative appraisal of informal journal writing. The first step was to collect the data. So students were directed to start and keep a journal for two purposes: to record at least twice a week both stressful and non-stressful events and experiences in their personal, academic, and social life, and to brainstorm and problem solve for specific writing assignments for the course. These two goals reflect the differing assignments given by Smyth et al. to the experimental and control groups in their 1999 *JAMA* article. The 71 participants in their experimental group were to "write about the most stressful experience that they had ever undergone," while the 41 patients in the control group were to "describe their plans for the day" (Smyth et al. 1305). The purpose for our project was left intentionally vague until two weeks before the final paper was due. At that point, students read and discussed Smyth et al.'s 1999 JAMA article, "Effects of Writing about Stressful Experiences on Symptom Reduction in Patients with Asthma or Rheumatoid Arthritis," along with Spiegel's accompanying commentary, "Healing Words. Emotional Expression and Disease Outcome" (Smyth et al).

I then asked the students to examine their own journals. Presumably, the majority did not suffer from asthma or arthritis. But did their first term experiences, as recorded in their journals, include stressful occurrences? Did writing about them improve their emotional, mental, or even physical well-being? Or was there no change? Maybe even an increase of stress when writing about stressful events? I also pointed out three important differences between our study and Smyth et al's.

First, our project would only run for ten weeks, not the four months that Smyth et al. covered. Second, in contrast to Smyth et al.'s carefully monitored experiment, my student-subjects determined when, where, what, and how they wrote. The only criterion was that they were to record events, stressful and non-stressful, as well as brainstorm for paper topics at least twice a week in their journals. Third, in their role of critical evaluator, they were to write an essay that supported or contradicted Smyth et al. and Spiegel by assessing their emotional and mental condition before, during, and after their journal-writing. Their conclusions would therefore be subject to the oft-noted weaknesses and strengths of self-reporting.

On the one hand, there would be a lack of the hard evidence gained by the objective measures recorded in the four clinical examinations of Smyth et al.'s asthmatic and rheumatic subjects. On the other, by collecting data from 54 reporter-researchers, we might be able to chart just how many reported finding relief from stress and note as well where, when, and how they had individually found stress reduction through journal-writing. There would be three positive outcomes. First, backed by their assessment of the evidence in their journals, they would with confidence contradict or sustain the assertions made by professionals. Second, they would be able to contribute to scientific research, and third, they might acquire a useful stress relief technique to use in the future.

Interestingly, despite significant differences in experimental goals and design, my students' self-reported results were remarkably close to those reported by Smyth et al. Smyth et al. had reported that of 70 experimental patients, 33 or 47.8% showed "clinically relevant improvement," compared with 9 or 24.3% of the patients in the control group. Out of 54 subject-evaluators in my classes, 25 or 48.3% reported positive mental and/or emotional relief in writing their journals. Eight members (14.3%) reported experiencing temporary relief in writing their journals, but also a return of stress when not writing. (This variable was not included in Smyth et al.'s report.) Ten members (18.5%) experienced an increase in stress by writing about stressful situations. Four members (7.4%) reported feeling neither stress nor relief in writing about stress events. Three members (5.5%) did not find any data in their writings about stress. They compared themselves to Smyth et al.'s control group. Two

(3.7%) reported medical problems that would have excluded them from Smyth et al.'s study, and one member reported a temporary increase in anxiety while writing about stressful events, followed by an ultimate reduction after "getting it off my back and onto paper."

Even more enlightening were individual student comments. Those who found relief while writing journal entries supported their stand with insightful self-assessments such as: "If I have anxiety, I simply pick up a pen and start relieving my stress by writing. I am completely in control over what I write and my feelings. No one can dictate how you feel or what you're writing when you write a journal." And: "When you start to write what's in your head, your problem seems to unfold right in front of you." Several saw journal-writing as a means to solve stress-producing problems: "Writing in the journal allowed me to picture the thoughts on paper instead of them being jumbled in my head." And: "[...] to sort through my thoughts and emotions to eventually find a solution." And: "After writing in my journal for a semester, I found that I could figure out events in my life and it also released built-up tensions."

Contradicting Smyth and Pennebaker's speculation that a coherent narrative, a "good" story, is essential for stress relief, several students reported that the unlimited freedom of being able to write whatever, whenever, and however they pleased provided much more stress relief than did assigned essays. They contrasted the stress provoked by assigned essays, burdened with requirements and due dates, with the informality of free-writing in a journal, which they equated with talking to a friend. One student who experienced severe family problems even stated: "Without writing in my journal, I do not know if I could make it through each day." Another compared the comfort of discussing a problem privately in his journal with the discomfort of discussing it with others: "Instead of turning to a friend and discussing the issue in long detail, I can just turn to myself and let everything flow, knowing that my thoughts are mine alone."

Those students who contradicted Smyth et al.'s positive correlation between writing and stress reduction supported their view with equally informative comments. This was particularly true of those who found only temporary relief. One evaluator remarked that writing about stressful experiences, while providing a momentary respite, merely pushed back problems to be dealt with later: "What kind of help can a piece of paper really offer anyway? It cannot give advice or logically evaluate the situation." Another reported that though she felt better after writing about her anxiety caused by missing scholarship funds, the next day, "I was plagued with the virus of uncertainty." Other students discovered that writing about stress only increased it. One found that his anger intensified after writing about his stress; another, that as the term progressed, so did his anxiety: "... it has gotten to the point that just writing about stress freaks me out." A student who disclosed a learning disability that made it difficult to write intelligently questioned Smyth et al.'s protocol to exclude subjects who were unable to write for the prescribed twenty minutes: "To make their study more effective, Smyth et al. should have had more a variety of people." Many students came to the logical conclusion that further studies stretching beyond the term would be needed to test whether the results were indeed temporary or permanent.

By ending their papers with a call for further studies, the student-evaluators demonstrated that they had gained a number of important outcomes. First, they showed their understanding of academic research as an ongoing activity in which each new study builds on the conclusions of its predecessors by introducing new variables and testing them, just as they had done as a group. Instead of following Smyth et al.'s division of subjects into experimental and control groups, they had all become experimental subjects. Their test would not be whether physical ailments such as asthma or arthritis had been measurably improved by writing twenty-minute essays but whether they had experienced relief by writing informally in their journals about stress, and whether that relief continued beyond the moment of writing. Collectively, their individual evaluations could form a statistical analysis that curiously ended up echoing Smyth et al.'s findings, despite being based on new variables, including one that contradicted Smyth and Pennebaker's assertion that because journal-writing is less coherent, it would be a less reliable medium to reduce stress.

Second, by playing the double roles of recorders and critics, students learned to value journal-writing as a medium to gain insight and control not only over stressful situations but also over the ability to express themselves. Often this occurred serendipitously. After critically assessing his journal, one student discovered that by writing about the stress caused by the mediocre grades that he had received for previously assigned essays, he had acquired a new ability to express himself. Another analyzed a remarkable change in vocabulary in her journal-writing about stress: ". . . in week 1, my vocabulary consisted mainly of depressing words such as 'loneliness,' 'fear,' 'unhappiness,' and 'worrying.' The second week journal entries included the words 'getting better,' 'hopefully,' and 'I'm learning to cope' . . . by the third week, . . . the words 'relief,' 'confident,' and 'everything is okay now' saturated my personal journal." Their recognition that gaining expressiveness in writing aids in stress reduction echoes more recent research that reported a positive correlation between expressive writing and coping with distress or disease (Largo-Marsh and Spates; Smith et al.; Creswell et al.; Barry et al.).

Third, students' use of their personal journals as evidence for assessing the validity of professional researchers' assertions brings to life the elasticity of writing as a means of communication. If we adopt Webster's definition of a medium as "that through which anything is accomplished," we can conclude that writing as a medium spans an enormous range starting with writing private journal entries about personal stresses and ending up with a critical analysis about the potential benefits of keeping a journal that adds to the ongoing professional discussion on writing as a stress-reducer. In the intervening decade, the Internet has opened up new media for both keeping a journal and critically assessing it. The global accessibility of blogging sites such as LiveJournal.com, Blogger.com, or WordPress.com and social networking sites such as Facebook, MySpace, or Twitter offers new paradigms that transgress the traditional boundaries between the private journal and public discussion that operated in our study. Transferred to the networking capacity of the Internet, our project's two distinct activities become one continuous flow oscillating between recording and critically assessing data and between the personal and the public.

Will these new media provide more relief from stress because the private journal becomes open to others' comments, as reported by Atkinson et al. (2009)? Or will they create a new and perhaps dangerous level of anxiety when others are invited to interact with private experiences and emotions? Even more provocatively: will the fluidity encouraged by social networking result in our exchanging our private selves for a series of "masks" contingent on our interaction with others, as suggested by Kreps (2010)? Only a new study by participants willing to play the double role of recorder and critical reporter can answer these questions.

Works Cited

Atkinson, R., Hare, T, Merriman, M., and Vogel, A. "Therapeutic benefits of expressive writing in an electronic format." *Nursing Administration Quarterly* 33 (3(2009)): 212-215.

Barry, L.M., Hudley, C., Kelly, M., and Cho, S.-J. "Differences in self-reported disclosure of college experiences by first-generation college student status." *Adolescence* 44 (173(2009)): 55-69.

Creswell, J.D., Lam, S., Stanton, A.L., Taylor, S.E., Bower, J.E., and Sherman, D.K. "Does self-affirmation, cognitive processing, or discovery of meaning explain cancer-related health benefits of expressive writing?" *Personality and Social Psychology Bulletin* 33 (2(2007)): 238-251.

Feathers, K.M., and White, J.H. "Learning to learn: case studies of the process." *Reading Research and Instruction* 26(4(1987)): 264-274.

Gardner, S., and Fulwiler, T. *The Journal Book*. Portsmouth: Boyton/Cook, 1999. Print.

Kelly, A. L. "Write Away." *Shape* May 2000: 70-71. Print.

Kreps, D. "My social networking profile: copy, resemblance, or simulacrum? A poststructuralist interpretation of social information systems." *European Journal of Information Systems* 19 (1(2010)): 104-115.

Largo-Marsh, L., and Spates, C.R. "The effects of writing therapy in comparison to EMD/R on traumatic stress: The relationship between hypnotizability and client expectance to outcome." *Professional Psychology: Research and Practice* 33 (6(2002)): 581-586.

McAuliffe, K. "The undiscovered world of Thomas Edison." *The Atlantic Monthly* 276 (1995): 80-93.

Smith, S., Anderson-Hanley, C., Langrock, A., and Compas, B. "The effects of journaling for women with newly diagnosed breast cancer." *Psycho-Oncology* 14 (12(2005)): 1075-1082.

Smyth, J.M, Stone, A.A., Hurewitz, A., and Kaell, A. "Effects of writing about stressful experiences on symptom reduction in patients with asthma and rheumatoid arthritis." *Journal of the American Medical Society* 281 (1999): pp. 1304-1309.

Smyth, J.M. and J.W. Pennebaker. "Sharing One's Story: Translating emotional experiencesinto words as a coping tool." Coping: *The psychology of what works*. Ed. C.R. Snyder. New York: Oxford Press, 1999.

Spiegel, D. "Healing Words: Emotional expression and disease outcome."*Journal of the American Medical Society* 281 (1999): 1328-1329.

Wapner, J. "The Healthy Type: The therapeutic value of blogging becomes a focus of study." *Scientific American* 298 (2008): 32.

Albert DiBartolomeo
Double Life

I'd been hanging doors for my brother in the trapezoidal doorframes of his old house, and sawdust clung to my clothing and had even found its way into my hair. Earlier in the day, I had contorted myself into the tiny cabinet space beneath the kitchen sink to fix a leak, and I had run a string of receptacles in the basement. My sweaty tee shirt and tattered jeans were dirty and a cut on my knuckle had crusted over with dried blood—not exactly the way I looked on campus.

But my appearance was nothing new or unusual to me. I always do home renovation or repair of one sort or another between semesters and on weekends, and it often leaves me smudged and sometimes scarred. I'm not complaining; I like the work, always have, and I'm pretty good at it. Maybe this goes back to my early schooling.

In ninth grade, my aptitude test scores indicated that I might best be served by learning the electrical trade—it was clear that I would never be a neurosurgeon or a CPA—and throughout my last three years of high school I took two weeks of "shop" every month and the balance studying the usual liberal arts courses. I wound up preferring shop to class, and didn't mind studying more about voltage than mitochondria. But when the SATs rolled around, I didn't do so well, and my college choices were limited. On the other hand, I knew how to wire a house, which has proven more useful over the years than identifying the innards of a frog.

My first summer job was as a laborer with a construction company that built townhouses in New Jersey where my stepfather worked. The job introduced me more intimately to the building trades and, more importantly, I realized later, to the men who worked at them. Most were masters at their trade, incredibly skilled and efficient, and deeply knowledgeable about what they did. They also had skill in the trades outside their specialty, having learned from watching one another, as I learned something about plumbing while helping my stepfather with "side jobs" on the weekends.

I was impressed by the confidence the men had in what their skills could always be counted on to supply: a means of making a buck and, what is perhaps more important, the ability to "do for yourself." I came to realize this, too, at certain points in my life when I was laid off or simply needed more income and worked weekends or summers as a handyman to get it, or when I found the need to build bookcases or repair some trouble in the apartment or house I was living in.

Although the construction workers and men like them that I've met since prized hand skill, they were virtually unanimous about the value of college and the affluence it promised. They wanted their children to go to college and worked hard toward that goal. They advised me to go when I began to waver after the superintendent on the construction site saw something in me and offered to groom me as his assistant. It was a tempting offer, but I attended college that fall, and eventually went on to graduate school. I learned a bit about literature but I never stopped working with my hands.

This seems to make me an oddity at the university, where I teach English. When I mention that I had spent the weekend putting in a skylight, say, or tiling a bathroom floor, my colleagues often look at me in bafflement or awe, as though I'd just climbed Mount Everest. They can't quite reconcile the professor me with the guy who routinely uses hand and power tools to do a wide variety of tasks. For my part, I'm amazed that most of them, and other of my white collar friends, have little, if any, manual skill, nor much interest in acquiring any.

Perhaps this is a financial calculation and nothing more. Why spend time learning a hand skill when the time can be more profitably spent in some other manner? Makes sense, I suppose, until the drywall is damaged or the lighting begins to blink and individuals like some of my colleagues have to bumble through a repair attempt or call someone, hoping for the best in terms of cost and good, honest workmanship. I wonder if they see themselves when the clueless male in a TV sitcom or film smashes a big hole in the wall when trying to hang a picture or who nearly electrocutes himself while tinkering with a faulty toaster. I hate to think so. Knowledge of Shakespeare or the law is a wonderful thing, but so is the ability to change out the works in a toilet tank, an uncomplicated job that takes an hour, an hour for which a plumber would charge about $100.

A few weeks after completing the renovations on my brother's house, I visited him and, looking at his new heater, noticed that the vent pipe to the flue was missing; luckily, it was the summer and he and his family weren't asphyxiated. He simply didn't know there was a problem, and I'm certain that he's in a vast company of homeowners ignorant of even basic handyman skills—to the peril of their health or their wallets.

I rolled up my sleeves.

Leonard Finegold

My Penultimate Crematory Visit

At a party, I was asked "Have you done anything out of the usual since we last met?" I was about to mutter my usual "nothing much," and then remembered I'd visited a crematorium. My friend admitted this was unusual and worth hearing. This is the story of my penultimate visit to a crematorium—we were fortunate, for many people visit but once. It came about because the board of the Funeral Consumer Alliance (on which I serve) regularly visits the funeral homes they list. I had never been on one of these visits, and I volunteered—with some trepidation (for I didn't know what to expect)—for the next one, which was to a crematorium. It was truly memorable.

My dictionary says that "crematory" is from the Latin "To consume by fire, to burn; specifically to reduce (a corpse) to ashes." The crematory is a separate building in the Ivy Hill Cemetery; there is also a chapel on the site. We were met by Superintendent Dave Drysdale, in a rectangular reception hall with seats for perhaps a hundred people. He explained, at length, the many laws and procedures which control how a body is brought to the crematorium, that these laws can vary within states and even counties. I suspect that these evolved to make it awkward for someone (for example, Mafiosi) to bring a body for cremation, inadvertently forgetting to inform the authorities. We heard the protocols for rigorous identification of the remains, from entrance to exit, which ensure that it's the correct body. Each body is given individual service.

Our questions, which were often piercing, were answered well. Why cremate? Cremation is popular among many religions, and I recalled that some faiths have been doing it for millennia. Apparently many people like cremation because "it is clean and natural," like a refiner's fire. Recently, cremation has become more popular, partly due to lack of land.

After a while, we were invited to see the crematorium. I expected to go outside to another part of the building. Instead, behind where a speaker might hold the memorial service, a curtain which I'd ignored was drawn back, and—to my surprise—the crematorium proper was immediately behind. The oven looked so familiar, that one of the group asked if pizzas were ever cooked in there. There were a great deal of controls and temperature measuring equipment to automatically run the process.

I had wondered if the mercury fillings in my teeth would be a pollution problem. This is answered by the "afterburner," a wondrously beautiful flame that oxidizes all gases, so that the resulting pollution is negligible. (Afterwards, we agreed that this flame was the most impressive item of our visit.) The flame is natural gas.

We came across large (seven feet long, two feet wide, about a foot deep) open cardboard trays, in which a body is placed prior to being wheeled into the ovens. During a cremation, some people wish to see this wheeling phase, and Ivy Hill arranges it. (We have a photograph of one of our group trying the tray for size.) After cremation, the bones basically crumble, and (after careful archival-quality labeling and comminution) the ashes are put into a robust inert plastic container, which will stay intact for centuries. The overall cleanliness and tidiness were close to that of a restaurant.

The staff and surroundings (including the people and things that visitors would not see) were sedate, respectful and comforting. The surroundings were also pleasant—not at all dismal. Ivy Hill could be the crematory *crème de la crème*. Unusually, it is a not-for-profit organization, so on first seeing the ".org" in their electronic address, I was immediately favorably disposed. We had quite free access behind the scenes, and could take photos freely. Our ex-funeral director commented that Ivy Hill was perhaps the best crematorium around. It was a gift, from the crematorium, to have the opportunity to see something so unusual.

Valerie Fox

Manifesto

I can't walk and look in windows at the same time
I lined a shoebox with photographs of the hot-air balloon and put a hole in it

For Reflection
What personal experiences have you had with hot-air balloons? How does
that influence how you read this poem? Do you think about this balloon
often? Never? Why?

For Writing
Do you still consider this poem a poem, even though it is called a manifesto?
Compare and contrast this "manifesto" to other examples of this form.

For Lifelong Learning
From now on, every time you notice yourself looking into lit-up windows at
night, try to note what tv programs people are watching. Assuming these
people have got nothing better to do, burst through their door (or window) in
the guise of your favorite character from *The Wizard of Oz.*

For More Comparison
Compare the points of view in the first two stanzas.

Concerning Imagery
Why do you suppose the author lined a "shoebox with photographs" as
opposed to say, a breadbox with paper money? Does bringing in a visual
art form reveal a deep, psychological sense of doubt concerning the ability
of the literary mode, on its own, to suffice in revealing the emotion of the
moment(s) portrayed in the poem?

For More Writing
Where is the emotion here? Where does it reside? Does it reside anywhere?
What kind of emotions can an author such as this feel? Do you wish the
author had written something different, or nothing at all?

In Aristotelian Terms
Consider the spectacle here.

And What If
You turned the page and saw something else:
How can a child disappear, just like that?

Valerie Fox, collaboration with Arlene Ang

We Wrote a Letter to Jesus and He Told Us to Buy a New Car

There were sinister red marks on the dog where its hair came off

I had just moved back to the city after having been away for three years at school

It was around the same time I went out on a blind date with someone and dropped my keys under the bar at the Villa de Roma

Although I had no money I had several typewriters

In our childhood, we were all victims of DDT

I kept wiping my mouth on parts of the table napkin that I hadn't soiled with my lipstick

The more I learned about my driving from rude strangers, the more I understood extinction

It seemed like everyone back then was making a film using one of those toy video cameras Fisher Price had come out with

On the ground, an egg sandwich absorbed the rain and disintegrated down the gutter

The sound of the CAT scan was just gaining prominence, getting louder and louder with each passing season

Poor as I was, I had friends with less

The museum was free on Sundays but I had to buy them coffee and once, a tuna melt

Since that day at the beach my digestive tract began to exist outside of my body

In the back of our heads somewhere—voices of our great-grandparents speaking in German, comfortable in their lonesome canal-town

The new car turned out to be a rainy-blue '64 Buick Skylark with taped-on plastic material for the rear view mirror instead of glass

The way I'm lighting all these candles to save electricity makes me a real fire hazard

A lot of pretending goes into the appearance of water and electricity

For larks, we used to pretend we were courtiers, and our dog was of the 5th rank

I documented many aspects of our lives, but not our dog's

Fifteen years later I remember the look of the crowd but not what the speaker said

Once I start listing them I can remember hundreds of these crowds

That must mean something

I see plenty of famous people (celebrities) around town but I forget them within seconds

Dear Me, I used to start a lot of letters that way

One conversation stands out, on a beach in Atlantic City

We had nicknames for everyone both consequential and inconsequential

I got a bit of advice from sisterly types about what to do about my name at the neighborhood bar

We heard people spray graffiti on the side of our house and it wasn't even that late

Homes were sinking too, there were sinkholes

The whole time everything was happening I kept trying to find words to describe our own small, austere circumstance

Dogs woke us up early each and every day

It was alright to waste our time as long as we could choose how to waste it

Maria Hnaraki

We Speak What We Eat:
My Big Fat Greek Language

"A hungry bear does not dance..."

Greeks do not spend but eat time. They eat their years studying and working, but also their liver, when they try hard to achieve what they want. Greeks eat their words, when they forget, are stressed or say fat lies. They eat rain, when wet, their moustaches, when they intensively argue, their tongues, when they do not mean what they just said, cabbage and straw, when they easily believe, and noodles, when the ones they love set them aside. They may even eat you as onion stew, unless they like you so much, and thus crave for you.

Greek clocks do not waste but eat minutes. Greek noses, when curious, eat you. If Greek hands are hungry, you will soon get money, or be beaten. In Greece, too much work does not harm but eats you; you are not being scolded but eaten, you are not getting a boot but being eaten or even... eating wood (namely, getting beaten with a stick), your head is not itching, but eating, and you are not searching thoroughly but you are eating the world, hoping you won't be eaten by the woodworm. Not only do you have to be aware of eating someone with your eyes, but also not forget that getting older you are actually eating your own bread.

Ancient Greeks seemed to know the dialectics between language and food. Pindar offered food via his poetry, and thought of his lyric works as refreshing drinks and his melodies sounding sweet as honey. Several literary species in classical Greece were expressed via cooking metaphors: satyr was the "sampler dish" whereas the farce functioned as an interlude, "stuffing" amidst a serious performance. The general idea was that both books and men of letters were technicians producing pleasant mixtures for the mouth or the mind so as to satisfy the hunger of the word-eaters (lexifágos).

For Ancient Greeks, "the beginning and the root of each good was the pleasure of the abdomen," or, as Greeks today say, even "love goes through the stomach." The ancient Greek "table" became the word for the Modern Greek "bank" (trápeza). Greeks still speak of the Epicurean feast, a sumptuous meal, and the Meal of Luculus. They recall the famous symposia, the thirty

Sophists who sat around a dinner table to discuss a wide range of topics in the *Banquet of Scholars* by Athenaeus and "the dining philosophers problem," which combine learning with...eating.

A central life concept, time (hrónos), is a word which etymologically relates to Kronos (Krónos). According to mythology, Kronos was the rather unaffectionate father of Zeus, who ate his children, in an effort to give himself more authority time. The great tragic poets of Greece attributed to Zeus adjectives such as caterer (trofodótis), alimentary (trofónios), fructuous (epikárpios), of the apples (milósios) and of the figs (sikásios). In addition, the word diet (díaita) stems from the Greek name for Zeus, namely, Días. Even the word nutrition, *diatrofí*, is a composite of the words *Días* and *trofí*, thus, Zeus and food. In that context, nutrition is the proper diet, the one Zeus had, that consisting of dittany tea (díktamo), honey (méli) and goat milk (gála).

Greek words may be sweet as sugar coming out of a mouth as a river of honey. They may be silent as a fish or as a pillar of salt, or calm as yogurt. When Greeks speak rudely, elders put pepper on their tongues. But when they get angry, they need to swallow vinegar. "Good appetite!" "To your health!" and "Good digestion!" are frequently used expressions in Greek, absent from English. In a country where hospitality is lavish, village rules deem that one who enters the coffeehouse must treat those already present.

In Greek, "language" and "tongue" are one word: "glóssa." "In the beginning was the Word," the "lógos," something born in the mouth. The Annunciation is nothing else but a verbal conception: As the Virgin Mary absorbs the words of the Holy Ghost, she becomes pregnant, and gives birth to Christ. Words, thus, using the human body and brain as transportation vessels, are getting into the mouth, down the larynx to the pharynx and the esophagus, to be devoured and assimilated.

A closer look at the anatomy of the body tells us that Greek men have the Adam's apple whereas Greek women continuously complain about their little breads and not... love handles. In general, Greeks grow almond trees instead of tonsils whereas they may get barley on their eyes (but not a sty). In their brains they have almonds—not cerebellums, and on their skin olives—not spots.

In the Greek worldview, bread (psomí, ártos) is a symbol of continuity and healthy life. Greeks pray for the daily bread. A Greek in a relationship is mature or convinced because he has been baked. To earn money, Greeks are making their own bread, sometimes even through sweating. Procrastinating is not blending the bread ingredients but keep sifting. The hungry dream of bread loaves, and may even eat the tablecloth, whereas the greedy want both the dog fed and the pie untouched.

Synaesthetically, Cretans "hear" the smell, and Greeks "flavor" colors: tints may be of the rotten apple, the orange, the carrot, the eggplant, the cabbage, the plum and the fish; the green of the olive, the cabbage and the pistachio; the brown of the chocolate, the hazelnut, the coffee and the cinnamon; the white of the milk; the cherry red; the yellow of the lemon, the corn and the honey. When sunburned, a Greek looks like a dark-fired frying pan or pot.

Greek wine (krasí) is the nectar of gods. At the sounds of traditional music, Greeks open their wine barrels to festively honor saints (such as Saint George the Inebriant) or merely to socialize and have fun. The grape (stafíli) is a symbol of fertility. "Wine and children speak the truth," a Greek proverb says, whereas—inspired by the Aesop fable—"the grapes the fox cannot reach it calls them sour." Ancient Greeks rarely drank wine waterless. Thus, *krasí* stands literally for wine mixed with water and the phrase "I put water in my wine" means compromising. Lastly, to a Greek, *oínopas póntos*, what Homer called the "wine-dark sea," makes perfect sense.

Greece's ethnic identity is recognized in its language. Bean soup is Greece's national food. When beans insist on being raw, they behave like the country's old-time enemies, the Turks. During Lent, bean soup reminds Greeks of sacrifice and restraint. This legume may be giant (gígantes) or black-eyed (mavromátika). Another legume, yellow split peas (fáva), may get married when mixed with onion and tomato, and, if you mash it and make a hole in its middle, then be careful, because there might be something wrong in your life.

Speaking of condiments now, salt is a necessary ingredient for human nourishment, and a symbol of duration, concord and devotion. When Greeks throw salt to someone else's plate, they are interfering with other people's business. Stingy Greeks don't even give you a grain of salt. Greeks who have eaten bread and salt together are like brothers and sisters. The family man is the salt of the household.

Fruits, like the pomegranate (ródi) and the apple (mílo), symbolize fertility. According to Greek mythology, the pomegranate sprang from the blood drops of Dionysus and symbolized Hades. Pluto, the god of the underworld, gave Persephone, Demeter's daughter, a pomegranate to eat, so as to remember him. Traditionally, Greeks, for good luck, would break a pomegranate in front of their doors upon reentrance to their houses on New Year's.

The apple is a symbol of good luck, fertility and fruitfulness. It symbolizes devotion of the one partner to the other, particularly at weddings. It also stands for the acquisition of knowledge, heritage and progress. As a Greek proverb says, illustrating Newton's discovery and imaginativeness, "The apple will fall under the apple tree." It is a purely erotic fruit. In Greek mythology, the apple tree is the gift of the Earth to Zeus for his wedding. Paris offers an apple to Aphrodite as the winning prize of a beauty contest—the apple of discord. Its name is also associated with beautiful Milos, who hanged himself from a tree when he discovered Adonis' death. Upon his death, Aphrodite converted him into a seed, which was named apple (mílo).

Food expressions also mark Greek cultural ideals. The wise person's children cook before they get hungry. The pot rolls around until it finds its lid. Too may cooks slow down the cooking process and spoil the broth. The guest and the fish stink after the third day. When a Greek brags about many cherries, bring along a small container, and if you get burned on the pumpkin, blow even the yogurt.

On Greek months which do not contain an "R" in their names, Greeks must put water in their wine. Everything is seasonal, thus Greeks consume mackerel in August. Most Greeks have generous hearts, like artichokes. Mean Greeks may profit fat out of a fly or milk out of the male goat. Old Greek women are rich in broth, because they have eaten the sea by the spoon, whereas wealthy Greeks also own the bird's milk.

You may think what I have been sharing with you is "zucchinis" (kolokíthia), squash words (kolokithokouvéntes) or vegetable marrow pies (kolokithópites). But I will teach you how many pears fit in the sack, so let's call the figs figs and the wash-tub a wash-tub. By the way, did you know that in ancient Greece figs were very important in cooking and whoever stole a fig from someone else's tree was immediately accused as a sikofántis (slanderer)? So, please, don't hide behind the leeks, as I may catch you, and, as a Greek, dance you on the roasting pan.

Greeks do not put on layers of clothes, instead, they dress themselves as onions. They are hospitable; they may prepare a whole meal out of an onion only. Greeks should not eat like pigs, even if they are as hungry as wolves. Eating as light as a bird is best, especially with golden spoons.

Food is a basic societal need. As Greeks claim, "Appetite comes by eating" and "if the pot boils, friendship lives." Sharing a meal is the most common Greek social activity. Perhaps fast food was invented to house the lonely: the faster the process, the shorter the sense of solitude. We may drink alone, but food presupposes companionship, exchange of understanding. Perhaps that is why, unconsciously, Greeks always speak to their babies when they feed them: to accustom them timely to the sociality of food.

For example, the Greek word nóstimo (tasty) shares the same root with the word nostalgia. Nóstos means the return, the journey, while ánostos means without taste. *Nóstimos*, thus, is the one who, from the Homeric Odysseus to the contemporary Greek, has journeyed and arrived, has matured, ripened and is, therefore, tasty, and, in extension, useful.

I have tried to nibble on this spicy, meaty, juicy honey of a topic in order to savor and relish. I asked you to feast your eyes on the veritable potpourri of mushrooming food expressions that grace the table or Greek language and season your tongue. As I chewed the fat about the food-filled phrases that are packed like sardines and sandwiched into everyday Greek conversations, I tried to sweeten the pot with some tidbits of food for thought, guaranteed to whet your appetite.

I hope this essay is food for thought. In that case, I don't need to eat my words. (Otherwise, I'm ready to eat my hat.) After all, Greeks speak what they eat, and their big fat Greek vocabulary could make Greek a piece of cake!

Scott Gabriel Knowles

Building Under Peril

Nature will always challenge developers, but landmark studies of wildfire in California and flooding along the Mississippi are showing new ways of living in America's most dangerous regions.

This past October, when the Santa Ana winds returned to Southern California as they do every autumn, they caused 18 devastating wildfires to rage through the region. The largest of these—the "Witch Fire"—charred 200,000 acres, consumed 1,125 homes, injured 40 firefighters and killed two people. And at the center sat Rancho Santa Fe.

With a median home price of more than $2 million, this unincorporated bedroom community—described by a local real estate broker as "the new pleasure ground of America's landed gentry"—ranks among the most affluent in the United States. Its 2,400 homes on the frontier of San Diego County are situated on two-acre-plus lots where sidewalks and streetlights are banned.

But Rancho Santa Fe, despite its proximity to the fires, did not burn down. In fact, only one house in the community was lost. And the explanation is simple: A strict set of land use and construction codes called "shelter-in-place."

Diversion

Shelter-in-place is straightforward: First, accept that wildfire will be part of your new home's ecosystem. Then, deprive it of fuel: Avoid flammable landscaping and construct a house that's as fire-retardant as possible.

But how do you get developers, construction companies, insurers and homeowners to bear the costs of this new construction regimen?

"It's real simple," say Rancho Santa Fe fire marshal and 37-year California fire-service veteran Cliff Hunter. "Don't approve the plans. If you don't approve the plans, they don't get a house."

Just like that, Hunter is helping to rewrite the drama that has long played out in communities from San Diego County to the Gulf Coast and in the multitudes of other regions across America where catastrophe and construction are co-stars. This drama stars the "greedy developer" and the "sentimental environmentalist." Should we build or shouldn't we build? It's the land-use equivalent of a Shakespearean dilemma, and just like Shakespeare's plays, it may seem real but it's ultimately fiction. Even with Hurricane Andrew and Hurricane Katrina firmly lodged in our collective memory, development in hazardous regions continues. Even if construction were to stop entirely in these regions, we would still have generations' worth of property and citizens to protect from a changing risk environment that now includes the effects of climate change and the realities of aging infrastructure.

Hunter's shelter-in-place gospel is only one of many possible solutions currently emerging in a national move towards hazard realism, which seeks to get beyond the age of "should we build or shouldn't we?" Many of these ideas have been around for a while, including shelter-in-place, but they are only now being applied as the stakes of failure grow higher and higher. Others are less well-known, intermingling sustainability theory and sophisticated new mapping and modeling technologies in order to profile hazards and predict their effects with greater accuracy. It's a trend that cuts across the disciplines of planning, architecture and ecology; it includes first responders and emergency preparedness experts. And, if successful, the hazard realists will more and more be shaping national trends of development in America's most hazardous regions.

Life in the WUI

Max Moritz sees a philosophical puzzle in the way Californians think about hazards. "We fight fires—it's very military—but we don't fight earthquakes," he says. "We avoid them or we engineer against them." Moritz co-directs the Center for Fire Research and Outreach at the University of California, Berkeley. He wants to correct this inconsistency. Not fighting earthquakes, Moritz argues, has led to strong building codes and reasonable expectations of the built environment in earthquake-prone cities. It coincides with a century-old history—a post-1906-quake reckoning of the costs involved in rebuilding San Francisco or Los Angeles every generation. "We don't co-exist with fire and we need to," Moritz explains. "That's a fundamental difference."

Between 2000 and 2006, the United States witnessed five new records for acreage burned in wildfires, according to statistics collected since 1960 by the National Interagency Fire Center. The U.S. Fire Service reports that losses from "Outdoor and Other Fires" have averaged $260 million per year over the past decade. The National Fire Protection Association estimates that in 2005, there were 800,000 fires in this category, resulting in 50 civilian fire deaths and 950 injuries.

Moritz has an explanation. "Part of this has got to be, while we are learning more, we are seeing the results of climate change, the accumulation of fuel and an expansion of the WUI." WUI is fire-ecology-speak for the "Wildland Urban Interface"—that region of development where the suburb meanders into undeveloped space. As people move out into the WUI they start doing what you would expect—they put out fires that threaten their homes. Fire season after fire season, this leads to the fight, with Herculean efforts by thousands of firefighters called out to save the day. Such efforts, even when successful, are costly.

To Moritz, who looks at the problem with a scientific eye, the real trick is not in denying development in the WUI outright, but in understanding when, where and with what frequency wildfires strike. With this knowledge, a set of rational land-use policies and building codes can be developed—policies that don't necessarily say no to developers but do entail accountability when developers and homeowners insist on taking risks with the full knowledge of what they are doing.

Moritz has spent much of his career studying the interactions among the large-scale forces that cause wildfires, the elements that make up a "fire regime"—like vegetation, geography and weather patterns. While the fire regime changes over time, it can be mapped. And mapping means decisions about fire-resistant building codes, for example, can be based on hard data. "The last real solid work on [fire weather patterns] was done in the '60s for civil defense reasons," Moritz notes. It seems that the federal government was worried about nuclear war-induced firestorms, so a set of fire maps was developed. In the '80s and again in the '90s, California's Department of Forestry and Fire Protection (CAL FIRE) commissioned "Fire Hazard Severity Zone" (FHSZ) maps after especially bad fire seasons, to assess risk in wildland areas controlled by the state and to show areas where local residents are responsible for fire protection. But the pace of construction in the WUI has been brisk since then, leaving these maps outdated.

In response to the accelerating threat of wildfires in recent years, the California Building Standards Commission initiated a revised mapping effort in 2007, intended to guide the next generation of development in the WUI. A major break with past efforts is now possible thanks to the introduction of computer-based Geographic Information System (GIS) tools. Applying GIS to fire hazards in California (think Google Maps for disasters) enables experts to create maps that integrate potential fire locations with locations of buildings and the past fire history of a given area. The new FHSZ maps are designed to give realistic probabilities for fire behavior in areas rated according to "moderate," "high" and "very high" levels of risk. These areas show up on a map in yellow, orange and red bands that reflect not only the history, but also the possible future of the WUI.

Drafts of the FHSZ maps were discussed in localities across the state for months, and they went into effect on Jan. 1, 2008. The result, hopes Max

Moritz and many in the fire protection community, is a science-based system of understanding risk and allocating responsibility in a rational way across the state's WUI. Moritz's lab and CAL FIRE even co-host a Web site where people can input a physical address and see where their property sits in relation to fire hazard. If the property sits in one of the highest-risk zones, enhanced building codes kick into effect. The state estimates the cost per home to meet the new codes in the highest risk fire zones will run about $1,800. Enforcing codes, of course, is another matter—but it will be more and more difficult to keep on building in the same old ways in the WUI. So, where will development go from here?

From the individual structure up to neighborhood design, Moritz says, "we can use what we know about fire in educating urban planners." Moritz's lab holds workshops to demonstrate these new tools and has local fire agencies and planners engage in cooperatively crafting the new building codes. Better understanding of fire could also point the way to innovations in architecture and construction. We can soon expect to see technological revisions of household sprinkler systems, attic vent covers and fireproof roof materials to protect against flying embers. We can also expect the prohibition of traditional favorites like cedar shake roofs, which tend to burst into flame at the slightest provocation.

Moritz's lab is also charged with providing information and outreach to homeowners—in a sense, the final frontier of fire hazard mitigation—and he has developed what he calls a "Fire Information Engine Toolkit." The toolkit offers a Web-based diagnostic allowing a homeowner to find out whether his home might be susceptible to fire and includes a fire mitigation guide that advises on fire protection for everything from decks to landscaping plants. Moritz expects that homeowners might be incentivized to use the toolkit by lowered insurance rates. Or, by simple common sense, perhaps. Either way, Moritz's fire research lab is trying to accomplish something rather radical these days—taking the products of macro-level hazards research and making them available at the micro level of the homeowner.

Rediscovering the Mississippi

In 1993, the Mississippi River flooded for several months, from Minnesota down to the Gulf of Mexico. It was a "500-year event" in the lingo of flood experts, costing $15 billion before all was said and done. In historical memory only the Great 1927 Flood matches it. As the waters receded, landscape architect and professor Anuradha Mathur and her husband, architect Dilip da Cunha, started getting interested in what they saw as a very narrow, very shortsighted, post-flood conversation about what to do next with the river. In the introduction to their 2001 book, *Mississippi Floods: Designing a Shifting Landscape*, they recall:

> From one side we heard calls for more control of the river; from the other, for the withdrawal of settlement from the floodplains; even as the Mississippi was erasing property lines and dissolving boundaries of all kinds, it was not shaking the distinctions by which this landscape has been looked upon and inhabited for the past three centuries: River and settlement, nature and culture, water and land.

Shaking these distinctions would come to define Mathur and da Cunha's research method. They traveled up and down the river, conducting interviews, digging up old maps, and eventually riding along on one of the massive Mississippi barges for a week. They channeled Mark Twain, in whose *Life on the Mississippi* they found a respect for the water—as both a resource and muse. That made more sense to them than the dry calculations of the Army Corps of Engineers. They met old blues musicians, studied the racial history of the land alongside the water and at last came to a rather startling conclusion: The Mississippi River is not separate from the land through which it courses.

To say that land and water are part of one ecosystem with permeable boundaries is a rather difficult proposition in a country founded on the sanctity, and fixity, of property rights. Liberated from this concept, one immediately sees the road, or the stream, not taken. And, in fact, if one searches out the history of the river, the "fixed river" appears only as an apparition. Rising water was a seasonal guest. Travel out of New Orleans up the river to the sugarcane country and see the 18th-century Creole mansions. They were built to flood, with permeable basements and front doors that opened right to the river. Think about the land before industrial oil and gas production cut up the wetlands and real estate developers built houses in the lowlands. It's like the Nile in Egypt: Flooding brings life, replenishes the land; it gives rise to culture—a culture that values cycles and feels a deep shudder of memory and respect when the waters rise.

Moments of profound disruption in the American system don't come along often, but surely Katrina was one. In such a moment new ideas are often aired; and so, after Katrina, Mathur and da Cunha set about again to tear down the psychological boundaries between land and water along the Mississippi. The result was "New Orleans: Inhabiting a Fluid Terrain," a 2006 design project that developed into an exhibition. Mathur took her students down to the Gulf, where they studied the geography and met the people and imagined the possibilities of the space for themselves. They developed plans that conjured up the city of New Orleans as a submersible space for living. The

"Roof/Ramp" by Huiqing Kuang was one concept. It's an enormous multi-level ramp with housing, retail and public space inside the structure—on the roof is a garden. Day by day, it is a place to live, to work and to play. But, when the waters rise, as they invariably will again, the ramp becomes a lifeline to safety. And when the waters are high, the ramp could even be used as a temporary city, a place to locate housing for evacuees, keeping them rooted to the city where they live rather than dispersing them to the four corners of the nation as refugees.

High-density housing along the natural levees formed by the riverbank was another idea that grew from the process. Again emphasizing traditional use of land in New Orleans before the current levee system existed, the designers made use of a common sense proposition: Build on the high ground and restrain development in the lowlands. Another proposal called for the creation of new canals in the city that would simultaneously channel water to Lake Pontchartrain, but also discharge rainwater into the natural "bowl" that is New Orleans. Such a plan would "allow once more the Mississippi Water to flow through the city." This may seem counter-productive, except that the new canals will allow for more construction on high ground—the canal banks—and also return sediment to the city's naturally swampy areas, thus lifting the overall elevation.

At their core, the visionary designs of Mathur, da Cunha and their students seek to remind us of two key lessons for life along the Mississippi: First, the city and the water are not separate. Second, separating them insults history, and, if the past is ignored, eventually you find yourself marooned on a rooftop in a sea of survivors who can't connect.

Know your Enemies

Such lessons perfectly echo the thinking of Louisiana State University hurricane researcher and Hurricane Center deputy director Ivor van Heerden. "Be very careful of expanding the footprint of your city into wetlands—they are wet for a reason," van Heerden warns. Like Mathur and da Cunha, van Heerden and his research team at LSU started with the history of the river and the history of its big floods to understand the bad planning that led to Katrina's devastation.

Sediment is a big player in van Heerden's analysis. Rather than turning the river into a canal, a process begun after the 1927 flood and renewed after Hurricane Betsy in 1965, van Heerden believes we need to allow periodic flooding of the Mississippi's surrounding lands. The flooding provides the sediment that builds land and nourishes the wetland plants—land and plants that counteract subsidence and erosion that serve as powerful buffers against hurricane-induced storm surges. "We've lost over a million acres of protective apron," says van Heerden. "The river is in straitjackets, and it pours into 400 feet of water out in the Gulf. But, we could siphon the water and sediment out and into the wetlands, we can use diversions, we could even allow the river to take a different course."

Like Mathur and da Cunha, van Heerden laments the fact that the Army Corps of Engineers seems to be drawing just the opposite conclusion. It's "a mad rush to get a plan and start working, [with] very little thought to effectiveness. They've dusted off old Corps plans and put them in a shopping bag." Echoing Mathur and da Cunha, van Heerden believes that a fundamental philosophical shift—let the land and the water co-exist—must come first. He argues, "Our river levees cause or exacerbate the flooding, because we don't look at it as a system—we have to start taking the European systems approach."

The European system to which van Heerden looks for guidance evolved from the greatest modern flood disaster to hit the Netherlands. In the winter of 1953, an enormous flood engulfed the country's vast lowlands, killing over 1,800 people, destroying 4,000 homes and causing an evacuation of 100,000 people. Just as with Hurricane Katrina a half-century later, this was a disaster caused by a failed levee system—a disaster predicted and still sadly endured. The remediation strategy was a highly technological one, involving the construction of massive surge barriers at the meeting of land and sea. Rather than barring the two from meeting, however, the barriers have gates that can be raised and lowered, allowing saltwater estuaries and tidal zones to continue to exist. The gates are only closed when the seas are high and flooding is imminent. The Dutch looked at the hazards they faced after 1953 and calculated that they wanted to reduce the risk of serious flooding in their cities to an extraordinary ratio of 1:10,000. Within four years, the protective barriers were complete, and they continue to build and monitor them as the environment changes. Van Heerden laughs when he remembers showing pictures of the piecemeal Mississippi levee system to Dutch scientists. "Compared to the Dutch, ours are little sand castles," he says. The emphasis here is less on copying the Dutch exactly, but in adopting the seriousness with which they approached the issue, and making a long-term societal commitment to protecting our cities. By cutting siphons through the current levee system, building serious levees where they are needed, and restoring the wetlands, van Heerden sees a way to co-exist with the mighty Mississippi. He also cites the need to mimic the Dutch process of opening the levee design process to competition. The Corps can build, in van Heerden's estimation, but visionary designs are quite another matter.

As with Max Moritz's work in California, there is new promise in using computer-modeling and GIS technology to project the implications of certain remedial actions, or of taking no action at all. The Dutch, according to van Heerden, are once again showing the way forward, with sophisticated computer models allowing researchers to play out any number of scenarios and rediscoveries along the waterway. If van Heerden can get his models done in time, he might just be able to win over the politicians, the engineers and the developers who are right now building the next generation of flood controls along the Mississippi.

Back at the Ranch

Back in Rancho Santa Fe after the fire, Fire Marshal Cliff Hunter's gamble paid off. The local and even national press were jamming up his phone line, wanting to know what the success of shelter-in-place meant for the rest of the country. Hunter is optimistic, but also realistic. "I don't recommend that people stay in their homes during a fire," he says. Shelter-in-place is, in fact, a second line of defense, intended to protect people who can't escape because of age or illness or panic. Still, he is obviously pleased when he explains he knows some people who stayed behind during the Witch Fire, despite the robocall warnings to evacuate. And they were fine, he says. The strict requirements of keeping a vegetation-free perimeter around the home, blocking attic vents from flying embers and liberal use of fire-resistant building materials in addition to wider than usual escape roadways add up to a winning strategy for co-existing with fire, in Hunter's view.

The downside, of course, is the increased cost of construction and upkeep, and the risk that people will try this on their own but forget that shelter-in-place design must be maintained and monitored all the time. At Rancho Santa Fe, this is accomplished by inspectors who come around every fire season to catalogue code abuses, and through private restriction rather than public law. Recently, one woman put 22 forbidden cypress trees around her home and was flagged for a code violation. "Why did you do it?" Hunter wanted to know. "I never thought you would inspect," the woman replied. This attitude troubles Hunter, and especially agitates those who are concerned that shelter-in-place is unsustainable without costly and constant oversight.

Hunter sees another big problem: It's too expensive to retrofit all of the homes in California's WUI that don't already make use of shelter-in-place. Such requirements, despite the new code structure and Max Moritz's fire maps, would take political courage that is currently untested, but historically weak. This is the same sort of problem that faces the Gulf Coast. Those levees along the Mississippi? Not coming down anytime soon. This means more living on borrowed time as the water and the land remain temporarily separated.

For years, developers have built unsustainably in harm's way. Every disaster necessitated more government oversight, more firemen and rapid reconstruction to demonstrate that the "fight" with nature was being won. Now, as we settle into the 21st century, realists are working hard to redefine how to best live with hazard. They know people want to live in disaster-prone areas, for cultural and economic reasons that are out of the control of any governing entity.

However, with new construction methods and more rational building codes facilitated by accurate map-making and computer models, it is unlikely that residents of the WUI will remain heedless. A fundamental realignment of construction with ecological reality—rather than feebly trying to push the ecology away from the construction site—will present new design options and ecological philosophies to be discussed in classrooms, town halls, laboratories and firehouses. And as the discussion continues, disaster realists will make their case: You can live where you want to, but have a good, long look at a map first.

Miriam N. Kotzin

Hag

The day Sean told her that he was moving out was the day he dug his video camera out of the box of stuff that he'd kept in the back of the closet. They'd never set it up on a tripod and aimed it at the bed. They'd never taken it to the shore or anywhere else. It had always stayed in the box, loaded.

Now he aims it at Anna as she paces around what had just become her bedroom again. She's crying, and she's been crying off and on for hours while Sean packed. Her face is red and swollen with grief and anger. Her long, gray hair falls into her face and sticks where her face is wet with tears and snot.

The bed is a staging area between them. Sean's belongings and clothes cover the bed in heaps. He hasn't started putting things into suitcases yet. A six-pack of cartons from Staples leans up against the bed.

The Kleenex is on the same side of the bed as Sean, and Anna won't go there. She wants him to stop the camera. She grabs a shirt from the pile of clothes and holds it up, open like a curtain in front of her face. "Stop," she says, from behind the shirt, and then says it again, "Stop it."

She's sobbing, "Don't. You have no right." She lowers the shirt and he's still filming.

"No...." her voice trails into a whimper. She hates melodrama, hates being out of control.

"Erase it! Erase it now!" She's begging though the words are commands. Later she will not remember what else she said.

"Look," he says. He presses some buttons, watching the monitor, and then he turns the screen towards her. She sees herself reduced, holding up the shirt and hears herself say it in a tinny voice, "Stop, Stop it. Don't. You have no right. No...Erase it. Erase it now."

She sees herself, diminished, lower the shirt, and the zoom-in closeup of her face. She sees herself as he will remember her and as she will remember herself, like this: her hair wild, her face puffy and streaked, bags under her tiny red-rimmed eyes.

Anna's mouth opens and closes like a ventriloquist's dummy's when Sean turns off the sound.

Miriam N. Kotzin

Should, Shouldn't

"People who feed songbirds shouldn't keep cats," Franny said as I drove, "especially, feed strays." I heard our mother's tone in her voice, and I was amused because Franny had hated being told what she should and shouldn't do. When we were teenagers she'd sit on her bed in our room and chant, "Should, shouldn't, shit."

"Shh, Franny," I'd say, "She'll hear you, and we'll both get in trouble."

"Are you telling me I should shut up?"

"I'm saying that if you don't shush we'll get both in trouble, that's all."

Somehow we never did. Not for that. We caught it for the usual: undone chores, curfew violations, when the neighbors called the cops because we gave a loud party the one time our mother left us home alone for a weekend. "I guess I can't leave you two alone after all," she'd said, her voice a mixture of anger and frustration. Much later I realized that she was chiding herself as well.

And now Franny was telling me how to live. "Should, shouldn't, shit," I said.

"You know I'm right," Franny said, and then she told me how the cat would leap up on the terra cotta bird bath and break it.

I began chanting Franny's, "Should, shouldn't, shit."

She told me how the cat would get the baby finches in the nest on the lamp next to the front door.

I chanted louder.

She told me about the presents the cat would bring, the tribute of the half-dead mouse or, she said, practically shouting now, the wounded bird.

I chanted louder still.

"Someday you'll see," she said, "You'll see I was right. You'll learn the hard way, and you'll be sorry."

I kept on chanting Franny's teenage chant; in response she kept on scolding, warning me with mounting frustration. I kept on chanting to hear the echo of our mother's voice fill the car. In her lap, Franny held two beautiful stones. It was our first time like this, the two of us alone, going to visit her grave.

Lynn Levin

Thistledown

At the moment of what we thought was our death
that seemed to be coming for us in a Vauxhall
on the wrong side of the road,
Patsy, Lulu, and I just happened to be debating

the existence of the immortal soul.
"Is it the same as consciousness
and thus perishable? Organically based,"
I submitted, "like a tulip or thistle?
Or are the soul and body from two separate worlds?"
In the backseat Patsy was horrified
by my thoughts and the way the traffic whirled
around the roundabout. I myself was not at all certain

about which side we should be on. So it was
a great surprise to find Patsy, the satirist,
to be the most secure in her faith.

"Don't you believe
in reincarnation?" she asked as we motored
past fields of sheep and cows.

I agreed that animals had souls
but felt their spirits decomposed
with their bodies. It was just the same for us:
we were nothing

but big apes, bald chimps.
"Speak for yourself," she said holding fast
to the edge of her seat.

"I'm the eternal pessimist," said Lulu
who was driving and smoking. "Hell's the only thing I know,"
she said as she swerved and saved the three of us
who gulped back our ghosts.

When we saw that those white puffs
in the blue air were not us
but thistledown looping like paratroopers

loathe to touch ground, Lulu parked by the side
of the road, and we flew out, the three of us,
spinning, laughing, waving our arms
in the down that caught in our hair, our clothes.

Lynn Levin

The Fox and the Neighbors

I was a monster strange and wild
a walking tree with birdless boughs
and to the fox not food, not friend
though to a shy thing like that
what could be a friend?
Like a dot before the dash
a dog that took itself for cat—
the fox posed for a moment
dainty in its gloves and fine mustache
below the planted pines
that set the neighbors' lot from mine
and these were good neighbors.
You could not want better neighbors.
We lived side by side for twenty years.
When snow or sickness came
they helped me and I helped them.
Though in things not health or weather
we felt a border better.
One night an ice storm glassed us in.
Next morning everything outside
gleamed like clear sugar candy.
I chopped a path to Bea and Ben's
to see if they needed
bread or heat or medicine.
And by the pines
chandeliered with ice, halogen-bright in the sun
I spied the fox—threadbare as an old jacket
scratching at the frozen egg
of the world for its breakfast.
And I should not have, but I fed it.

Harriet Millan

Girl in Cap and Gown

Next morning
over coffee
on the porch of a guest house
in a seaside town, I'm introduced.
Tom says, "You're the girl in the street
last night we called Kim. The one who looks like Kim."
Bob swallows a sip,
then, amid the clatter of china, says,
"You could be Kim's sister."

I say I don't know who she is,
and because it is raining outside,
the yellow tarpaulin over the upstairs deck
flapping in the wind,
filling with emptiness,
I go back to my room.
They're still there
when I come down,
sprawled out on the glider.

They scrutinize me, darken my hair,
square off my chin
and I am blotted out. I cannot hear
my own thoughts, voice, story.
The rain and the slap of waves.
The clatter of china. The flapping tarpaulin.
Until, at last, I'm off the porch,
having reached the path,
standing in the salvaging downpour
but you have to realize I am writing this
after I have found out.

At the end of that path
I walk smack right into
a pole (literally bumping into it
because it is raining and I walk face down)
where someone stapled a photocopy
onto the gouged out wood
of a girl in cap and gown

splattered with raindrops,
staring at me, that reads:

KIM MISSING LAST SEEN IN WELLEFLEET
6/22/06

I gasp. So this is Kim.
It doesn't matter anymore who she is
or I am or if we resemble one another
or not at all—it had been a pick up line
or at best, a punch,
if Kim were not already dead.

What happens is
they put me in her place
at the bottom of a deep ravine.
I close my eyes. I hold my breath,
the possibility becoming next.
And then it stops,
and I come back.

Harriet Millan

In the Community Garden
(33rd and Powelton Sts.)

Sparse, that first spring, we could project growth,
a marking on a cellar wall to tout as comparison.

Healthy roots build resistance like a measles inoculation,
rhizomes, antibody tithers, spathes of the arum lily,

and despite accusations against the use of pesticides.
Native gardens are not special. All flowers belong to the world,

because orchids sealed in plastic on the grocery store shelf
help indigenous growers to compose new songs to stars

rising onto late night stages. You don't have to speak English
to read the applause meter. The peonies amassed with ants
give it rain forest status on the patio of the row home

where I live. According to neighborhood lore,
the Lenni Lenape farmed tracts of ant hills.
Now those ants' ancestors swarm through cement cracks.

The perennials we planted stake out inches of beauty,
spreading leaves overcome asphalt,
stride over the garden's fence, cascade down spires,

blacked-out warehouses, and crystalline lots with Sleeping Beauty sleep.
You don't remember waking. You remember ingesting something,
tilting the glass back, then your hand holding the glass grows limp

and it shatters to the ground. If you haven't realized your mistake,
the broken glass tells you. Is it possible that pollen dust,
propagated in spring, mixes with finger print marks

and that, when the jogger's body is buried underground
she becomes entangled with roots? For example, the myth of
Daphne, her calling out to
      her father, a god already,

his patience at the boiling point, especially after that charade of hers,

the commotion she caused, the upheaval, disturbing the pinnacle of power.
Apollo at her heels, she snaps back branches trying to trip him,

someone has to throw it back in his face—the privileged assumptions,
the leaf mold.

Anne-Marie Obajtek-Kirkwood

Le Monde on a "Likely" Iraq War: Of Current Events, History and a French Newpaper

Musing on the relationship between current events, history and the acceleration of time, Marc Augé writes:

> History—I am referring primarily to what is called contemporary history—is not protected from the profound mutations our world is undergoing. On the one hand, national and regional histories are more caught up in planetary development. On the other hand, we are experiencing an "acceleration of history"—another expression for shrinking of the planet that involves both objective interactions within the "world system" and the instantaneity of information and image dissemination. Each month, each day, we experience "historical" events; each day the border between history and current events becomes a bit more blurred. The parameters of time, like those of space, are changing, and this is an unprecedented revolution. Just as our modernity uncontrollably creates otherness, so it is uncontrollably creating the immediate past-history even as it claims to stabilize history and unify the world.

His statement rings particularly true in conjunction with the events preceding the Iraq War, resounding throughout the planet through satellite dishes, the Internet, the audio-visual and written press. Faced with the abundance of daily news and developments ever-changing, one experiences difficulty at absorbing this impact of ongoing news that soon make history or rather are history in the making. This complexity is further magnified when events go on unfurling into the present and do not seem to reach a conclusion as is the case with the Iraq War so far.

Months have passed since the military end of the 2003 Iraq War, and so much has happened since in Iraq, the U.S., Europe and the world that needs to be forgotten if one is to go back to 2003, namely February and March—the weeks and days preceding the armed conflict—and give an accurate account of the French press coverage of events with the current data then.

Reflecting the population's attitude and the government stance, French press at large was not in favor of another Iraq War but could feel it coming inexorably. Apart from some (and really, quite few) dissenting intellectuals and politicians, there were in France, before the war, not many attempts at finding justifications or reasons for the conflict, but on the contrary resignation prevailed at what was coming, when not resentment and criticism. Articles were questioning motives and rationale of this "likely" war, pointing out that war should be the last resort when all other channels of communication and constraint would have been exhausted. Others, before the war itself, were imagining the scenarios when not stating the consequences that could/would unfold out of that war, for the U.S., Iraq, the Middle East, or the world, not forgetting the French-U.S. relationship.

This paper delineates how the French daily *Le Monde* focused on what was to be or not engaged, in which terms, with what arguments. Politically speaking, *Le Monde* is center left but in the instance of the Iraq war, the political left was of the same opinion as the right. As objectivity is a high ideal but does not ever totally exist in any newspaper, the choice of Le Monde was mainly motivated by its high intellectual standards and the best, deepest coverage it offers as a French daily. When need be, contributions from *Libération* (left wing daily) or weeklies such as *Le Nouvel Observateur* (left wing) or *Le Point* (right wing) will be added.

January 1 2003 and the Franco-French Debate on the "Likely" Iraq War

War was on the horizon at the dawn of 2003. In his article, "Will the Iraq War happen?" Serguei summed up French worries: "The year 2002 is ending up on big international uncertainties. Is the military offensive, wished for by the United States to topple Saddam Hussein's regime, inescapable?" And assessment of the situation: "2002 had started with American president Bush's declaration placing Iraq at the head of the list of the 'axis of evil.' It finishes with still Saddam Hussein's regime at the heart of international issues at stake." France's position and the role it could play was delineated:

> France is to take the United Nations Security Council presidency
> this January 1st. It considers that only this body is qualified
> to decide the Iraq case, and that no armed intervention can be
> engaged without a new resolution of the UN. On the military plane,
> it is holding minimum preparations. Will the war against Iraq that
> a major part of the American Administration seems to have backed,
> take place? Is it inescapable? What will the UN inspectors say in
> their final report, the delivery of which is set to January 27, 2003?
> What will France's position be if the United States maintain their
> determination?

Serguei's January 1 article was followed by an analysis of the international situation and a parallel drawn between the possible intervention in Iraq and that of Kosovo in July 1999. Special Representative of the Secretary General of the United Nations and Head of the UN Mission in Kosovo Bernard

Kouchner, philosophers Alain Finkielkraut and Bernard-Henri Lévy, director of Esprit Olivier Mongin, European Parliament member Daniel Cohn-Bendit, and emeritus researcher at l'Institut d'Etudes politiques Pierre Hassner were faced with three questions: Can Kosovo be equated with Iraq, Milosevic with Saddam Hussein and thus armed conflict against Iraq be justified? There was general consensus on the similarities between the two heads of state and their brutal regimes. If Kouchner spoke of Saddam's "criminal productivity" and the barbaric nature of his regime, Mongin and Cohn-Bendit asserted this was nothing new, nor a late development, nothing having fundamentally changed since September 11, 2001. Proofs of the monstrous character of the Iraqi regime already existed while the U.S. backed, even guided, Iraq in its war against Iran from 1981 to 1988, while France armed Baghdad just as the U.S. did, and neither Washington nor Paris felt morally tormented when Iraqi armed forces used gas against Iran.

The urgency of an armed conflict with Iraq was questioned on several fronts, namely the danger that Iraq represented and American aims. The reasons put forward by the White House to justify an armed intervention, namely Iraqi WMDs, that Iraq might avail to Al Qaeda which might use them against the United States, seemed fragile for lack of substantial proof. Differences between Kosovo and Iraq were stressed: "We were in favor of an intervention in Kosovo in the name of regional stability. With Iraq, we are afraid of de-stabilization," Kouchner said, and Mongin added: "Iraq lies in the midst of a troubled region where a war may reinforce repressive regimes." For Pierre Hassner, the Israeli-Palestinian conflict could not be subtracted from the equation and was related to it. Doubts existed about what Americans had in store after Saddam's removal. According to Mongin, "One of the principle of a 'just war' is to foster an after-war setting likely to be better. In the present case, one may question this outcome." Washington intent prompted Kouchner to formulate the following misgivings: "An after-Saddam under a UN mandate is needed. If it is sole U.S. business reeking of oil and American home politics, it won't be good. This is the reason why everything is perverse, distorted in this case." Pierre Hassner also questioned the democratic goal put forward and the credibility of a battle against an "axis of evil" led with allies who, in Tchechnia, have committed crimes equivalent to those of Saddam Hussein.

This January 1, 2003 article stressed that September 11 had upset the new paradigms of international relations that had been setting in since the end of the Cold War. The nineties were marked by efforts at creating a kind of international law order where the United Nations was to play a pivotal role. Both vulnerable and all powerful, the United States were perceived as holding the monopoly of power and morals; they were, according to Pierre Hassner, "Both emperor and pope." As with Kosovo, but in a different way, the whole conception of international order was at stake with Iraq.

More Franco-French Debate from Various Personalities

These two articles from *Le Monde* January 1, 2003, a month before the period under scrutiny, were emblematic of the major worries of the new year. These issues constitute the Franco-French debate on the "likely" Iraq War among various French citizens, from various walks of life and intellectual status, to which will be added the analysis of French politicians from the political spectrum, the position of the French government, and incidentally its stance in the European Union, the United Nations, and vis-à-vis the United States.

Presenting viewpoints from intellectuals was undertaken in February 2003 by *Le Monde* again with 27 personalities (artists, writers, architects, lawyers, sportsmen, filmmakers and more), all very well-known by the French in their various disciplines, being asked the following questions: 1. Is a new war against Iraq justified? 2. Do you approve of the French position? Only one man, Arno Klarsfeld , was resolutely in favor of the war, because of Saddam's regime and atrocities, and also because of the comparison between the lack of eventual French warfare and European inertia against Hitler in 1936 and 1938. Klarsfeld also deemed it France's duty to line up behind the U.S., France's liberator in WWI and II. Kiejman had this ambiguous answer: "No to war. Yes to the possibility of it happening." He thought that the United States, in spite of its errors, remained the sole safeguard of an imperfect but perfectible world fit to live in.

The rest of the panel approved of the French position while some feared that it would bring a rift in the French-American relationship, that France would suffer economic sanctions and retaliations for its opposition to the U.S. views. Others still applauded France's courage (and also Germany's) since "few nations dare oppose the Americans"; they praised its determination, encouraged its duty as an old country to utter its own point of view and say no to "the arrogance of a badly brought up person like Bush or the shameful lies of M. Blair," while deploring American sarcasms, "like those of Peter King's, a Republican congressman who described France as 'a second-rate country' and the French as 'yesterday's people.'"

Though it was recognized across the board that Saddam Hussein was a frightful tyrant, nobody found war against Iraq justified at this stage and that on several counts: out of all existing tyrants, Hussein was the only one to be pursued. Was it because other tyrants did not possess a strategic product interesting the U.S. like Iraq's? The American war plan was a caricature: In 1991 Saddam Hussein was spared and kept his tyrannical power against all logic while the Iraqi people put up with an unfair embargo and suffered from it, regardless of any humanity. If there was to be war, it would be again regardless of the Iraqi people.

The Iraqi menace seemed greatly exaggerated; no real link could be established between international terrorism and Saddam Hussein. On the contrary, Saddam was said to entertain anything but cordial links with Muslim extremism. After ten years of embargo, the country was not economically sound. How could it therefore have the resources to hide the military arsenal that the Bush Administration attributed to it? The population was suffering. Iraq since Kuwait had not been an aggressor, so why attack it? Hussein was contained and should be contained still through pacific means.

War is justified if one is attacked or on the verge of being so, which did not seem to be the case. There was musing on what a "just" war is and how violence was really not the solution, all the more in this context as forces in presence were so disproportionate, so heavily in favor of the West. Any war is horrible and a preemptive war is worse yet. The concept of "preemptive war" was judged both dangerous and ironical juxtaposed to the "obscene and current massacres in Tchechnia." It was strongly condemned: "The world is not an American protectorate. Preemptive war is the law of the jungle." Henri de France was vocal against it: "No preemptive war can be justified. It would mean opening the gates to chaos. In this case, no serious proof has been provided by the UN inspectors of the existence of weapons of mass destruction in Iraq. An old saying expresses quite well, it seems to me, the present will of the American power: 'Who wants to kill his dog shows it rage.'"

The consequences for the world of a possible war were evoked. For Soulages: "Starting a second war nowadays is a remedy worse than the evil; it would, by enhancing fanaticism, provide the best pretext to all those who aspire to oppose the Muslim world to the European-American West. It is the best turn that could be given to Bin Laden and terrorists." Desmarest further agreed: "A war in Iraq may have destabilizing consequences on lots of Middle-Eastern countries already shaken by the fact that lots of the attackers of September 11, 2001 originate from there and more yet by the deadlock of the Israeli-Palestinian conflict. One may also fear the repercussions on the Muslim world at large, in Southeast Asia, in North-Africa and in Western countries."

Since there was no established link between international anti-American terrorism and Saddam Hussein, Nourissier painted a very bleak picture of what war might mean:

> The Americans' determined bellicosity expresses this apocalyptic acknowledgment that big religious, ideological, economic blocks are doomed to a fatal death struggle. [...] No 'progress'

is to be hoped for from history. Comparing forces in presence? The 'Western' military power is overwhelming; but the anti-American, anti-Christian fury, etc., with its paroxystic discourse, its anachronism, its kamikaze, is no less spectacular. Justifying war—which would be an American counter-attack—by all means would boil down to proclaiming/deploring that big human societies are promised to collective suicide.

Finally the rationale for war advocacy was questioned: "I have no certainty, no proof backing up the arguments given by the Americans to launch war," "I can't believe the proofs that the Bush Administration pains to gather," "War is not justified as long as the United States attempt to convince us with false proofs and fake photos," "None of the advanced arguments is convincing, there only appears the Bush administration determination which, in its way, is as fundamentalist as those it denounces." The reasons recognized behind the American pro-war position are acknowledged again and again as electoral and economic, boosting the faltering American economy through vested interest in Iraqi oil, as Ernaux summed it up: "The war that the United States want has not much to do with the proclaimed democratic ideal but all with their interests: hold economic and political sway on the Middle-East, relaunch the home economic machine, etc."

George Bush was "not an idiot, but he is convinced of being inspired by God and he is dangerous." His warmongering and religiousness were no solution: "Opposing the fundamentalism of the 'axis of Good' to the terrorism of 'the axis of Evil' won't have the world progress in the right direction, when there is so much to do: reduction of inequalities between rich and poor countries, tolerance and comprehension of others, improvement of living conditions of the planet and its inhabitants..." The underlying condemnation of American aims was strong as was on a moral plane the hypocrisy Bush and others were accused of: "I find it extremely shocking to receive moral and political lessons from politicians who did their best at arming a dictator whom they denounce today as dangerous. A people is asked to destroy weapons that the American but also the English and the French governments provided! I'll believe in the democratic intentions of the Americans and in their will to fight terrorism the day they deal with financial support to Islamist terrorist networks."

A total loss of credibility in American arguments and deep criticism of the way in which they were presented to the American citizens and the world ensued. The Administration was bluntly accused of having manipulated data and shaped their presentation accordingly. Writer Rufin analyzed the Administration procedure very sternly:

The United States have built up justification, in an artificial manner, using methods of manipulation of public opinion. The subject first emerged in Bush's declarations on the axis of Evil. It was worked on by reports, formal demands, rhetorical dramatization. Finally the "failure" of the inspections came about. A perverse dialectic then transformed this negative assessment into guilt: "If there is nothing, it is because nothing has been shown to us. [...] Those who are against the war, are 'against the disarming of Saddam,' therefore pro war! The honor of democracies during the Cold War had been to utter the truth as opposed to totalitarian lying. It is shocking to see nowadays bad faith pass into the camp of the country that symbolizes freedom.

Ernaux deconstructed the Administration rhetoric too:

What differs from the first Gulf War is that the wrong reasons for killing thousands of Iraqis have been made manifest and prevail on the 'right' ones in most opinions. [...] Like any hegemonic nation, the United States make the error of thinking that their most obvious lies won't be caught by citizens from other countries. In a way, they overdid it, and allowed to emerge to consciousness the fact that 'means are part of truth as well as results' (Marx), of course, but is this not the foundation of any morals and science and the foundation of not wanting this notoriously imperialistic war?"

This opinion gathering by *Le Monde* concluded with a critique by its very readers who reproached the paper for airing mainly anti-war statements and the "mediator" tried to balance opinions by showcasing those of two strongly pro-war readers. And thus one Parisian wrote: "I am pro-war, as it can be a just war like in Serbia or Afghanistan, and because I remember September 11, 2001 and so many numerous murders which demand condemnation, reparation and memory," while another added: "How lucky Europe is to have statesmen the like of Blair, Aznar and Berlusconi, who having to face contrary winds at times, manage to direct it in the direction of honor. How lucky for Europe that the countries which have just joined it remind old France that it is more than high time for it to wake up from its wintery torpor."

In spite of his trying to balance opinions, Solé had to confess that *Le Monde* had difficulty in finding pro-war opinions, that some solicited people refused to answer so that it finally had to close this series of articles on February 21 for want of participants. He concluded that "the French in general and *Le Monde* readers in particular are in their vast majority opposed to the preemptive war wanted by Bush."

By March 20, there appeared again in *Le Monde* two articles in favor of the war as the paper still tried to balance views. Kendal Nezan, director of the Kurdish Institute in Paris, really wished for a war to oust Saddam but with the UN sanction, not led unilaterally by the US. The other pro-war article featured writer Pascal Bruckner, philosopher André Glucksmann, and film-maker Romain Goupil. They had on March 10 launched in Le Monde a petition to be signed, the title of which was: "Saddam must go, by choice or by force." That petition started with recalling Milosevic's ethnic cleansing atrocities in Croatia and NATO intervention; it then focused on the atrocities and ethnic cleansing that were going on in Iraq similarly, for lack of concrete action, and finished with the following paragraphs:

> It would be regrettable to reduce the present crisis to a Franco-American conflict when the two countries' point of view could have been complementary [...]

> It would be catastrophic if, out of vainglory and stubbornness, Paris resorted to the veto, at the risk of shattering Western solidarity and leaving Europe somewhat shaken (which, let's remember, cannot be reduced to the Paris-Berlin axis alone) [...]

> Saddam must go, by choice or by force! The Iraqis, the Kurds, Shi'ites, but also Sunnis will breathe freer and the peoples of the region will be relieved [...]

> After Milosevic, the Balkans are no heaven but there is more peace and less dictatorship. The post-Saddam era will not be rosy, but less black than 30 years of tyranny, summary executions and war.

Glucksmann's criticism of France's independence from the United States and fear of its persistence, the possible repercussions and political and economic isolation (particularly from future Iraqi deals) were shared by all pro-war intellectuals or politicians as was their stressing of the nature of Saddam and his regime.

Yves Roucaute thus deemed that moral demand alone would justify the removal of Saddam. Generally speaking, there was, in the pro-war articles or petitions, no criticism whatsoever of American actual or ulterior motives and no doubt that a military intervention could only benefit Iraq and the whole Middle East. Roucaute expressed forcefully that camp's views:

> As the war is just because of its political and humanitarian ends, it is also just by its means [...] The war will soon appear as a wise decision to the world. In spite of the doomwatchers, there will be

no resistance from a population waiting for the tyrant's removal. And just a few cameras will be needed to reverse international opinion which is fooled today [...] Thus this region powder keg will be reorganized, Saudi Arabia and the Emirates security comforted, Israel existence assured and Palestinian authority democratized while the war started against the hooligan states of Afghanistan, carried on in Iraq will continue imposing on the globe this perpetual peace treaty that universal conscience demands [...] Right without a sword is just a word, and morals without will a hollow dream.

Two days earlier than the pro-war petition appearance, four well-known Europeans, Spanish filmmaker Pedro Almodovar, German literature Nobel prize-winner Günter Grass, Swedish writer Per Olof Enquist and Finnish political top-editor Helle Klein signed a kind of tribute titled "Continue, Jacques Chirac," in which they underlined the consequences a war with Iraq would entail: great loss of human lives, increased spread of terrorism, worsening of ties with the Southern part of the world, especially Muslim countries, weakening of international law and the UN, marginalization of Europe engaged in a major constructing phase of its political identity. They thanked Chirac for the course and the actions he had taken so far and begged him to steer the same course all the way to a UN veto to stop the war, if need be. They also stressed the long-standing ties between France and the U.S. throughout history and pointed to the fact that France's position evidences authentic solidarity with the American people and institutions and that France in its continued action would thus follow its destiny of independence and responsibility, serving Europe and the whole world.

Analyzing the pros and cons of war, trying to make sense of the whole situation, Jean Daniel stated that the more countries rallied directly or indirectly to the American position, the less there were public opinions in favor of war, that there were already two winners in this story: Bin Laden, whose aim was not war for the sake of war but vengeance for centuries of Arab humiliation, and George Bush, not altogether correctly elected but who managed to get his whole country's support after September 11, and following an indecisive and botched operation in Afghanistan, financial scandals and an economic crisis at home, took the Iraq operation where his father left off, comparing in the process Saddam Hussein to Bin Laden, as he couldn't back his moves on Hussein annexing another country anymore. Pierre Hassner blamed both the U.S. and France for having greatly undermined the European Union, NATO and the UN and the United States for having managed, after two years of aggressive unilateralism and Manichean rhetoric, to have Saddam Hussein appear as the first victim of an adventurous enterprise, both regionally and worldwide .

The Debate among French Government and Politicians

The Franco-French debate on the Iraq War gave voice to public opinion expressed by thoughtful, enlightened people, on the basis of what Michaux wrote: "The democracies in which we live are public opinion and media regimes, which means that in principle, public affairs are treated in a transparent manner with the media operating as a fourth power." In turn, the media is used by governments to convince or shape public opinion at times; as Augé states: "Every government today—given that it governs at least in part through word and image—must convince a majority of citizens." Yet, on the subject of a likely Iraq War, the French government did not need to do much convincing as the lack of pro-war opinions, also noticeable among politicians, echoed the citizens'.

On January 31, 2003, Lionel Jospin broached the subject of Iraq and expressed himself as a former statesman in very similar terms to those previously encountered. He agreed to a military intervention in case of a proven link between Iraq and Al Qaeda. He did not believe Iraq was able to strike without risking its own destruction. Though he recognized the Iraqi dictatorship, he wondered if the UN was going to make a list of all dictatorships and act militarily against them. He declared that "it is not true that only principles are at stake in this conflict." Musing on a possible war, he reminded France of its role:

> This war would be led exclusively by the United States forces, the other participating countries being there only as political caution. It is not France's calling to be reduced to back-up troops, even less so when the outcome is uncertain. If this war takes place, France should not participate in it. I wish that together with Germany, we may convince our European partners to adopt this position. If not, let us decide for France.

As for as the traditional left/right divide which dominates French politics, there was consensus across the board—albeit with some nuances—with the policy followed by Chirac and Dominique de Villepin, then Foreign Affairs minister. Actually, differences lay within some members of the UMP (Union for the Presidential Majority, Chirac's party) since some, but very few, did back a military intervention, a few individuals from Chirac's party and the Démocratie libérale party (those people were sometimes referred to as "Atlantists"). A part of the UMP feared that a veto from France at the UN Security Council would antagonize the U.S. even more and entail political and economic isolation on the world scene, and that France should finally choose to side with the U.S. There was a faction of the right, the very right and extreme right, that was openly supporting a possible veto from France (with some among them fearing that France might back out of it at the last minute). All of the left (Socialists, Communists and extreme-left) were strongly in favor of France's veto. One Socialist deputy said: "One can't reason only in terms of repercussion which, of course, might be considerable for the European Union, NATO, and the UN. One has to accept this stage of tension with the United States and reconstruct afterwards. There will be an after-Bush."

By mid-February, there was talk that the National Assembly and Senate would vote on the issue of Iraq to comfort France's position by showing how the country was behind its President. Then this motion weakened as some did doubt what the voting issue would really be about with the uncertainty of international politics, and finally Chirac upheld the Gaullist view that foreign policy really was his turf alone so that it was up to him to decide in the final analysis. Nevertheless a debate about Iraq did take place in both chambers and summary was given in *Le Monde,* notably abundant extracts of Prime Minister Jean-Pierre Raffarin's speech to the National Assembly. It entailed meaningful and concerned passages on the pre-war situation as Raffarin redefined France's position in regard to the conflict, the UN or the U.S., and assessed the nature of a possible conflict, plus its consequences:

> Today's crisis may be tomorrow's war. This perspective mobilizes
> public opinions [...] Beyond the current crisis what is at stake
> is people's confidence in the future of international law. Such is
> the deep meaning of France's engagement and its diplomacy in
> this crisis [...] Nobody can assert that the path to war might be
> shorter than the path to inspections. Nobody can assert either
> that it could open up on a safer, fairer and stabler world. [...] War
> is always the outcome of failure. [...] France relies on the United
> Nations. [...] Our differences on Iraq should not challenge the
> strength of our relationship with the United States [...] We are old
> allies, we cooperate on many vital dossiers, starting with the fight
> against terrorism. [...] We share on Iraq the same objectives, those
> of Resolution 1441. We diverge on the means of achieving them.
> We have a duty of truth towards Allies who respect each other [...]
> Today, a military intervention, when all the avenues of a pacific
> solution have not been explored, would divide the international
> community [...] It would emphasize fractures and tensions in a
> complex country and region [...] War would weaken the coalition
> formed against terrorism after September 11. It would cause an
> increase of this phenomenon whereas this scourge which threatens
> us all, in that part of the world as here, needs to be fought against."

Alain Juppé declared that the disarming of Iraq was first on the agenda, and contemplated pessimistically that instead of "democratic contagion" in

Ryad, Damascus, and Teheran, after the end of Saddam's dictatorship, there might be on the contrary "a prolonged occupation of Iraq under American administration" which "might end up causing rejection reactions and even maybe an increase in terrorism."

Noël Mamère, fully approved of France's position "against a war decided unilaterally by a hyper power," criticizing "the new doctrine of 'preemptive action,' according to which the United States take upon themselves the right to invade countries and topple governments hostile to their interests." This doctrine reflected "the methodical organization of imperial globalization, on the basis of preeminence of the American order in every domain." Its danger was underlined: "As it feeds upon the consequences of North-South inequalities, tied to liberal globalization, and the alibi of the fight against terrorism, it is a global war without time or space limits."

Alain Bocquet added that "the war policy of the American Administration is not accepted but rejected by public opinion throughout the world, mobilized more by anti-hegemony than by anti-Americanism." He then envisioned the consequences for the Middle East but also French suburbs: "The whole of the Middle-East and the Muslim world would live through an American war as a provocation, an extra humiliation, an injustice adding to others, noticeably the one endured so harshly by the Palestinian people. We are not immune in our popular suburbs to the difficult consequences of such a hypothesis."

After that debate, *Le Monde* in its analysis and account of it, stressed another factor not so forcefully nor openly expressed before then by politicians: the fact that, while backing France's anti-war position and wanting the UN as arbiter, quite a few leaders were already then (i.e., about a month before the outbreak of war itself) strongly foreseeing the likelihood of war. Pessimistic about the overruling of the UN, Raffarin said: "We do not discard war." Balladur, inviting the government "to prepare for the future, reflect on the consequences on the world balance of this conflict which seems unavoidable," uttered: "Will France manage or not to avoid war and have its conception of law respected? It is far from being certain." Alain Juppé bluntly affirmed: "I won't beat around the bush. Of course, we all want to hope still that there remains a chance to avoid war. But rumors of mobilization are starting to cover voices which still call for reason. Nevertheless it won't be said that we did not express our worries loud and clear."

On March 6, a UMP member accompanying Chirac and Villepin on a visit to Algeria confided to *Le Monde* that the President was convinced that Americans wouldn't back out but go to war against Iraq, come what may. On the same page of *Le Monde*, Guy Tessier, president of the Defense Commission at the National Assembly, commented that Americans have been in a war logic since September 11, and see evil everywhere, that they would not change course for fear of losing face, unless Saddam Hussein were to go into exile. He doubted the presence of WMDs, convinced that "the Iraqis have accepted all conditions. What remains is only conventional weapons."

On March 15, fears of war approaching inexorably were even more confirmed as Blair and Bush renounced bringing to the UN Security Council vote the U.S., UK and Spain resolution asking Iraq to disarm before March 17 and blamed France heavily for what in their eyes was a diplomatic failure which France did not recognize as such. This last step was illustrative of what had been developing throughout 2002 and even more 2003, that is a rift among pro- and anti-war European Union members. This divide between its members was at times forcefully promoted by Donald Rumsfeld and in turn initiated by Jacques Chirac against new pro-war European Union members like Poland. This was also another episode of the widening gap between the U.S. and France in their appraisal and decisions about Iraq, which engendered Francophobia in the U.S. on a scale never witnessed before. Finally it concretized the failure of the UN as an international body and the supremacy of international law and the worst fears of might against right as Kagan had promoted it. No wonder, then, that *Le Monde* on its front page of March 21 had this big title above a picture of the first explosions in Baghdad: "The American War Has Started."

Last Points of View before the Outbreak of the War

Finally on March 20, there appeared two articles underlining the lack of logic and rationality, the madness and the absurdity of the whole situation. Martin Amis's article bore in French a more provoking title than in the original English: "Bush against Saddam: delirium shock." At the start, Amis stressed the confounding proofs backing the American and British decisions: "We accept that there are legitimate *casus belli*: acts or situations 'provoking or justifying war'. The present debate feels off-centre, and faintly unreal, because the U.S. and the UK are going to war for a new set of reasons (partly undisclosed) while continuing to adduce the old set of reasons (which in this case do not cohere or even overlap)." He then expanded on the change of terms from "the axis of hatred" to "the axis of evil" (reminiscent of Reagan's evil empire) to underline Bush's religiousness and the heady mix of religion and politics that are his, Bush "being intellectually null," with these scathing remarks:

> [...] we are obliged to accept the fact that Bush is more religious than Saddam: of the two presidents, he is, in this respect, the more psychologically primitive. We hear about the successful "Texanisation" of the Republican party. And doesn't Texas sometimes seem to resemble a country like Saudi Arabia, with its great heat, its oil wealth, its brimming houses of worship, and its weekly executions?

Amis questioned the attack of Iraq on the basis of WMDs, as there were two countries in his view that would deserve such an attack more: Iran and North Korea (but then South Korea would have suffered too which therefore could not be envisioned). He doubted the validity of the whole enterprise:

> There are two rules of war that have not yet been invalidated by the new world order. The first rule is that the belligerent nation must be fairly sure that its actions will make things better; the second rule is that the belligerent nation must be more or less certain that its actions won't make things worse. America could perhaps claim to be satisfying the first rule (while admitting that the improvement may be only local and short term). It cannot begin to satisfy the second.

In the order of comparisons, Bush versus Saddam or Bush versus Bin Laden as "his opposite extreme twin," another opposition was made between war and peace served by faltering rhetoric. Morin and Saussure based their analysis on the fact that European and world opinions were not as receptive as American public opinion to the Administration thesis, presented as expert and competent. Recalling the means which totalitarianism regimes used to convince the masses, they inferred that Bush has had recourse to similar methods where the individual is to adhere to the position of the power in place, not thanks to rational arguments illustrated by facts but simply because the power in place rests on an unconditional demand of allegiance to the State, as opposed to dangerous enemies, sometimes real, but often fantasized. They added that the big conflicts led by the U.S. in the last decades "have regularly distinguished themselves by the absence of ethical and rational justification." Jean-François Kahn held the same view, finding it strange that after the Cold War, the United States picked up Marxist dialectics, and "like the Communists," are "ready to resort to their methods, photos, montages, arbitrary imprisonments [...] to put forward their point of view."

Of Newspapers and War and Consequences

What to conclude from this selection of mainly *Le Monde* articles on the "likely" Iraq War? In our "paradoxically intimate relation to the world, a relation which is both image-charged and abstract [...] though we are informed of all that is happening, we generally only know what we are told about it," Augé writes. This is obvious and particularly well illustrated by the people from various walks of life who expressed themselves in *Le Monde*. They all reacted to the looming event with data then known to them and also their own analysis according to their psychological, political or professional make-up. Two years after their pronouncements, one is struck, all the more with the benefit of hindsight, by the clairvoyance most of them evidenced on the motives or so-called proofs invoked for starting the war. One must also acknowledge that the positive outcomes of the war, so forcefully put forward by the pro-war camp have so far not materialized or so little, and admit with sadness that lots of the misgivings or dire predictions resulting from the war have materialized to a lesser or greater degree, causing the now French Foreign Affairs minister, Michel Barnier, to beg the world to come out of "this black hole which is in the process of aspiring the Middle-East and beyond it, the world."

What also stands out is the sense of utter helplessness engendered by such a situation. As Augé has it again, we live in a world which gives us the illusion that we know everything but we are also helpless to do anything about what we know. Ours is "an anxiety-producing world," and our new century is most brilliantly described as follows: "after a fanfare start, the third millenium crashed at take-off!" People of good will or wisdom seem powerless to counteract what was mainly one country's decision. Baudrillard rightly points out that in this Iraq war there was "an absolute schism between power on one side and the will of populations on the other, mobilized everywhere against this incomprehensible war, without this bringing the slightest change whatsoever." Since international institutions and treaties are not respected by the United States, it flows out that events occur against or next to various peoples, governments, or nations, all powerless to influence the course of events. September 11 has been our Sarajevo, and has allowed the Bush Administration to use that event to launch the basis of "the new American century." Using might against right has undermined the existing world order by creating a "new world *disorder*," as it is often termed, or world chaos. Says Michel Barnier, again: "All the principles we hold dear—respect of human dignity and international law, force as ultimate recourse, solidarity in striving for dialogue between cultures and civilizations—all these principles have been shaken."

In the final analysis, it has to be agreed with Augé, that history is "dirty," "mad," and "with desires and delirium running through it." September 11, through the shock and phenomenal dimension of the event, has set the U.S. on a "gigantic task of retrospective contraception," striving to erase that fall cataclysm by attacking terrorism and therefore Iraq as a choice target. Baudrillard perceives it as a humiliation that the U.S. wants to see vanish but that is always there, traumatic, the reverse of the positive American Myth, the myth of American destruction. It results in an asymmetrical confrontation of a world power which attacks who it wishes when it wishes and an underground adversary which keeps on reproducing all the more as it is being exterminated. It has led to the paradox that identity reflexes which used to be the weapon of poor people and nations have since September 11, under a nationalistic-evangelical guise, become those "of the highest State instances of the world hyperpower." Are we then living in a "safer world" as President Bush claimed it in 2004? Will we? The answer, my friend, is blowing in the wind.

Don Riggs

How Do Dune and Winter Differ apart from the Weather?

When Frank Herbert's *Dune* appeared in 1965, the first novel ever to win both the Hugo and the Nebula awards in one year, Ursula K. LeGuin, whose *The Left Hand of Darkness* would be the second ever to do so four years later, could hardly have been unaware of Herbert's creation. Indeed, the two novels share several striking motifs: a planet known by a single word that describes a dominant environmental characteristic—"Dune" and "Winter"—an indigenous population that is encountered by one or more "offworlders" who must learn enough of the culture to interact with the inhabitants successfully, a major focus on gender complementarities, and an awareness of exploitation of traditional peoples by more "advanced" civilizations.

Cross-cultural communication, and especially miscommunication, is foregrounded in both novels. The postwar American intellectual environment that nurtured both Herbert and LeGuin was characterized by attention paid to the structural aspects of explicit and implicit communication, and an awareness of problems arising in dealing with other cultures. In 1958, Lederer and Burdick's novel *The Ugly American*, which depicts an American ambassador who doesn't understand the language or the culture of the country where he has been stationed, was a bestseller. In 1959, anthropologist Edward Twitchell Hall published his study *The Silent Language*, in which particular aspects of nonverbal, and to a certain extent unconscious, communication are analyzed. However, S.I. Hayakawa had published his *Language in Action* in 1941, and the revised version, *Language in Thought and Action*, in 1949; Brian Herbert states that this last book influenced his father significantly (177). Hayakawa's distinction between "reports," or statements the truth of which can be checked, and "inferences," or speculations about the unknown based on the known, underlies the miscommunications illustrated in *The Ugly American* and *The Silent Language*, and provides a convenient critical tool for analyzing aspects of those communication failures pictured in *Dune* and *The Left Hand of Darkness*.

For Paul Atreides, much of *Dune* consists of his learning to participate in and understand the native Fremen culture, ultimately to bend it to his "terrible purpose," the nature of which he only gradually realizes. However, another aspect of his journey is learning the language—in the larger sense— of the Fremen culture, and to fuse that somehow with his eclectic training as an Atreides ruler, as a Mentat, and as the first male to become as one of the Illuminati-like sisterhood, the Bene Gesserit. In LeGuin's novel *The Left Hand of Darkness*, the Terran envoy from the Ekumen of civilized worlds, Genly Ai, must learn the language, also in the larger sense, of the complementary native cultures of Karhide and Orgoreyn. He has been supplied with vocabulary and grammar before landing on Gethen, or Winter, but the deep structures of the culture inform the literal word meanings in such a way as to impede his understanding of what the indigenous people tell him. Thus, there is a disconnect between what is stated and what is inferred similar to that in the Atreides-Fremen communications, but instead of the "word sounds...not being linked up...in the normal manner" (Herbert 210) because of the aridity of the planet, the misunderstandings occur as a result of "shifgrethor," which is described as "prestige, face, place, the pride-relationship, the untranslatable and all-important principle of social authority" in the planet's cultures (Le Guin 14).

Most of the misunderstandings between the offworld Atreides and the native Fremen arise from the Dune native's attunement to the extreme scarcity of water. However, whereas in *Dune*, only the offworlders seem aware of a disjuncture between the Fremen's use of language and the offworlders' understanding of it, in *The Left Hand of Darkness* we see that the Gethenian Estraven understands that differences in shifgrethor, a culture-specific deep structure, seriously impede the flow of communication between him and Genly Ai, as does Ai himself. As the sinister Gethenian Tibe says to Genly Ai, "'I keep forgetting that you come from another planet. But of course it's not a matter that you ever forget'" (9).

Even though Tibe's comment is ironic, it does underline a central theme of *The Left Hand of Darkness*, that of isolation within an alien culture. Genly Ai, a Terran, is in the novel a male on a world of neuter people, where people become sexed only during *kemmer*, a monthly period of a few days during which the Gethenians become either male or female, depending upon context. Ai, as someone who is constantly male, is regarded as a pervert. At the same time, since he is the only earthman on Gethen, he is the only member of his culture in his surroundings; the other few members of the Ekumen on his spaceship are in stasis in orbit around the planet's sun. He has no one who understands his cultural *Weltanschauung*, let alone his sexual constitution, with whom he can confide.

It is in the nature of the contacts between offworlders and the planets' aboriginals that *Dune* and *The Left Hand of Darkness* differ with respect to invasiveness and exploitation. Herbert's offworlders, particularly the Atreides' mortal enemies the Harkonnens, see Arrakis as a planet to be mined for its valuable spice, and the natives to be exploited for their labor and oppressed, even exterminated. The Atreides family, on the other hand, sees in the Fremen possible allies, as the constituents of a highly effective fighting force. The latter is what ultimately happens, although Paul Atreides "goes native" and becomes a fusion of Atreides and Fremen. LeGuin's offworlders, represented by the one envoy presented in the novel, want to gently introduce the Gethenians, when they are ready, to the possibilities of cultural exchange, and trade to the extent that trade with planets at the distance of many light-years is possible. Exploitation and the development of a fighting force are both distinctly discounted by Genly Ai.

Donald Palumbo's analysis of *Dune* as a Monomythic text emphasizes the initiatory quality of Paul's experiences as he develops into Paul Muad'dib; one stage in this process is the symbolic burial and rebirth, the first literal instance of which is Paul and Jessica's night in a stilltent, fleeing the Harkonnen troops, during which they are buried by a sandstorm (Palumbo 174). It is during this tomb/womb experience Paul shares with his mother that he comes to a series of inner realizations about his identity and adumbrations of his "terrible purpose" (Herbert 187-205), part of which involves his inheritance, genetic and educational, from her. One of the most strikingly parallel motifs in Herbert's and LeGuin's novels is this sharing of the tent, as Genly Ai and Estraven escape the Orgota authorities by trekking across the polar ice cap in midwinter. Just as Paul has come to know his mother, and thus his identity, far better during this incubation period in the stilltent, so Ai and Estraven come to understand each other far more deeply in their periodic rests in their tent during the winter nights.

A pivotal sharing in this tent signals LeGuin's debt to, and transformation of, Herbert's novel. Estraven asks Ai why the Ekumen sends one sole Envoy to a planet; Ai responds that one Envoy cannot transform a planet, but that planet can transform the Envoy, which is significant in that the Ekumen "is not a body politic, but a body mystic." This first contact is important, as the Ekumen "considers beginnings to be extremely important" (259). This rather strikingly recalls the very first sentence in *Dune*: "A beginning is the time for taking the most delicate care that the balances are correct" (3). Indeed, in both books the offworlder is transformed by the world; the difference is that the reader sees Paul Muad'dib transform the Fremen on Dune, while the transformations on Winter seem, in the course of the novel, to be minimal. Possibly this has to do, in part, with the fact that the politics of the Galactic Empire in *Dune* are Machiavellian, while Ai explains that the Ekumen's "doctrine is just the opposite of the doctrine that the end justifies the means" (259), or precisely anti-Machiavellian. One explanation Ai gives for this is the devastation of the intergalactic war of the Ekumen against the Enemy, "several centuries ago" (137), making the Ekumen less interested in conquest and profit than in evolution, both that of the worlds newly admitted into its sphere, and of itself. Both Herbert and LeGuin react against destructive elements of the sociopolitical and economic order of their times; Herbert's fictional world is characterized by *yang* and Machiavellian tactics, while LeGuin's is characterized by a *yin* and Taoist dance.

I presented a significantly longer version of the above paper at a conference where it was well received; about a year later, I had an opportunity to send a copy of it to Ursula K. Le Guin herself. Here are excerpts from her generous email commentary:

Hello Don Riggs—

I did read your paper. I enjoyed it and it seems sound to me: but I think Dune didn't have as much to do with LHD as it might seem to.

...

I had Hayakawa's text as a freshman in English A at Radcliffe, and rebelled feebly against much of his laying down the law; but Edward Hall, later, was a great discovery, and a genuine influence on my thought.

...

Anyhow, back to *Dune*, I did read it, not when it first came out but somewhere within the first few years, therefore probably before I wrote LHD: but honestly I am not certain.

I read the book while I had a quite bad flu—I was mentally impaired, and little of it remained with me when I finished it. I liked the setting but wasn't emotionally engaged by the characters, found the complicated politics and plotting boring, the narrative style flat and clunky and the dialogue stilted. Pseudo-references such as the name Atreides galled me, and the semi-Arabic culture didn't persuade me. What I am saying, obviously, is that I didn't like the book—which I still hate to say, because I liked Frank Herbert very much—he was a good, generous man, a mensch. I have never wanted to reread it.

If I did read *Dune* before I wrote LHD, it may well have subliminally influenced me—probably in the negative, as you suggest. I do not recall any consciousness of this, any intention to "do what Frank did, only do it right." But as you see, my memory is so imprecise as to be nearly useless.

The one parallel you make that I feel (and it can only be a feeling) is truly wrong, despite the seeming close resemblance, is the two scenes in tents— Paul with his mother, you say, and Estraven with Genly. I have no memory whatever of the scene in *Dune*. Zilch. It didn't register. (One should not read with a temperature of 101 degrees.) I think I can state with certainty that this episode in *Dune* is unrelated to the scenes in the tent on the Ice. (The principal ancestry of those scenes, of course, is the journals of Scott, Shackleton, et al., particularly the emotionally wrenching last journal of Scott.)

...

I wish I could be more useful to you. Anyhow, if you want to use any of this, feel free. (Le Guin)

The basic lesson I learned from Le Guin's e-mail response is that two works can have either an affinity or a point-by-point contrast without one work necessarily having "influenced" another; it is a lesson one of my graduate school professors emphasized, and for some reason I had wanted to make the contrast between the novels such a conscious statement on Le Guin's part that I created a factual link where there was none. Stating that Le Guin "could hardly have been unaware" of *Dune* is the kind of assertion I slash with my pen when reading stacks of student papers, but it is one's own blind spot which goes unnoticed.

Works Cited

Hall, Edward Twitchell. *The Silent Language*. Garden City, NY: Doubleday,1959.

Hayakawa, S. I. *Language in Thought and Action*. New York: Harcourt, Brace,1949.

Herbert, Brian. Dreamer of Dune: The Biography of Frank Herbert. New York: Doherty, 2003.

Herbert, Frank. *Dune*. 1965. New York: Ace, 1987.

Lederer, William J. and Eugene Burdick. *The Ugly American*. New York: Norton, 1958.

Le Guin, Ursula. Message to the author. 29 March 2006. E-mail.

The Left Hand of Darkness. New York: Ace, 1969.

Palumbo, Donald E. *Chaos Theory, Asimov's Foundations and Robots, and Herbert's Dune: The Fractal Aesthetic of Epic Science Fiction*. Westport, CT: Greenwood, 2002.

Scott Stein

Big Switch

The stock market was down. Gas prices were up. Home values were down. Inflation was up. Savings were down. Unemployment was up. Production was down. Foreclosures were up. The people were down. Way down. Something had to be done.

Something had been done. Many somethings. Most of them involved printing green paper and giving it away. For some reason, this didn't work. No one seemed to know why, but it didn't. More green paper was supposed to make the things people wanted to go up, go up, and the things people wanted to go down, go down. But it didn't.

Worse still, new things started going up that people wanted to go down, and vice versa. Crime had been going down for a long time, but was now up. Life expectancy had been going up for a long time, but was now down. The people were down, way down, and so were their politicians' approval numbers. Something had to be done. And something was. A brilliant something, maybe the most brilliant ever to come out of Washington, which is saying something indeed, for many brilliant somethings had come out of Washington before. But never a something like this.

The problem, at its core, was that what people wanted to go up, was going down, and what people wanted to go down, was going up. The solution, at its core, was to make what was going up, go down, and what was going down, go up. It was obvious. An executive order was issued and executed; a new congressional committee convened.

Thus began the first session of the newly formed Linguislature, which, in its first linguislative act, ordered that henceforth up was down. The President signed it immediately, and it was the law of the land, a breathtaking piece of linguislation.

Up was down.

Some people didn't like it, but the law was the law. The nation was in a bad way and everyone had to rally behind this new plan. Politicians called on citizens to be patriotic. Saying that something was up when it was down was not only illegal but also un-American.

Up was down.

Unfortunately, down was not yet up.

The companion piece of linguislation that would change down into up was prevented from going forward (one could no longer say "held up" without meaning "held down," but "held down" did not yet mean "held up") by a committee member who insisted that funding for a highway rest stop in his home state be added to the bill. The wrangling went on for three days, as other committee members argued that their states also needed highway rest stops. In the end, it was agreed that all of their states needed highway rest stops, and down was linguislated to be up.

It had been a rough three days for Americans. When up is down, and down is down, that's one too many downs, and one too few ups. During those stressful days, if a woman, tired after a long day of work, had enough of watching television and wanted to leave the couch to go to the bedroom, she could not say to her husband, "I'm going upstairs to bed." Not without breaking the law. And she could not very well say, "I'm going downstairs to bed," since down did not yet mean up. She could simply say she was going to bed and leave up or down out of it altogether, but that would be rude. The only polite option was to stay on the couch late into the night while her husband watched reruns of *The A-Team*. Unless, of course, the bedroom was in fact downstairs. If the bedroom was downstairs, she could just say she was going down to bed. But as luck would have it, the bedroom rarely was.

Fortunately, wiser heads prevailed in the Linguislature, and seven states started planning construction on highway rest stops, named after dedicated and selfless public servants, on the same day that down officially became up. This made life better for everyone. Now people didn't have to sit on the couch watching reruns of *The A-Team* unless they wanted to. That's not to say the transition was easy. It wasn't.

People had no idea how often they said up and down without really thinking about it. Adjusting took some time. Those first few weeks, people kept saying down when up was what they meant, and up when down was what they meant. They weren't trying to break the law, but they did, over and over: "I'm going down to the market." "I'm sure the hat will turn up somewhere." "The rain came down in buckets." "Wake up, already." Many a basketball coach watched in dismay as his players stretched out on the floor when told to do laydown drills.

But Americans are a hardy people. Plus, everyone was scared that the economy would never recover—if calling down up and up down would help, most were willing to go along. Also, after a two-week grace period, using up for up or down for down was punishable by a $50 fine, which no one could afford to pay. The Linguislature had funded massive enforcement for the Up-Down initiative. Up-Down agents were everywhere, correcting people's word choices (the way grammar-conscious parents used to in the old days for *who* and *whom*) and handing out fines.

People adjusted. They always do. Before long, they were seeing downlifting movies, looking down old friends, and doing upward-facing dog in yoga class. They went uptown and downtown the way they always had. They just said to the cab driver, "Take me downtown" when they meant up, or "Take me uptown" when they meant down. Midtown, mercifully, remained unchanged. Not that it mattered—most people didn't have enough money to take a cab anywhere, on account of the economic upturn.

The transition cost billions. Boxes had to be reprinted to say "This Side Down." Elevator buttons had to be switched. Although perhaps the linguislators only meant to switch down with up in the directional sense, the law was written without such a limitation, so to be in compliance, millions of winter coats and comforters had to be relabeled "genuine goose up." Linguislators held a press conference to note that all of this stimulated the economy.

If any of this seemed to be a waste of money, an empty gesture, it wasn't. Within a few weeks, the astonishing brilliance of this landmark linguislation became clear. Newscasters reported on gas prices going down. On inflation going down. On taxes going down. On the stock market going up at a historic rate. Neighbors told their friends that they had just upgraded their cable service or their car lease to save money. People were feeling good about the news for the first time in many months. It got better still.

The news reported that the literacy rate was going up and the obesity rate was going down. Best of all, millions of people were told by their doctors that their cholesterol was down and even their blood pressure was down. Maybe this last one was caused by hearing that their property values were up, or by hearing that their retirement portfolios were up. People lost their jobs as fast as always and faster still, and their homes, and their investments, but the overall picture seemed brighter than it had in a long time. Unemployment was going down, after all.

A nation's morale had never before received such a desperately needed boost. The linguislators were hailed as heroes. In the halls of Congress they shook each other's hands and agreed that they were. Up-Down had accomplished so much. Yet there was still more work to be done. There were so many other words. The task ahead was immense, but the linguislators were committed to the American people and pressed on through the night, knowing that, as salaries went up and food prices went down, down, down, hungry families across the nation were counting on them.

Elizabeth Thorpe

Punctuation

Part One: Common Problems

Cody was seventeen.
Cody was in love.
Cody's curfew was midnight.
Cody's girlfriend had freckles.
She had a freckle on her right hip.
Cody circled it in pen.
Cody wrote "Cody's" above the freckle.

Cody left the party, and he died.

The SUV broke the thin skim of ice over the gravel pit and sank to the bottom.

Cody's girlfriend told him not to leave the party, and he didn't want to, but went anyway.

Cody's mom didn't want him to drive fast, but didn't want him to be late, so he drove fast.

Seeing the hole in the ice the next morning, Sgt. Benjamin feared the worst.

The dispatcher who answered Sgt. Benjamin's call knew Cody's family.
Everyone in town knew Cody's family.
Everyone in town knew everyone else in town.

Cody's parents, who had only one child, had been up all night.

Cody, their baby, was below 100 feet of water.
Water, black gravel pit water, surrounded the SUV.
Sarah, Cody's girlfriend, didn't know yet.
Marcia and Phil, Cody's parents, didn't think to tell her.

Cody had, a few years ago, stopped telling his parents everything.
Cody knew, or thought he knew, he was going to die.

He dreamed he was in a car accident (driving his father's car, not his mom's SUV) and the dream ended in darkness.

Cody told his girlfriend—he told her everything—and she made him stop talking about it.

She put his finger on her freckle, his favorite one, and made his finger trace back and forth across her stomach until he wasn't thinking about the dream anymore.

Who would open his Christmas presents, he thought, if he died? Would they just stay, with big homemade bows on top, in his parents' bedroom closet?

(That made Cody cry sometimes, as he lay in bed, thinking of the Christmas presents getting dusty, the boxes warping from summer heat, the paper fading.)

The gravel pit was deep, the weather was cold, and visibility was poor. Cody's mother wanted the police to send divers, a crane, and a submarine, if that's what it would take to get to her son (she couldn't say the word "body").

Part Two: End Punctuation

Marcia was amazed that people could continue on as normal.
She felt skinless.
The police wanted to wait until spring to recover the car.

Marcia asked them how they could leave a kid underwater all winter.

Marcia had always avoided confrontation. But not now.

Sgt. Benjamin said, "I'm sorry, Marcia. I can't endanger my men." She would have gladly traded all of his living men for her dead child.

"The divers can't do their jobs?" Marcia said, "Is that it? Or maybe you don't think the car's really there?"

Sgt. Benjamin said, "It broke through the guardrail, remember? We know it's there. Why don't you sit down?"

"You have children!" Marcia yelled. "I know you understand!"

Part Three: Making Transitions

The other Sarah, Sarah Bunker, was the one who told Cody's girlfriend Sarah; Sarah Bunker's father was a volunteer firefighter.

Sarah and the other Sarah weren't friends; still, the other Sarah thought Cody's girlfriend should know before everyone else.

Sarah skipped the assembly and left the school building; in the meantime, Sgt. Benjamin was on the phone with the Environmental Protection Agency, at Marcia's request.

Here's what Sarah saw as she walked: icy trees, shining in the sunlight; a pink knitted mitten, frozen into a snowbank; a pothole, layered with thin ice.

Sarah jumped on the pothole until it was filled with nothing but snow. She kept walking, even though it was five below and she didn't have her jacket; she didn't stop until she got to the 7-11 where her mother worked.

Sarah's mother stood behind the cash register, selling Chuck Salsbury a breakfast sandwich; Sarah waited in line to talk to her.

Sarah told her mother what she knew: that Cody was dead, that she had left school, and that she needed permission to get a tattoo.

Sarah's mother had plenty of questions: What happened to Cody? Would her daughter be all right? Why a tattoo? For God's sake, a tattoo? Now?

While Sarah's mother hesitated, Sarah blinked back tears and stared at the sign by the register: "Leave a penny, take a penny."

Sarah's mother looked at the clock: 8:45. A woman she didn't recognize stood behind Sarah holding a booklet, "We, Like Sheep: Bible Verses for Every Occasion." While she thought about the tattoo request, Sarah's mother rang up the woman's purchase. Looking for a sign, she opened to a random passage: Luke 1:34. "'How will this be,' Mary asked the angel, 'since I am a virgin?'" This didn't help.

"Mom," Sarah said, almost whispering, "It's going to wear off."

She turned down the waistband of her jeans, and her mother saw the word written above her daughter's right hip: Cody's.

At the crash site, Marcia hadn't given up.

Now Charlie O'Hallahan, the local diver, was talking to Sgt. Benjamin: "Guess if I can dive for urchins in the winter, I can't refuse on account of the cold. I d'no but it'll be tough, though, Benny, getting' that car door open."

"Just try," Marcia said. "I won't leave him there; don't ask me to."

Part Four: Possessives

Cody's family's house was already lit up for Christmas. In two weeks' time, Marcia's sister Pam and Cody's cousins, Chuck and Casey, would be there for Christmas Eve.

Marcia sat in her husband's car after he had gone inside. She looked at the sign next to the mailbox: "The Joneses' Abode." Her husband's best man gave it to them as a wedding present 25 years ago. He thought it was funny: keeping up with the Joneses, ha, ha. Phil and Cody had wrapped lights around the signpost in a candy cane pattern. The lights were off, but covered in ice and catching sunlight.

They'd been on a fool's errand. She sat up straighter.

"It's a mistake," she yelled, hitting the cold steering wheel. Her hand stung. "It's just a mistake. Cody, I thought you were dead!"

Phil came back out, opened her door and reached for her. "It's time to come inside," he said. "It's been a long morning."

Part Five: Emphasis

Phil felt punch-drunk. Three days ago, he had returned from a fact-finding business trip. His company had taken care of him: he had flown first-class and enjoyed a few well-earned in-flight drinks. But he had felt unsettled. While he waited in the baggage-claim area, he had a feeling that something was wrong at home. Cody had been testing the limits lately, pushing for more independence. Phil had often felt like the go-between in conflicts with his wife and son. He called home. Everything was fine there.

Still, the strange feeling remained. Phil stopped in one of the airport stores. He looked at the quarter-, half-, and one-pound bags of dark chocolate. Cody loved dark chocolate. It had been a while since Phil had bought him a present on a business trip.

Now Phil went into his son's room. The one-pound bag of chocolate sat on Cody's desk, half empty. Phil hesitated, then reached into it. He put a dark wafer of chocolate on his tongue and let it melt.

When Sarah and her mother left the tattoo parlor, the sun was setting—the days were so short this time of year. Sarah looked at the trees—evergreens, mostly—silhouetted in black against the orange-pink sky. In the cold car, Sarah tried to shrink into herself, make herself as small as possible and touch as little as possible. The tattoo felt sticky—sticky and sort of scratchy—and Sarah wondered if the dressing would freeze to it. The other Sarah had left a message on her cell phone: "They're sending Charlie O'Hallahan down to get Cody. Tomorrow morning, early—if the weather's okay. I just—I thought you should know. I almost said I thought you might like to know, but that's not exactly—I mean—I'm just really sorry. About Cody. I'll see you at school."

Sarah thought—she couldn't help it—about Cody's body, how it would look when they pulled him out. She wondered if he'd look like himself. She touched the gauze pad over her tattoo and tried to remember the way it had felt when he wrote on her—the point of the pen, his little finger on her skin.

"Marcia, I strongly recommend that you do not...yes, I know. But I don't think you're gonna want to be there when we... Still, I... Yes, we talked to the EPA, and...right. They want us to get the crane in...well, I didn't think it was an option before. I know, but... I KNOW, but... Well, if the EPA wants us to pull the whole car out, that's what... I was just worried about the diver, Marcia, not... I know. See you tomorrow, I guess...okay. Try to get some sleep. Goodnight."

Part Six: It All Falls Apart

It was snowing again the ground crunched under marcias boots as she shifted back and forth phil was still in the car he didnt want to watch he didnt understand why marcia wanted to my baby she thought my baby and she thought about once when he was two blond hair big eyes and he fell in her sisters pool he was a good swimmer she thought he loved the water how strange that it would be like this charlie the diver was underwater and then he came up and marcia assumed he had clipped the cable onto the car like they said he would onto the front of the car next to the dent where she ran into the light post at the supermarket god shed loved that car and why was she thinking that and why were her feet cold how could she feel or think anything besides my son my son and it seemed like a long time before the sound of machinery the crane pulling back phil coming to stand behind her and the ice cracking around the car her car as the front bumper came up and she didnt want to look and she couldnt help but look and the silence then the murmuring as they all realized he wasnt there he wasnt at the wheel was he in the back no no he wasnt he wasnt anywhere and marcia didnt feel the gravel mixed with snow on her knees through her pants but she saw the scrapes later

Scott Warnock

School Budgets? We Vote Every Day with our Wallets

Letter to the Editor

Tell me the one again about the crisis we're facing supporting and financing our local public school. Tell me how we're all broke and suffering and we have to vote "no" on the budget.

We can start our conversation at a Phillies game, where—forget the overpriced tickets—one round of beer for me, you, and your two friends costs $29. We can focus our frustration while we watch *Avatar*, which grossed over $740 million in the U.S. After dropping $21 for tickets, we'll commiserate over a $5 popcorn and a couple $4 sodas. We can share our anger after we plunk down $50 for a Pay-Per-View sporting event that we watch in front of your $1,500 widescreen HD TV.

There's more to say on this topic—we're really angry now—so we can continue ranting for several days over our daily coffee (two on Sundays!), ringing up over $1,000 a year each.

We can finalize our decision to vote "no" while taking a ride in your $50 thousand car, which does everything a $30 thousand car does with a little more leather and some extra buttons. Vote how you will for your local school budget, but vote honestly. Let's stop pretending that when it comes to our schools we're overstretched, finished, financially defeated.

The money spent on beer at one Phillies game could bail out many small school districts. One person's coffee expenses could save an after-school activity. With the car price differential, some schools could save their entire extracurricular programs this year. If the money we spend on *Avatar* and other movies went toward education... well, now I'm really creating my own fantasy.

Don't vote to direct your ire at schools and teachers for trying to take what you don't have. Just be honest and say you'd rather spend your money elsewhere. Movies not art classes. Pro athletes not teachers. Shiny cars not school computers.

Don't vote out of the feeling that you don't control where your money goes. Why? Because it just wouldn't be true. When it comes to our money, we vote every day.

Jason Wilson

A Game Journey

The day before the wild boar hunt, we'd eaten horsemeat, which was the traditional weekend lunch of chef Olivier de St. Martin's childhood. Olivier had earlier taken me along to visit the village horse butcher, who complained that the younger generation of French didn't eat so much horsemeat anymore. The butcher blamed it on inferior supermarket horsemeat, which he said came—like everything else—pre-packaged from America. "There's also this idea that the horse is the friend of the man," said the horse butcher, who also happened to be an old schoolfriend of Olivier's.

That night, in Charleville-Mézières, near the Ardennes Forest, we drank champagne with Olivier's uncle Jean, who proudly showed off a local hunting magazine which had published his snapshot of a huge, bloody, dead boar he'd recently killed. "That's what you'll be flushing out of the bushes tomorrow," Olivier said to me with a laugh.

Olivier de St. Martin is a French chef who now lives in Philadelphia. He's a superb chef and his restaurant Caribou Café was recently named Best French Restaurant—this in a city with exceptional, renowned French restaurants such as Le Bec Fin and Lacroix. At his restaurant, Olivier insists on bistro staples like organ meats, skate, and snails—and if Americans weren't so fond of horses, he'd offer *viande de cheval*. Olivier is also a friend of mine. We'd both been complaining about the present fussiness of contemporary foodie culture, and he expressed a desire to get back to the basic, primal roots of the cooking of his childhood in hardscrabble Picardie and Champagne. This is cuisine based on unsexy vegetables like beets, turnips, endives, and leeks, as well as forest mushrooms, pungent Maroilles cheese, "pre-salted" lamb (grazed on salt marshes), and game—including boar. Olivier suggested we visit, and he invited me to go on a wild boar hunt with his uncle.

The next morning, still reeling from horse and champagne, it was time for the hunt. Olivier and Jean showed up before dawn at the hotel. "I've been up early salting the lamb for lunch," Olivier said. Uncle Jean wore his brimmed hat cocked to one side and with his trimmed mustache looked a little like Ernest Hemingway.

There was frost on the autumn ground as the sun rose and we arrived at the meeting spot in the forest. Two dozen hunters gathered around in a semi-circle, receiving instructions from the hunt master. No blaze orange for these guys—they were dressed in spiffy outfits and most opted for tweed caps and berets. Some wore scarves. One guy wore a cape. The hunt master explained where some boars had been spotted the other day, and explained the forest was full of deer.

We munched bits of a pastry called *galette au sucre* as horns blew and the dogs barked inside their kennel. "Where are our guns?" I asked.

Olivier laughed and handed me a fluorescent yellow vest. "They're not giving us guns," he said. "Today, we are *traqueur*."

This meant our job would be to walk through the woods, crashing through the low-lying brush, shouting, and generally trying to flush wild boars out of hiding. Meanwhile, two dozen hunters would stand ready to shoot. I was thankful when I heard the hunt master tell them, "No one is to shoot directly into the forest."

They released the dogs and we traqueurs followed them into the woods as the hunters took their positions. The head traqueur told us to advance together in a line, at arm's length, so none of us would accidentally be shot.

We were a motley bunch. I was positioned next to a girl who had dyed her hair bright red—for today only, a pretty good style decision. On my other side was a tough-looking bald guy wearing a ridiculously tiny knit cap that didn't cover his ears. An odd camaraderie developed as we wandered through the forest, waving our arms like idiots, growling "Ho!" I learned that the other traqueurs were mostly local people who were looking to pick up a little extra cash on the weekend. Some of the women gathered chanterelle mushrooms that grew on the forest floor. The hunters meanwhile were middle-aged, upperclass men who had some bucks. So being a traqueur was sort of like caddying, except of course you might be shot.

As the morning wore on, we could sometimes hear the snorts of boar, and would catch a whiff of their musky smell, but we had no luck flushing any. A few times we flushed deer, and some of us would yell, "*À la houe! Derrière!*" and within seconds we'd hear the crack of gunfire.

After a few hours, everyone regrouped in the clearing and we took a break for lunch. This was when the real class system of the hunt revealed itself.

The traqueurs lit a makeshift bonfire, unwrapped sandwiches, and sat down on logs for lunch. The hunters, meanwhile, set up at long, covered picnic tables. Since we were with Uncle Jean, we were upgraded and invited to the hunters' lunch. We ate pre-salted lamb and lentils and vegetable potage. Other hunters grilled sirloin au poivre, and tripe. There were meat tourtes and pâté. There was lots of red wine. I asked why the hunters and the traqueurs had to eat separately and someone said, "Well, you know, you don't wash the towels with the rags."

As we finished our lunch, a group of traqueurs came over to the hunters' side and—seeming to be offended—insisted that we come join them. It seems the traqueurs had broken open a bottle of local moonshine called *bistouille* and were drinking shots. They insisted we join in, too. "You had better be careful," Olivier told me.

The bald guy with the tiny knit cap, in particular, kept passing us the bottle, trying to get us drunk. After a couple of good-comrade sips, Olivier and I just pretended to swig from the bottle. The bald guy, on the other hand, kept tossing back the firewater. Soon enough, the hunters were eager to find a postprandial boar to shoot, and called for us traqueurs to trudge back into the forest.

The first area we flushed after lunch included a steep hill that went up several hundred feet. After all the wine and bistouille, it seemed somewhat discourteous, or even sadistic, of the hunters. At that point, the ways I might die on the boar hunt seemed to be mounting.

All of the traqueurs appeared to be in bad shape when we finally arrived at the hilltop, but the bald guy with the tiny knit cap was in the worst. He swayed back and forth, holding onto a tree. He tried to stand and fell forward, head over heels, nearly a hundred feet down the hill. After that, he couldn't get up at all and lay back down in wet leaves. Olivier and another guy dragged him, on his ass, to the bottom of the hill and left him lying on the trail. His dog stood guard nearby, and would not let anyone near its drunken owner.

We continued waving our arms and shouting. We continued to hear and smell boar. But all we seemed to be flushing was deer. "*À la houe! Derrière!*"

Finally, we neared the end of the last flush, and stepped into the clearing. I could see the line of hunters, guns trained. Suddenly, directly in front of me, a deer popped up and broke into a sprint. "*À la houe!*" someone shouted. With the deer directly in front of me, this was my first thought: The hunters won't shoot into the forest. Second thought: I am not in the forest, I am in the clearing, and therefore I will be shot. Panic immediately set in. And without thinking, I lunged headfirst back into the woods. Like a total wuss.

At least, I thought I looked like a total wuss. When I stood and brushed myself off, some of the Frenchmen came over with admiring faces. They actually seemed impressed. "You tried to tackle that deer!" they said.

No one ended up shooting a boar that afternoon.

Afterwards, over cocktails in the hunt lodge, there was much bemused talk about the barbaric American who had tried to tackle a deer and wrestle him to the ground with his bare hands. "You are a cowboy!" they said.

After the hunt, we joined the rest of Uncle Jean's family at a rustic hilltop inn. There were heads of wild boar lining the walls. Dinner was, of course, game. In this case, we were served *grives*, or thrush. Tiny birds cooked whole and served in a sage butter sauce. We dove in, little heads and beaks first.

In the middle of dinner, a woman at the next table became short of breath. She seemed to be clearly experiencing a heart attack. Uncle Jean calmly stood to help, and her dining companions laid her down on the ground in the middle of the dining room. The waitress phoned an ambulance. About 45 minutes later, the ambulance finally arrived, with the most nonchalant paramedics I have ever witnessed strolling into the dining room—one stubbing out a cigarette. They offered the woman a cup of water and sat her on a stretcher.

The chef, furious that this was happening during his Saturday dinner rush, kept poking his head out of the kitchen. "Did she die yet?" he hissed at his wait staff.

After dinner, as we prepared to leave, Uncle Jean introduced the chef to Olivier, explaining that his nephew "owns a French restaurant in Philadelphia."

"Pffffft," the chef said, a classic French mouth fart, with a dismissive wave of the hand. "Ah," he said. "It's barbaric over there, no?"

Contributors

Stacey E. Ake is an assistant professor of philosophy in the Department of English and Philosophy at Drexel University. She holds two doctorates from Pennsylvania State University. One is in Biology, the other in Philosophy. Her primary area of research is in semiotics, where her interests range from Kierkegaard's idea of the God-Man as a sign to the real world implications of biosemiotics and evolutionary theory. She also does work in religion and science as well as in bioengineering and ethics.

Marquerita Algorri is a Nutrition and Foods major currently in her sophomore year at Drexel. She is hoping to pursue a minor in English in the upcoming year to nurture her love of writing and literature. Her passion for reading and writing began at an early age and was encouraged by her grandmother. These days, she can be found immersed in the pages of the works of Kafka, Plath, and Bukowski. Her interests include fashion, vegetarianism, punk rock, classic literature, art, health, and writing.

Adam Barnett is a strapping young lad enrolled in Music Industry with Music and Film Production minors. He enjoys tap dancing, playing hop scotch, and fiddling with the accordion. He constantly ponders whether his biggest influences, Gambit and James Joyce, would appreciate his writing, but then he realizes it doesn't really matter. What does matter is that he wants to be a good person when he grows up, and nothing else.

Genevieve Betts received her MFA in creative writing in 2006 from Arizona State University, where she reviewed poetry for *Hayden's Ferry Review*, as well as *Sotto Voce* magazine. Recently, she was a finalist for the ABZ First Book Award and her latest work appears in *Western American Literature, Quarter After Eight, Midwest Quarterly*, and *NANO Fiction*. She currently teaches at Drexel University.

Ron Bishop is a professor in the Department of Culture and Communication at Drexel University, where he teaches courses in news writing, sports writing, news media law, and the cultural history of fame. He holds a Ph.D. in communication from Temple University in Philadelphia, PA.

Clinton Burkhart is a Biology major who will be starting his senior year at Drexel in the fall of 2010. When he's not on campus he enjoys trail running and reading in his free time. He prefers classic literature and science fiction. He gets writing inspiration from his favorite writer, Isaac Asimov. Clinton's post-graduation plans are to further his education in the field of clinical psychology.

Sam Chattin is a Screenwriting/Playwriting major whose love of writing spans multiple mediums. His greatest influences are the world around him and the people he meets in life.

Paula Marantz Cohen is distinguished professor of English at Drexel, host of *The Drexel InterView*, and co-editor of jml: *Journal of Modern Literature*. She is the author of eight books, including, most recently, *What Alice Knew: A Most Curious Tale of Henry James and Jack the Ripper*. She holds a BA from Yale College and a Ph.D. from Columbia University.

Ingrid G. Daemmrich teaches writing and literature in the Department of English and Philosophy at Drexel. Her textbook, *The Changing Seasons of Humor in Literature*, now in its sixth edition, aligns humorous literature with the seasons in moving from springtime farce to winter absurdity. The *Handbook of Themes and Motifs in Western Literature*, co-authored with Horst S. Daemmrich, is used as a reference guide by students of literature throughout the world.

Ryan Debski is a sophomore Architecture student. He is originally from the Philadelphia suburbs, but he enjoys the convenience and pace of the city. In his free time Ryan plays basketball, spends time with friends and family, and expands his understanding of architecture. He finds that his biggest inspiration for writing comes from his observations of the world around him.

Amanda Decker is currently a sophomore Chemical Engineering major at Drexel University. Up until her freshman year of high school, Amanda had planned to become a journalist. Although her aspirations have changed slightly, she still enjoys writing for herself. Amanda also enjoys music and theatre, and eventually wants to work in pharmaceutical research after graduation.

Katherine Devanney is a freshman Psychology major minoring in Philosophy. In her free time, she enjoys playing competitive Scrabble, watching television, and traveling. Her favorite book is Oscar Wilde's *The Picture of Dorian Gray*, although she also enjoys reading contemporary authors including Kurt Vonnegut and Jodi Picoult. After graduating, she hopes to earn a Ph.D. in psychology.

Albert DiBartolomeo is the author of the novels *The Vespers Tapes (Blood Confessions* in paperback) and *Fool's Gold*. He has published numerous essays, memoirs, and articles in *Readers Digest, Philadelphia* magazine, the *Philadelphia Inquirer*, the *Newark Star Ledger, Italian Americana, VIA, Woodwork Magazine, Peregrine* and *Catholic Digest*. His publications have been anthologized in the *Chicken Soup for the Soul* series, *Wild Dreams* and *Human Ecology*. One of his essays is used in testing in the Texas Public School system. He co-wrote the short film *Tiramisu* with Len Guercio. He was the founding editor of the *Drexel Online Journal* and *ASK* (originally the Journal of the College of Arts and Sciences), and is a co-director of the Drexel Publishing Group.

Autumn Elliott is a junior majoring in Anthropology at Drexel University.

Leonard Finegold is a self-proclaimed standard-issue faculty member in the Department of Physics at Drexel University. Two things that make him slightly different from the norm is that he teaches the Issues in Science and Religion course 137 (the number is meaningful to physicists), and is on the editorial board of *Annals of Improbable Research*. His favorite place on this planet is Colorado Plateau. Sadly, his knee no longer allows backpacking—only car camping.

Valerie Fox's most recent book is *Bundles of Letters Including A, V and Epsilon* (Texture Press), a compilation of poems with Arlene Ang. Ang and Fox have published collaborative writings in *Admit 2, qarrtsiluni, Per Contra, Arsenic Lobster*, and other journals. Fox is also a Co-Editor for the journal, *Press 1*. Her latest volume, *The Glass Book*, will be out from Texture Press in 2010. She teaches in Drexel's Department of English and Philosophy.

Lauren Gatto is a graduate student working on getting her Masters of Science in Public Policy, specializing in education policy. She is also law school bound and would like to end up working in education law. She received her BA in English from George Washington University. She developed a love of poetry there when first introduced to poets ranging from William Blake to Sharon Olds. In addition to writing poetry, she is also currently working on a novel.

Katrina Gaudier graduated in 2010 as an English major at Drexel University, but is excited to return to Drexel in the fall to continue her studies towards a Masters degree in Communications.

Giby George is a pre-med Biology major, currently in her second year. Inspired by both her job in the operating room and modern literary-physician icons such as Dr. Atul Gawande and Dr. Jerome Groopman, Giby hopes to continue to bring to light the more philosophical facets of medicine. She also notes that it was Professor Rebecca Ingalls, of the Department of English and Philosophy, who first encouraged her foray into the realm of medical-philosophy writing.

Justin Gero is a senior majoring in World History and Politics (BA) and Science, Technology and Society (MS). He was the editor of *The Triangle*, but he is best known for his starring role as "Free Food Guy" in the Commuter Freshman Orientation video of 2009. No acting was required, as Justin actually has the ability to detect free food anywhere on a university campus.

Alison Grant is an International Area Studies major with a concentration in Human Rights. She believes in equality for everyone and is currently working in a Women's Studies Research Center in Costa Rica. In her spare time she enjoys teaching English and taking long walks on the beach (seriously, she is in Costa Rica—the beaches are beautiful). As soon as she returns to the United States, she will start planning her next study abroad to Peru.

Michael B. Harris-Peyton is an English major with a Philosophy minor. His childhood dog was named Godot and his cat Meursault—accordingly, from a young age, he had a passion for books that were well beyond his grade level. His hobbies include constant fiction writing, obsessively reading the works of Haruki Murakami and Jhumpa Lahiri, cooking, and studying languages. Having graduated from Drexel, he continues to live in Philadelphia and refuses to leave until another city can prove, conclusively, that it has superior food.

Maria Hnaraki is the Director of Greek Studies at Drexel University. She is author of *Cretan Music: Unraveling Ariadne's Thread*. Her wide-ranging circle of activities includes, among others, international publications of articles and book reviews in journals and periodicals, translation as well as instruction, and presentations and performances on several aspects of Greek culture.

Emily Homrok is a junior at Drexel University, where she studies Film and Video Production. Her work has been published in the *SNReview* and *Gargoyle* magazine. She writes for the *Philadelphia Examiner*

Donna Kapes is pursuing her Advanced Nursing Practice Graduate degree in Innovation and Intra/Entrepreneurship at Drexel while working full time as a certified emergency registered nurse. Donna plans to bring innovation at the end of life so that healthcare decisions are known and honored across the continuum of care. In addition to raising three teenagers, her passions include advancing opportunities for those with autism, prompted by raising an autistic daughter. In her more relaxing moments, Donna can be found reading a good book, swimming, or wafting through the latest research.

Scott Gabriel Knowles is an assistant professor of history in the Department of History and Politics, and serves as the director of the Great Works Symposium and the Custom-Designed Major. He is a co-director of the Drexel Engineering Cities Initiative. Knowles completed his Ph.D. at Johns Hopkins University in the Department of the History of Science, Medicine, and Technology in 2003, after completing an MA in history and BA in history and philosophy at the University of Texas at Austin. He is the author/editor of *Imagining Philadelphia: Edmund Bacon and the Future of the City* (UPenn Press, 2009).

Miriam N. Kotzin is associate professor of English at Drexel University, co-directs the Certificate Program in Writing and Publishing, and teaches creative writing and literature. Her fiction and poetry have been published widely in literary journals. She is a contributing editor of *Boulevard* and a founding editor of *Per Contra: the International Journal of the Arts, Literature and Ideas*. She is the author of two collections of poetry, and a collection of flash fiction, *Just Desserts*. She writes a bi-weekly column, "Second Acts," found in *The Smart Set*.

Grace Leonard is currently a junior at Haddonfield Memorial High School, and has no immediate plans for what she will major in when she eventually gets to college. She enjoys walking through the woods and reading drafts of her work to her two dogs, Charlie and Angel, who never seem to want to listen. Grace also loves painting, baking, and dancing in the rain.

Maia Livengood is a sophomore with dual majors in Business Administration and Hospitality Management. Though prolific use of "like," "ya," and "totally" often reveal her California roots, she considers herself somewhat of a misplaced native Philadelphian, keen on "wooder" ice, Yuengling, and, of course, the Eagles. In her spare time, she enjoys eating, baking, playing board games, attempting to knit (which almost always results in disastrously misshapen scarves), and identifying entirely too much with a variety of insane fictional Russians. And Salieri: Oh, mediocrity.

Lynn Levin is adjunct associate professor of English at Drexel University. A poet and translator, she is the author of three collections of poems, *Fair Creatures of an Hour* (2009), *Imaginarium* (2005), and *A Few Questions about Paradise* (2000), all published by Loonfeather Press. Lynn Levin's poems have appeared in *Ploughshares, Washington Square Review, Southwest Review, 5 AM*, and *Boulevard*. She is also executive producer of the TV show *The Drexel InterView*.

Carolynn McCormack is an English major in her junior year at Drexel. She is a member of *Maya*, the undergraduate literary magazine, as well as a copyeditor for *The Triangle*. Carolynn was an intern for the Drexel Publishing Group during summer 2010. Besides writing, she enjoys spending time with friends and family and going down the shore.

Ari Melman is a Marketing and Economics student with a minor in Psychology. In the vein of Jon Stewart, he writes comedic yet critical pieces on ending blind hate and conflict in society.

Robert Meyer is a freshman in the LeBow College of Business. He is a capable though extremely reluctant writer, having always found the process to be somewhat tortuous and interminable. Much of the credit for this and any future literary success must be shared with his professor, Dr. Raymond Brebach, for his time, counsel, patience, and encouragement.

Michael Meyers is a Biomedical Engineering freshman. He was raised in Doylestown, Pennsylvania, and has wide-spanning intellectual interests. His English writing has been influenced by his study of the German language and his various literary interests. His readings have spanned from holy books such as the *Bhagavad Gita* to scientific writings such as Stephen Hawkings' *A Brief History of Time*.

Harriet Millan's debut poetry book, *The Christmas Show*, was chosen by Eavan Boland for a Barnard New Women Poet's Prize and was a winner of the Poetry Society of America's Alice Fay di Castagnola Award, as well as an Ellen LaForge Memorial Poetry Prize. Poems from her newly released book, *Girl in Cap and Gown*, have appeared in publications such as *Antioch Review, Iowa Review, Kenyon Review, Cimarron Review, Ploughshares* and *Prairie Schooner*.

Nahjan Amer Nordin is an Environmental Engineering major who is currently in her sophomore year at Drexel. Originally from a country half the globe away, Malaysia, she believes that she is part-idealist, part-realist and part-environmentalist-wannabe—yet, wholly, a writer. Recently, she is looking into the possibility of minoring in English as a way to keep the writing passion alive. Aside from writing, she enjoys listening to her all-time favorite band, Hanson, and spending time with family and friends.

Anne-Marie Obajtek-Kirkwood is associate professor and head of French Studies at Drexel. She teaches French and Francophone 20th and 21st century literature, culture and film and also Women Studies and International Area Studies with a focus on the Maghreb, Middle East, and Iran. Her research and publications include the above topics but also minorities in France and autobiography and war (representations of the occupation, WWII, among others). She has published *Signs of War: From Patriotism to Dissent* (Palgrave MacMillan 2007), and is currently working on a manuscript of Patrick Modiano's first three novels.

Vennila Padmanaban is a sophomore Biology major who is also deeply interested in the humanities and writing—she hopes to apply these passions as a physician, to deliver good healthcare and treatment to those in need. Among numerous interests, she enjoys travel and exploration, James Bond movies, cats, and hip hop.

Steve Polsz is a Mathematics major currently considering Philosophy to be a much better choice. Along with writing (yes, there is a novel in the making), Steve enjoys painting in oils under the influence of Dali. It's likely that he might be found outdoors just after dawn, either trying to make a small bit of order within the mild chaos of his garden or sitting under the willow with his guitar singing to the ravens.

Ali Rahman is a student in the College of Arts and Sciences majoring in English.

Don Riggs specialized in Myth as an undergraduate, Comparative Literature/ Medieval for an MA and Ph.D., and focused on poetry in his second MA, which was in Creative Writing. He has presented papers at the International Conference on the Fantastic in the Arts—in both Science Fiction and Fantasy— since 1985, and has had the good fortune to have been seated next to Ursula K. LeGuin before she went up on stage to read. She admitted that she's always nervous before reading to an audience...but she wasn't nearly as nervous as he was talking to her!

Anjana Santhanam is a graduating senior in the Department of Biology. She is planning on a career in medicine and medical research—particularly internal medicine with a specialty in either endocrinology or oncology. As a multiple-time Week of Writing and Drexel Publishing Group winner as well as a contributor to the first-place entry in the Department of Biology's Senior Seminar project, she realizes the integral role that technical writing plays in the sciences. Anjana's guilty pleasures include reading bad fan fiction, celebrity gossip, and 19th century manners novels as well as listening to Britney Spears.

Angela J. Silverman is a 2011 MPH candidate in Drexel's School of Public Health. She received her undergraduate degree in Exercise Science from Appalachian State University with minors in Biology, Chemistry, and Psychology. Despite the scientific focus of her studies, Angela has a strong background in English literature and composition, music, and French. She spends most of her free time reading, traveling, practicing yoga, and volunteering.

Scott Stein is co-director of the Drexel Publishing Group and associate teaching professor in the Department of English and Philosophy at Drexel University, where he teaches Writing Humor and Comedy, Writing Fiction, Creative Writing, and Freshman Writing. He is the author of the novels *Lost* and *Mean Martin Manning* and founding editor of the online magazine *When Falls the Coliseum: a journal of American culture (or lack thereof)* <whenfallsthecoliseum.com>, where he blogs frequently. His short fiction, satires, reviews, and essays have been published in such places as *National Review*, the *Philadelphia Inquirer*, *Liberty*, *The G.W. Review*, and *Art Times*. He received his MFA from the University of Miami and his MA from New York University.

Joshua Dylan Stevenson is a sophomore International Area Studies major. His interest in poetry and prosody began in the fourth grade with an assignment to write a haiku. His interests besides poetry include humor, nonsense, games, and religion. He does not believe those items belong to a single category, of course. He loves his boyfriend, his mother, and his cats, in that order.

Elizabeth Thorpe's short stories and excerpts from her novel-in-progress have appeared in *Painted Bride Quarterly, Per Contra, Press 1, Puckerbrush Review, Stolen Island Review*, and *The Maine Review*, among others. She teaches Freshman Writing at Drexel University and Creative Writing in the University of the Arts Pre-College program. She earned her MFA in Writing from Goddard College.

Scott Warnock is an assistant professor of English and Director of the Freshman Writing Program at Drexel University, where he helps coordinate Drexel's initiative to offer online and hybrid composition courses. He is interested in uses of technology in writing instruction, particularly how learning technologies can help student writers and can facilitate better methods of responding to student work. He is the author of *Teaching Writing Online: How and Why*, and he has published a number of articles and has spoken at national conferences about teaching and technology issues and opportunities. He maintains a blog about online writing instruction at onlinewritingteacher. blogspot.com. Scott was also co-founder of Subjective Metrics, Inc., a company created to develop Waypoint writing assessment and peer review software.

Jason Wilson is the founding editor of *The Smart Set* as well as the series editor of *The Best American Travel Writing* (Houghton Mifflin). His book, *Boozehound: On the Trail of the Rare, the Obscure, and the Overrated in Spirits*, will be out in September from Ten Speed/Random House. Wilson is the drinks columnist for *The Washington Post* food section, and his column won the award for Best Newspaper Food Column in 2008, and has been nominated for the same award this year. His work has appeared in *National Geographic Traveler, Conde Nast Traveler, Travel + Leisure, Salon, McSweeney's, Philadelphia* magazine, among many other magazines and newspapers.

Abhishek Yeleswarapu is a BS/MS student in Biomedical Engineering with a minor in Computer Science, and is currently in his sophomore year at Drexel. He enjoys participating in sports, playing video games, and reading John Grisham novels during his free time. He is a member of the University of Pennsylvania NROTC program, an officer for Drexel EMS, as well as the Vice President of Penn for Youth Debate, a 501(c)(3) non-profit volunteer organization in Philadelphia. He hopes to go for his MBA and/or JD after graduation, eventually leading to a career in biomedical corporate management.

MEET
&GREETS

Fun, Food and Prizes!

The College of Arts and Sciences' quarterly Meet and Greets are an excellent opportunity for all members of the CoAS community to meet and connect in a relaxed social setting. Students have the opportunity to win prizes, make valuable contacts and establish new friendships.

Dates: Thursday, October 14, 2010
Thursday, January 27, 2011
Thursday, April 21, 2011

Time: 4:30 pm - 6:00 pm

Place: Paul Peck Alumni Center,
3142 Market Street

What Happens at a Meet and Greet?

1. Students and faculty mingle and enjoy a tasty reception.
2. Students receive raffle tickets from faculty members.
3. Students write their name on tickets and enter into drawing.
4. The Dean draws 6-8 names and winners receive prizes ranging from Barnes & Noble gift certificates to an iPod shuffle!

For more information, see the CoAS calendar: http://www.drexel.edu/coas/news/calendar/

DEAN'S SEMINAR

The Dean's Seminar Series is an opportunity for the CoAS community to learn more about the exciting research being done by our talented new and senior faculty members. Speakers present on topics ranging from the moral uncertainty of Harry Potter to the implications of geometry in the brain.

Day   Wednesdays during the 2nd, 4th, 6th and 8th weeks of the quarter

Time   3:30p.m. to 5:00p.m.

Place   Disque Hall, Room 109

D3s

D3 events highlight the interdisciplinary nature of the College of Arts and Sciences and serve as a forum in which students from all majors can meet and discuss a chosen topic of current interest. Events are organized by faculty members teaching complimentary courses, and include a brief performance, film screening, panel discussion or lecture, followed by an informal discussion and DINNER!

Day: **Wednesdays during the 3rd, 5th and 7th weeks of the quarter**

Time: 5:00p.m. to 7:00p.m.

Place: University Club, 6th floor MacAlister Hall (Location subject to change)

For more information, see the CoAS calendar: http://www.drexel.edu/coas/news/calendar/

MATH RESOURCE CENTER

The Math Resource Center provides students with immediate, on site assistance with their mathematics courses. The Resource Center is staffed with at least three tutors during all hours of operation; the tutoring staff is comprised of both Teaching Faculty and Teaching Assistants.

Location: **Korman Resource Center**
2nd floor of the Korman Building
Room 247

Hours: **Mondays to Thursdays**
10:00 am - 7:00 pm
Fridays
10:00 am - 4:00 pm

Contact: (215) - 895 - 2748

THE DREXEL
WRITING CENTER

Offering all students FREE tutoring by experienced faculty members and trained student staff.

Meeting with a tutor can help you:

> Add content to develop your ideas
> Improve the organization of your writing
> Properly format and document your sources
> Effectively use grammar and syntax
> Develop your thesis

In addition, we offer a face-to-face and online evening and weekend workshop series.

Location: **The Writing Center is located on the ground floor of MacAlister Hall, Room 32. However, we provide writing services at other locations across campus.**

Hours: **Vary by term.**

For more information on hours and locations, please call: (215) 895-6633 or 895-1799

The College of Arts and Sciences

RESEARCH DAY 2011

The College of Arts and Sciences' Research Day highlights the significant contributions that student scholars and researchers, both graduate and undergraduate, make to their respective disciplines. Students present their work, in poster format, in a supportive, collegial and festive setting.

Tuesday, April 5, 2011

Behrakis Grand Hall
Creese Student Center

Drexel UNIVERSITY college of arts + sciences